14-120-798

Teaching

mathematics in the modern

elementary school

CALHOUN C. COLLIER
Michigan State University

HAROLD H. LERCH
University of Illinois

Teaching mathematics in the modern elementary school

The Macmillan Company

Collier-Macmillan Limited
LONDON

372.7
C69t
c.1

Preface

Contemporary changes in the elementary mathematics curriculum have presented many problems for elementary classroom teachers. Demands on elementary teachers of mathematics are greater than they have ever been before. The problems facing teachers of elementary mathematics and the demands placed upon them are related to both the mathematical content of the elementary program and the instructional procedures to be used in teaching children the ideas of mathematics. In order to teach children the ideas in newer mathematics programs, elementary teachers must understand those ideas, appreciate the purposes and philosophy which underlie the concepts to be taught, and employ appropriate procedures for introducing and spirally developing those concepts.

Pre-service and in-service elementary teachers have become increasingly aware of the problems and challenges confronting them in the teaching of elementary mathematics. This book has been written to help meet those needs and interests as a textbook or as a reference to be used in undergraduate courses for those who are preparing to teach elementary mathematics, in certain graduate courses dealing with instruction in elementary mathematics, and in locally conducted in-service programs that are concerned with the improvement of elementary mathematics programs.

Although the book is primarily concerned with the methodology of elementary mathematics instruction, the major mathematical concepts of modern programs of elementary mathematics are also presented. Students who have studied the mathematics of modern

v

programs should find this material suitable for review and pertinent to their study of methods of teaching. Others, with limited backgrounds in mathematics, will be able to use this material to develop better understandings of the mathematics content in elementary programs. The issue in elementary mathematics is not one of "Shall we teach mathematics or shall we teach children?" but of teaching children the ideas of mathematics. For that reason, content and procedures are inseparable in this book. An attempt is made throughout the book to integrate the logical structure of modern mathematical concepts and contemporary instructional methods.

The content and procedures suggested in the text are in accord with the characteristics shared by "good" contemporary elementary mathematics programs. Reference to specific grade level placement of content and procedures is avoided because detailed specification is in conflict with the ideal of selecting and adjusting content, materials, and procedures to the needs and abilities of individual students.

Properties of numbers and other concepts relatively new to the elementary mathematics program are not treated as appendages or "little extras" in the program but as integral aspects to help develop pupils' knowledge, understandings, and skills. Emphasis is upon utilizing a "set approach" to introduce and develop concepts of number and of the operations upon number meaningfully. Applications in realistic situations (problem solving) are also stressed in introducing new learnings and in developing pupils' abilities. The "set approach" and probem-solving situations are integral parts of a discovery procedure in which pupils are asked to explore problematical situations, and in which the teacher's role is to aid and to guide. Attention is also paid to the spiral development of concepts in which instruction repeatedly returns to a topic, always expanding it and showing relationships with other topics.

A variety of approaches to introduce and develop concepts and to practice skills are discussed. Number sentences and number lines are introduced early and are used as instructional devices to aid in the development of concepts and in the practice of skills. Active pupil participation in instructional procedures is encouraged. Logical sequences of organizing and teaching topics or areas are suggested. Number patterns and relationships between operations are stressed. Verification of ideas and operations is treated as a continuing aspect of the elementary mathematics instructional program. In each chapter, instructional materials and aids are directly suggested and indirectly implied in the discussion and by illustrations.

Practice exercises where appropriate are built into the context of each chapter. At the end of each chapter, suggested activities and selected references are cited. These listings are not intended to be exhaustive, but are indicative of activities and references available to students for expanding knowledge of both mathematical content and instructional procedures. The suggested activities are directly related to preparation for teaching the ideas presented in the chapter. Care was taken to select references which would expand the material presented in the chapter. Descriptions of contemporary curriculum development projects are not given and research findings are not summarized because the authors feel that these materials and reports are best studied in their original form.

The authors of a book of this kind are always indebted to many people for various contributions, lasting influences, and special encouragements. Both authors have had years of experience in teaching elementary school pupils, pre-service elementary mathematics teachers, and in-service elementary teachers, as well as experience in consulting with elementary school mathematics programs, and conducting in-service mathematics programs and research projects. We are grateful for having had the opportunity to work with many pupils and teachers and appreciative of their innumerable contributions to and influences on this endeavor. We also wish to thank our colleagues in mathematics education and in other areas of elementary education for the ideas and encouragement received in both formal and informal conversations.

C. C. C
H. H. L

Contents

Trends and 1

changes in elementary

mathematics

Although there is little doubt in the minds of most people interested in education that mathematics programs at all levels are in a process of change, there does appear to be doubt on the part of some teachers as well as many parents as to (1) whether or not major changes are necessary at the elementary school level, (2) the methods which should be used in bringing these changes about, and (3) whether or not current and future modifications will be lasting changes.

Certainly teachers have read and heard a lot in recent years about Modern Mathematics. Educators, in general, seem to be interested and stimulated in reading and talking about the newer aspects of elementary school mathematics or arithmetic. Observation indicates, however, that many elementary teachers are uncertain and hesitant about changing their everyday classroom practices. Past history of the teaching profession indicates that teachers are willing and eager to change when they recognize there are good, sound reasons for changing what they are now doing. But willingness or even eagerness to change is not enough. Before we can implement changes in our elementary mathematics programs and practices for the better, we must understand the developments in mathematics education and see their possible applications in the classroom. In discussing newer developments in elementary school mathematics, it seems imperative, then, that we consider (1) factors that have given rise to the need for change, (2) changes in content and organization, and (3) changes in instructional methods.

Need for change

A study of the history of mathematics and of the history of the world reveals that mathematics has evolved in a dynamic relationship with the development of society. Looking at the kind of world in which we live today, it is easy to see that our mathematical needs are quite different than they were in the past decade. The fast-developing scientific and technological era with its great explosion of knowledge calls for uses of mathematics that were not even imagined, much less known, a few years ago. New discoveries and developments are occurring daily that demand more mathematical know-how on the part of more people. The world of tomorrow will undoubtedly make even greater demands. We are living in an increasingly numerically oriented world. Some people are now referring to today's culture as a mathematical culture. A true understanding of mathematics may now be considered a prerequisite for intelligent citizenship.

Schools need to help people fully develop their potential for mathematics in order that they can make more intelligent decisions in a highly technical culture. However, if students are expected to pursue mathematical studies at higher levels, a solid foundation should be developed in our elementary schools, for it is at this level that children must be helped to find early success and to establish an interest in and a liking for mathematics if they are to continue its study. Most people accept the fact that the foundation of all mathematics is laid at the elementary school level. Hence, it is essential that our elementary schools provide the kind of foundation upon which future mathematical learning can be built successfully. This calls for a program designed in terms of our changing times and changing needs.

Recognizing that mathematics is the tool by which cultural and scientific progress is made and that advancement is presently proceeding at an unprecedented rate, our mathematics program must (1) change fast enough to serve the needs of this advancement and (2) equip students to enter fields of study and work, the nature of which is at present difficult to predict.

Content and organization

In recent years much change has taken place in mathematics programs at all levels, elementary, secondary, and college. These changes take many forms and occur in varying degrees. These circumstances make it rather difficult to determine the status of the change or to say to what extent some of the newer concepts and ideas will become an integral part of on-going programs. Certainly, at the present time, mathematics programs can be said to be in a state of flux.

During the past few years teachers and administrators have probably been under more pressure from various sources to revise the existing programs, to adopt a new program, or to participate in some experimental program than at any other comparable period of time, all in the name of strengthening or updating present offerings. Frequently we read or hear people say that elementary school age children can and should learn much more arithmetic than they do.

The impact of this pressure for upgrading the mathematical program of children is gaining momentum. Much new mathematical material has been produced for use at the elementary level. Some of this material exists only in the experimental stage. Some of it has been commercially published for public consumption. The fact that much new material exists behooves all of us who are interested in the welfare of the learner to study, analyze, and evaluate it to see what applications can be utilized for our teaching-learning program.

Some of the newer developments have materialized because teachers have for some time recognized the need for carefully examining the mathematics that children study in school as well as the way it is taught. Other changing concepts are undoubtedly due to the recent world events that have spotlighted in the eyes of the American public the importance of mathematics.

Several rather large mathematical study, research, or experimental projects have appeared upon the American scene in the last decade. Most of these projects have been financed through grants, again indicating the public's increased interest in teaching more and better mathematics. Among the projects that have made a strong impact upon the elementary school program have been the School Mathematics Study Group (SMSG), the Greater Cleveland Mathematics Program (GCMP), the University of Illinois Arithmetic Project (UIAP), the Madison Project of Syracuse University and Webster College, the Institute for Mathematical Studies in the Social Sciences at Stanford University, and the Minnesota Mathematics and Science Teaching Project.

Recent developments in mathematics at the elementary school level resulting from the various studies and efforts are generally referred to as the *new* or *modern* mathematics. Surely, some of the ideas can be considered to be new, but many of them suggest a different emphasis on well-established basic concepts and operations. Contemporary developments also suggest a different placement than formerly of topics within the total school mathematics curriculum. Attention should be called to some of the changes and trends that reflect the newer points of view and new emphasis in content and organization. In the succeeding chapters these ideas will be discussed in more detail along with suggestions for implementing them in the classroom.

The nature, scope, and organization of the elementary school mathematics curriculum have been altered in many ways. Content changes have been and are being made to better meet the needs of children as well as of society in general. The opinion of most mathematicians and professional educators is that the content in our current programs is more functional and more vital because of these changes.

A very definite trend toward introducing mathematical ideas earlier than was previously considered possible has developed. Concepts that were not presented until high school or perhaps college at one time are now introduced at the elementary levels successfully, for example, inverse operations, sets, mathematical properties, and negative numbers. This trend was perhaps influenced by Bruner's often quoted statement, "any subject can be taught effectively in some intellectually honest form to any child at any stage of development."[1]

Emphasis on the earlier mastery of many fundamental concepts of arithmetic may be due in part to studies that indicate that American children's arithmetic achievement is below that of children of comparable grade level in other countries. A recent comparative study was made to assess the achievement in mathematics of two groups of students—thirteen years olds and those in their last year of secondary education—in more than 5,300 schools in 12 countries. The average test scores of both groups of U.S. students were

---

[1] Bruner, Jerome S., *The Process of Education.* New York: Random House, Inc. (Vintage Books), 1960, p. 33.

relatively low in comparison with test results of students from the other 11 countries.[2]

Perhaps a more important impetus for accelerating the mathematical progress of pupils, however, stems from the results of experimental programs in this country, such as those mentioned earlier in this chapter, that show that youngsters want to and can learn more sophisticated mathematical concepts at an earlier age than they have in the past and that they are capable of applying the concepts.

Introduction and study of more sophisticated mathematical ideas at the elementary school level are employed to (1) help children gain earlier insights into mathematical functions; (2) give meaning to heretofore rote responses; (3) develop firm foundations for the later study of mathematical concepts through emphasis on relationships, patterns, and structure; (4) stimulate interest and enjoyment in mathematics; and (5) encourage children of all levels of ability to greater achievement.

Much of the newer content has been placed in the elementary grades to help children not only master more mathematics but also to *understand* better what they are studying.

With an emphasis on understanding the *decimal numeral system*, we find in the elementary school more attention devoted to such topics as the history of mathematics, characteristics of systems of numeration, numeration systems with bases other than ten, the distinction between number and numeral, and the idea that there are many names for the same number.

As a result of the emphasis on understanding the *fundamental operations*, the newer materials devote a great deal more attention to the commutative, associative, and distributive laws and how they apply to addition, subtraction, multiplication, and division. Emphasis in newer materials on number relationships and principles of number operation is designed to help children recognize the basic structure and unifying ideas of mathematics.

The *concept of set* is finding its way into more of the content material being developed for elementary school use — a rather startling development to some people because the term set in the

---

[2] Husen, Torsten, et al. (eds.), *International Study of Achievement in Mathematics: A Comparison of Twelve Countries*, 2 vols. New York: John Wiley & Sons, Inc., 1967.

past found little or no use prior to the graduate level. Chapter 2 is devoted to sets and their application to elementary school mathematics programs.

A decided trend toward a more *precise use of vocabulary* has evolved. Some examples in point are the distinction made between numeral and number, the use of operations on number instead of fundamental processes, and inverse operations to refer to subtraction and division. Teachers need to be concerned with helping children develop a functional mathematical vocabulary. Care should be taken, however, that children's definitions and generalizations result from active involvement in problematic situations and not from memorizing terms and rules.

More *geometric concepts* are included in the newer elementary mathematics programs and are introduced in the early stages (primary grades) of the programs. The program has been expanded beyond experiences designed to help children recognize the shape and form of various geometric figures. An intuitive approach is used to develop basic concepts of points, lines, and planes in space. Emphasis is upon basic geometric ideas rather than on geometric proofs.

More attention than formerly is being devoted to *approximation*, particularly in terms of understanding measurement. The importance of approximation as it relates both to oral arithmetic and to paper and pencil computation is also stressed. Rounding numbers is still an important aspect of teaching approximation but it is no longer emphasized to the almost complete neglect of other aspects of the concept.

Other changes in content could undoubtedly be noted, but these appear to be the more important ones and certainly are indicative of the trend to introduce more sophisticated mathematical ideas and concepts in the elementary school program.

As is evident from the trends discussed in the previous paragraphs, there may be a danger that elementary arithmetic could become a pure mathematics that children are required to master, one taught with little concern for their interests and abilities, making the new arithmetic worse than the old. Although it is desirable that students develop a solid foundation to give them competence to deal with mathematics at secondary and college levels, it is also desirable that the program be appropriate for children in the elementary school. Fortunately, most of the experimental and new materials emphasize meaning and the ability to think quantitatively, rather than memorization and automatic responses. The dangers of developing a pure or unrealistic mathematics program should be avoided.

Instructional methods

Along with changes in mathematics content have come accompanying changes in methods and techniques of teaching. In past years the emphasis in teaching elementary school mathematics was on the mastery of skills through drill. Arithmetic was mainly a how-to-do-it subject.

Mathematics was once thought of as a vast number of specific and unrelated facts. For the most part arithmetic, then consisted of having children learn by rote the so-called number facts and how to do the four basic operations — addition, subtraction, multiplication, and division. Teaching-learning of this kind is not adequate for today's citizen, whose way of living and thinking, is affected by some quantitative aspect of daily life. Earlier methods probably contributed greatly to the lack of success and undesirable attitudes toward mathematics of previous generations of pupils.

An important objective of today's instruction is to help the elementary school age child to understand the *why* as well as the *what* and the *how* of mathematics — in effect to help the young learner to use his intelligence and creative ability to think *mathematically*.

Teachers cannot expect that learning geared to an automatic response will teach students to work creatively. Rote-type learners cannot be expected to metamorphose into creative mathematicians needed by society today or the citizen of the future who is expected to be able to handle the quantitative situations of the time, whatever they might be. That the basic structure and function of mathematical concepts be presented and understood at the elementary school level has become essential so that students may be adequately prepared for successful participation in more specific areas later.

Too many teachers have presented mathematics as something that is very difficult to learn. Children have been asked to memorize a great many singular facts and to drill on operational processes until they can repeat them by rote. As a result, mathematics, to many, has become a dull, monotonous subject thereby adversely affecting mathematical attitudes.

A number of perceptible trends indicate that significant changes are being made in the methodological approach to mathematical instruction. As these instructional changes, together with the content changes discussed earlier, are taking shape, both teachers and students, perhaps for the first time, are finding the study of mathematics fascinating, intriguing, challenging, satisfying, and enjoyable.

Believing now that the elementary school age child can grasp the meaning of number and the principles involved in computation, teachers should try to make his learning of mathematics an adventure in discovery from the time the child first enters school.

Teachers are making greater efforts to help the learner recognize recurring fundamental concepts and to discover patterns that help to integrate, unify, and strengthen mathematical ideas.

Programs are being planned to help pupils recognize the sequential, interrelated nature of mathematics. Therefore, instead of emphasizing distinct differences, a trend in instruction is toward helping children discover in each new topic some basic unifying idea that was operative in some aspect of number with which they are already familiar. New meanings are built on previous learnings. An approach to teaching-learning that emphasizes "using what you already know" should better equip students to face new situations with confidence.

A modern instructional approach emphasizes the relationships of the fundamental operations — of all of the operations to counting, of addition to multiplication, of subtraction to addition, of division to subtraction, and of multiplication to division. Children should be helped to understand that addition and multiplication are combining or putting together operations and that subtraction and division are separating, taking apart, or comparison operations. The fact that subtraction undoes addition and division undoes multiplication is emphasized. For example, if a child knows that $4 + 3 = 7$, he should also know that $7 - 3 = 4$. And if he knows that $4 \times 3 = 12$, he should know that there are 4 threes or 3 fours in 12.

With present-day emphasis on understanding the meanings of fundamental concepts and principles, the methodological approach is gradually becoming structure oriented rather than rule oriented. The learner can hardly be expected to use effectively a number system unless he understands its structure. J. S. Bruner believes that the basic ideas of mathematics ". . . are as simple as they are powerful"[3] and that they can be taught in some form to a youngster of any age. He suggests that the early teaching be done ". . . with scrupulous intellectual honesty, but with an emphasis upon the intuitive grasp of ideas and upon the use of these basic ideas"[4] and that these basic ideas be reinforced and expanded throughout the elementary school program.

Another trend is toward having students interpret quantitative situations and to structure problems for solution instead of merely arriving at numerical answers to numerous examples already structured for solution. Much use is made of number sentences as a means of expressing the problem situation mathematically as either an equality or an inequality.

More class time than formerly is allotted to children's demonstration and explanation, either orally or in writing, of *why* they did what they did as well as *what* they did and *how* they did it.

Current instructional procedures tend to have children spend more time reading and interpreting material presented in some type of pictorial graphic form as against the actual constructing of graphs. This certainly sounds like a logical change in terms of the ever-increasing quantity of material being presented in graphic form today through various communications media for public consumption, a trend also in accord with the new curricular materials in the area of elementary science.

A general agreement is that there are several mathematically correct approaches to solving most quantitative problems. Therefore, instead of insisting that this is *the* way, teachers are increasingly encouraging students to solve problems in *many* different ways. Such a methodological approach not only contributes to higher motivation and interest, but, perhaps more importantly, provides the individual learner with a basis for choosing the method that is most appropriate for him.

Another noticeable change in the teaching of mathematics is the use of more as well as a wider variety of instructional materials. A wealth of sensory materials can be utilized in the classroom to assist the learner as he attempts to deal with the many mathematical concepts, facts, and generalizations. Teachers are becoming increasingly aware that many children need to see, to feel or touch, to talk, as well as to hear or listen in order to develop meaning

[3] Bruner, *op. cit.*, p. 12–13.

[4] Bruner, *op. cit.*, p. 13.

and understanding. In addition to the familiar printed materials, the chalkboard, and the paper pad, teachers can easily make or find readily available any number of instructional aids such as manipulative materials, charts, audiovisual aids, models, games, and other devices to help each individual develop clear mental pictures of the truths of mathematics.

Counters, bundles of sticks, the number line, and some form of the abacus are examples of currently popular teaching aids in most classrooms. These teaching devices can be effectively used to help children visualize basic concepts, to add variety to the learning climate, to deepen understanding, to reinforce learnings, and to provide a simple form of proof.

Much of the discussion in this section has dealt with the trends and changes in methodological approach from an emphasis on the mastery of skills through drill to an emphasis on the meaning and structure of our number system and the mathematical principles involved in the operations on number. However, it is important to recognize that current methodology does not negate the need for practice. In fact, practice is considered an important aspect of present-day instruction. As new mathematical content and new ways of teaching develop, a balance between concepts and skills should be maintained. Along with the development of understandings of a concept, there needs to be a variety of meaningful exercises to develop skills related to the concept. Practice cannot substitute for understandings but should accompany understandings. A variety of practice experiences is needed to help the individual develop the ability to apply consciously and effectively mathematical concepts and skills in the solution of his problems.

The future of mathematics in the elementary school

All signals read "go" as related to improving the mathematics program in the elementary school. At this time, however, few *clear* signals tell us precisely in which direction to go or how far to go. Nevertheless, many signs *indicate* directions and guide our way. There are encouraging signs to increase and speed up the change and there are caution signs. Both signs are to be expected and in our opinion are needed—expected, because there always has been and perhaps always will be those who want to cling to the familiar and comfortable and those who recognize the need for change and are willing to lead the way. Both types of people are needed to keep us moving forward, but moving in sensible directions and at a practical pace.

All that is old within a program should not be condemned as being bad, nor should a program be changed simply for the sake of being new. No change, however, soon results in stagnation and change that is too rapid often results in confusion and sometimes in panic. Teachers need time to adjust to newly learned content and procedures.

World events in recent years and the result of (1) observing changes in the way people (children and adults) live and the things they do, (2) studies and research as to how children learn mathematics most effectively, and (3) the experimental programs such as SMSG, UIAP, and GCMP have engendered a climate for change and have effected and will continue to effect changes in mathematics programs in the elementary schools.

If elementary teachers pay any attention to the results of studies and research, they will no longer think of mathematics as a vast number of specific and unrelated facts to be memorized and of skills to be fixed through habit formation, nor will they be assignment givers, drill masters, and recitation hearers.

The elementary teacher of the future needs to plan the specific mathematics for her group of children systematically and sequentially both in terms of the nature of mathematics and the nature of the individual learner. The program for a specific age, grade, or ability group should also be planned within the framework of the total sequential program K–6 or K–12.

Modern mathematics programs represent some of the old, some of the new, and much of the revised and altered content and methodology. Although being classified as neither old nor new, modern mathematics programs certainly can be classified as being different. Alterations and changes are being made in content, organization, presentation, and application. The present trend definitely points toward a more vital and functional program, dealing with the concepts and ideas that provide a firm foundation for understanding and using our number system.

The modern program undoubtedly means more mathematics for our better students, but it also means better mathematics for more of our students. Improvement in our elementary mathematics will come about perhaps not so much through what is taught as through the manner in which it is taught. We certainly have enough knowledge of how people learn in diverse ways and enough teachable materials to make the underlying concepts and principles of mathematics important and meaningful for children of many abilities. In other words, the new arithmetic should not be limited only to the academically talented. There is really no just reason to exclude the slower child from rich and desirable mathematical experiences so that he may drill more extensively. A reasonable approach is to assume that all elementary school children can at least investigate the areas of mathematics usually reserved for the "gifted" youngsters; but, of course, the teacher should recognize and expect that the progress and success of the children will differ widely.

The world of today and tomorrow demands that we assist children in their early school years to gain deeper understanding of and greater facility in using mathematics. The mathematics the child learns should be useful to him as he learns it, but what he learns must also enhance his future study, not only in mathematics, but in all curricular areas.

The emphasis in most of the experimental programs that have been developed in the past few years has been on mathematical concepts, with relatively little consideration given to social applications. Now a trend appears to provide for more social application as these programs continue to develop. The elementary school programs of the future will provide for a reasonable balance between the purely mathematical aspects and the social aspects.

Computation and skill in acquiring the correct answer will continue to be a goal in the elementary school program. However, more emphasis will be devoted to understanding the nature of our numeration system, principles underlying number operations, structural relationships, approximation, certain aspects of nonmetric geometry and algebra, construction of models, development of thought patterns, and learning by discovery.

Suggested activities

1. At an orientation program for parents of children in your room, a concerned parent asks, "What are the advantages of a modern mathematics program over the kind of mathematics I had in the elementary school?" How would you answer?

2. List several factors that have influenced the changing mathematics curriculum in recent years.

3. An examination of a textbook series reveals an earlier introduction than formerly of many mathematical ideas. Do you agree with this trend? Why? Why not?

4. What criteria will you use in planning a mathematics program appropriate for the children under your supervision?

5. What do you consider the most significant changes in the methods and techniques of teaching mathematics in the past 10–15 years?

6. Choose a topic appropriate for a particular level of the elementary school. What instructional materials would you desire to have available? For what purpose(s)?

Selected references

An Analysis of New Mathematics Programs. Washington, D.C.: The National Council of Teachers of Mathematics, 1963.

Bruner, J. S., *The Process of Education.* New York: Random House, Inc. (Vintage Books), 1960.

Clark, J. R., "Perspectives in Programs of Instruction in Elementary Mathematics," *The Arithmetic Teacher*, 12:604–611, Dec. 1965.

Davis, R. B., *The Changing Curriculum: Mathematics.* Washington, D.C.: The Association for Supervision and Curriculum Development, NEA, 1967.

Glennon, V. J., "Is Your Mathematics Program on an Even Keel?", *Instructor*, 76:70–1+, Feb. 1967.

Goals for Mathematical Education of Elementary School Teachers, A report of the Cambridge Conference on Teacher Training. Boston: Houghton-Mifflin Co., 1967.

Hopkins, C. D., "Emerging Elementary Mathematic's Program," *Teachers College Journal*, 36:151–152, Jan. 1965.

Husen, Torsten, et al. (eds), *International Study of Achievement in Mathematics: A Comparison of Twelve Countries* (2 vols). New York: John Wiley & Sons, Inc., 1967.

Sister Mary Anne, "Emerging Trends in Mathematics: Impact on Elementary Schools," *Catholic School Journal*, 66:32–34, Jan. 1966.

Saudel, D. H., "Teach So Your Goals Are Showing," *The Arithmetic Teacher*, 15:320–323, April 1968.

Williams, J. D., "Effecting Educational Change: Some Notes on Reform of Primary School Mathematics Teaching," *Education Research*, 8: 191–195, June 1967.

Zant, J. H., "Use of New Educational Media," *The Arithmetic Teacher*, 12:640–644, Dec. 1965.

Utilizing 2

set concepts

In recent years a good deal of mathematical discussion has centered around the continuity threads or the unifying concepts of mathematics. One of the most promising ideas for helping students to deal effectively with mathematics as a unified field is the development of the concept of *set*.

Most sources credit the work of a German mathematician, Georg Cantor, during the latter part of the nineteenth century as marking the beginning of the mathematical theory of sets. Although the set idea in mathematics is not new, the inclusion of the concept of *sets* and utilization of a *set approach* in the elementary school is new.

Because many of today's basic, as well as proposed, elementary mathematics programs call for introducing some of the basic notions about sets in the primary grades and for using those ideas in developing other concepts, elementary teachers need to understand better the mathematical ideas relative to the concept of sets.

Teachers, and prospective teachers, should know that the sophisticated ideas of set theory are still to be taught at perhaps the college level, but at the same time they should recognize that sets and a set approach hold many implications and possibilities for the elementary school. Since ideas concerning sets are generally considered basic, the authors have purposely included a discussion of sets prior to a discussion of number and operations on number. Some specific suggestions are made for utilizing various set concepts with children. However, much of the material

14

in this chapter is designed to acquaint teachers with the language of sets needed in developing an adequate background for implementing the necessary concepts in the elementary grades.

Why sets?

Many elementary teachers are wondering why concepts of sets should be included in the elementary program. The expression is often used, "We already have more to teach than we can teach." What, then, does the set concept offer to justify its inclusion? A growing body of evidence is that the use of set concept offers a means of expanding students' understanding of number, number operations and of unifying concepts from the various areas of mathematics. Also, some evidence is accumulating that a set approach may be quite useful in improving pupils' abilities to solve problems.

When introduced on an intuitive basis, sets offer a convenient starting point for studying and learning mathematics. Many of the ideas related to sets are already within the child's everyday experiences; thus working with sets aids in the sequential development of concepts from the familiar to the new, from the concrete to the abstract. Although some modern programs introduce the formal symbolism of sets in the early grades, the use of such notation is not necessarily a requirement in developing mathematical concepts through a set approach.

Study of sets in the elementary school helps children express mathematical ideas more precisely. Understanding some of the properties of sets should also provide a better foundation for the mathematics of later grades.

What is a set?

In everyday conversation, entering school age children have heard used and have themselves used many words that refer to a collection of one sort or another. For example, we often hear people speak of a "flock" of birds, a "herd" of cattle, a football "team," a "crowd" of people, and a nice "family." All the words in quotes refer to a collection. In mathematics, when one desires to refer to a collection, the term *set* is used.

At an early age, children become familiar with the term set in their day-to-day experiences outside school through expressions such as "a set of dishes," "a set of towels," "a set of blocks," "a set of golf clubs," "a set of tires," or "a set of encyclopedias."

In mathematics no attempt is made to formally define the term *set*; however, it is used synonymously with class, family, aggregate, or collection. Mathematicians use the term set to mean a collection of objects or ideas. But to simply say that a set is a collection of objects does not really tell what a set is. A set is really a perception of our thinking. A collection of objects does not actually constitute a set until we think of the objects as belonging to the set. When we speak of a set, we regard the collection of distinct objects as constituting a single whole. Some identifying characteristic of the set always makes it possible for us to determine whether or not a given object belongs to it. The identifying property that characterizes the set can be almost anything. After this property or condition is perceived, we can then say any object meeting or satisfying the property or condition belongs to the set. Any object not possessing the property or condition does not belong to the set.

Consider, for example, the properties of being a girl and having red hair. This would define a set that we might call the set of "red-headed girls." The decision as to whether an object belongs to this set requires two acts of recognition. Given any object, we must decide if the object is a girl and, if so, whether the girl has red hair.

Those objects composing a set are thought of as belonging to the set and are called *members* or *elements* of the set. We can therefore describe a set by saying that its members possess some property not possessed by any other objects. The property of being over 6 feet tall identifies the set of all things over 6 feet tall. Objects not over 6 feet tall do not belong to this set.

Let us consider as a set all the dishes in the china closet. Some of the dishes in the china closet may be dissimilar. There may be other dishes in the house but not in the china closet. We must remember that the property used here to constitute a set is the fact that the dishes are in the china closet. The following examples will help to clarify how the term set is used in mathematics with elementary school pupils.

1. The set consisting of all children in Valley Elementary School
2. The set consisting of all children who eat lunch at Island Elementary School

3. The set consisting of the even numbers between one and twenty
4. The set consisting of a square, a triangle, and an addition sign
5. The set consisting of the days of the week

Any capital letter, for example, A, C, or Y may be used as a short name for a set. The symbol $\in$ is used to mean "is a member of" and the symbol $\notin$ is used to mean "is not a member of." For instance, we can talk about the fourth set described above as set A. Then if we wish to refer to the object triangle $\triangle$ as a member of set A, we can use the notation $\triangle \in A$. This expression is read, "a triangle is a member of set A."

The preceding five examples of sets are described in words. Frequently, however, we specify or describe a set by listing its members between braces { }. This method of describing a set is usually called tabulation. The symbol, { }, means "the set whose members are." Suppose we have a set made up of the numerals $1, 2, 3,$ and 4. We can specify this set as $C = \{1, 2, 3, 4\}$. This is read "C is the set whose members are the numerals one, two, three, four." Earlier (in example 4) we described a set in words as the set consisting of a square, a triangle, and an addition sign. This same set can be tabulated as $\{\square, \triangle, +\}$. This is read "the set whose members are a square, a triangle, and an addition sign."

Some additional examples of sets are tabulated and then described in words as follows:

$W = \{2, 4, 6, \cdots, 20\}$
    The set of even numbers two through twenty.
$X = \{+, -, \times, \div\}$
    The set whose members are the four fundamental operations signs
$Y = \{0, 1, 2, 3, 4, \cdots\}$
    The set of all natural numbers
$Z = \{\ \}$
    An empty set or a set that has no members

How would you describe sets T, R, S, and V?

$T = \{\text{Jon, Scott, Jan, Sue}\}$ $S = \{0.5, \tfrac{2}{3}, 0.75\}$
$R = \{1, 3, 5, \cdots, 15\}$ $V = \{0\}$

As has been illustrated, a set may consist of many members, a few members, or no members. When there are only a few members in a set, it is customary to list each member. Examples X, T, S, and V represent sets in which each element of a set is tabulated.

Sometimes a set contains too many members to list conveniently or efficiently. Sets of this type are sometimes described in words, for example, the set of all even numbers between 1 and 25, the set of children in Mr. Baker's room, the set of planets, and the set of minerals. We can also tabulate a set composed of many members, but we use a different way of tabulating this sort of set than we do a set with only a few members. Examples W and R are illustrative. Reexamine these sets and you will see that we write the first three or four members (enough to establish a pattern to indicate what members are under consideration), follow this with a comma and then three dots to indicate that some members of the set are not listed, and then list the last member of the set. In example W the set was tabulated in the following manner: $\{2, 4, 6, \cdots, 20\}$. This is read as "the set of even numbers two through twenty." How do you read example R? Try listing three additional sets in the way the sets in examples W and R were described.

It is also possible to have a set that contains no members. A set without members is called an empty set or a null set. We shall refer to a set with no members as the *empty set* and use the symbol { } to represent it; however, some people use the symbol $\emptyset$ to denote an empty set. Examples of an empty set would be the set of all women presidents of the United States, the set of all United States presidents under 20 years of age, or the set of proper fractions greater than 1. There are no members that satisfy either of the described conditions; therefore all three sets would be empty. Elementary school children will find the empty set a convenient and appropriate means of describing many ideas gained from various school subjects.

We call a set a *finite set* if it is empty or if we can count all the members included in the set. Examples W, X, Z, T, R, S, *and* V are finite sets.

Some sets contain an infinite number of members. In such a set there is no end to the list of members and we therefore cannot list a final element. Example Y, $\{0, 1, 2, 3, 4, \cdots\}$, is an *infinite set*. We cannot count the members of this set. The three dots (ellipses) after the 4 with no element following them tell us that we could list successive elements on and on in the same pattern. The set we have been discussing is the set of whole numbers. The number 4 is the last number listed in the set but the three dots tell us that we could continue the sequence of listing whole numbers but that we could never list them all. This shows how sets can be used to portray an important mathematical concept. Can you think of other examples of infinite sets? Try writing notations for describing some of them. Would the sets you just described be appropriate for use in an elementary classroom? For what purpose?

Equal sets and equivalent sets

Sometimes we want to know if two sets are equal. Let us assume that we have two sets of numbers: $X = \{11, 13, 15, 17, 19\}$ and $Y = \{17, 13, 15, 19, 11\}$. Does $X = Y$? If we say $X = Y$, then X must be "the same set as" Y. An examination of the two sets shows that set X and set Y contain precisely the same members, the five odd numbers between 10 and 20. The members of set X and set Y are listed differently, but the order in which members of a set are listed has no affect upon the set.

For two sets to be *equal*, they must contain precisely the same members. Using the two sets we have been considering as an example, each element in set X must be contained in set Y and each element in set Y must be contained in set X. Thus we can write $X = Y$ or $Y = X$. In this case we are using two different names for "the same set."

Two sets may not look alike, although they may be equal. Consider, for example, the set $\{3\}$ and $\{2 + 1\}$. If we are using two different names, then each of the two sets consists of the element "three" and we can therefore think of them as being equal. The term *identical sets* can be used synonymously with equal sets. Here, in dealing with sets, we are using different names for the same thing. This ties in with the common practice in most elementary schools of children using many names for the same number. In most arithmetic problems in the elementary grades, we are concerned with renaming equal sets or subsets.

Two sets may contain the same number of members, yet not be equal. For instance, the set $\{1, 2, 3, 4\}$ and $\{a, b, c, d\}$ contain the same number of members, but it is obvious that the members of the two sets are not identical; therefore the two sets are not equal.

When two sets are not equal, yet contain the same number of members, they are called *equivalent sets*.

Some other examples of equivalent sets are as follows:

$A = \{3, 4, 6, 9\}$ and $B = \{G, A, M, E\}$

$A = \{$ 👐,👐,👐 $\}$ and $B = \{$ 🎈,🍦,🇺🇸 $\}$

$A = \{$book, pencil, pen$\}$ and $B = \{$desk, ruler, chair$\}$

Which of the following examples represent *equal sets* and which represent *equivalent sets*?

$A = \{7, 8, 9, 10\}$ and $B = \{F, O, U, R\}$
$A = \{7, 8, 9, 10\}$ and $B = \{8, 10, 9, 7\}$
$A = \{3 + 4, 7 - 2, 2 \times 3\}$ and $B = \{5, 6, 7\}$
$A = \{$dog, top, orange$\}$ and $B = \{$pet, toy, apple$\}$

When developing concepts of cardinality of number or number names with exercises involving matching sets or one-to-one correspondence, we use equivalent sets. Developing cardinality of number through a "set approach" utilizing equivalent sets is discussed in Chapter 4.

Sets and subsets

Someone has said that much of modern mathematics is the generation of new sets from old sets or the formulation of subsets. One set may be related to another set in such a way that the first set is contained in or included in the second set. When we speak of the junior senators, we speak of a subset of all senators. If J denotes the set of junior senators and S denotes the set of all senators then we say J is a subset of S because all the members of J are also members of S. Other subsets of set S would be the set of all democratic senators and the set of all Republican senators. Each member of the subset is also a member of the whole set. If every member of A is also a member of B, then A is contained in B or A is a subset of B. This can be written in abbreviated form as $A \subseteq B$. The symbol $\subseteq$ is used to mean "is a subset of." Some people prefer to use a different notation. In some books you may find $\subset$ instead of $\subseteq$ to indicate "is contained in" or "is a subset of." In other books you may find $\supset$ or $\supseteq$ used to denote "contains" or "includes." There is more than one way to denote set inclusion; however, in this book the symbol $\subseteq$ will be used.

If all the members of A are not found in B, then $A \not\subseteq B$. This notation is read "A is not a subset of B." Now let us consider some more examples as we think about set inclusion.

1. If $A =$ {washer, dryer}   and $B =$ {heater, washer, dryer}, then $A \subseteq B$.
2. If $A =$ {6, 7, 8}   and $B =$ {6, 7, 8 $\cdots$, 20}, then $A \subseteq B$.
3. If $A =$ {Bob, Bill}   and $B =$ {Sue, Bill, Janet, Mary}, then $A \not\subseteq B$.
4. If $A =$ {cat, dog}   and $B =$ {all animals}, then $A \subseteq B$.

In examples 1 and 2 we say A is a subset of B. By mere observation it is easy to see that all the members of A are also members of B. In example 4, A is also a subset of B, but it is not quite as easy to determine this as it was in examples 1 and 2. Here you must think that cat and dog belong to the animal kingdom and that therefore the members of A are contained in B. In example 3, A is not a subset of B because one of the members of A is not included in B.

In mathematics an empty set is considered a subset of every set and any given set is a subset of itself. Determining all the possible subsets of a given set can be an interesting experience. For example, if $F =$ {apple, banana, orange}, there are eight possible subsets. If a boy were presented the above set when he came home from school and told he could choose what he wanted to eat, he might choose any one of the following subsets:

$$G = \{\text{apple, banana, orange}\}$$
$$H = \{\text{apple, banana}\}$$
$$I = \{\text{apple, orange}\}$$
$$J = \{\text{banana, orange}\}$$
$$K = \{\text{apple}\}$$
$$L = \{\text{banana}\}$$
$$M = \{\text{orange}\}$$
$$N = \{\quad\}$$

Notice that G is a subset of itself or of set F, because it contains exactly the same members as the original set. Sets H through N

are different than the original set, but every element contained in each of them is also in the original set; therefore they are all subsets of set F. Set N, the empty set because the boy did not choose to eat anything, is a subset because it does not contain any elements that are not in the original set F.

Sets H through N are special kinds of subsets called *proper subsets*. Set G is not a proper subset. Every subset of a given set is a proper subset if it does not equal the given set. In other words, if the original set does not contain at least one member that is not in the subset, the subset is not a proper subset. The only subset, then, that is not a proper subset is the subset that is the set itself.

In working with sets we frequently choose subsets from a dominant, or all-inclusive, set that is composed of all the objects under consideration. This dominant set from which we select some subsets is called the *universal set*. We employ a U to designate a universal set. If the universal set $U = \{$all animals$\}$, some of its subsets could be $\{$cats$\}$, $\{$dogs$\}$, $\{$cows$\}$, $\{$horses$\}$, and $\{$elephants, lions, tigers$\}$.

If the universal set $U = \{$all numbers$\}$, some of its subsets are $\{$even numbers$\}$, $\{$counting numbers$\}$, $\{$odd numbers$\}$, and $\{12, 0, 7, \frac{1}{2}\}$.

List some subsets for each of the following universal sets:

$$U = \{\text{automobiles}\}$$
$$U = \{\text{toys}\}$$
$$U = \{\text{fractions}\}$$
$$U = \{\text{shapes}\}$$

Operations on sets

We operate on sets for much the same reasons and in much the same ways as we operate on numbers in arithmetic. In arithmetic when we operate on numbers by means of addition or multiplication, the result is a new number of the same class. For example, if two natural numbers are added or multiplied, we get another natural number. When we operate on sets by means of intersection and union, we get another set. When we perform the operations of addition and multiplication on numbers, regardless of how many numbers are added or multiplied, we work with only two numbers at a time. When we perform the operations of intersection and union on sets, we work with only two sets at a time. We say that the four fundamental operations on number and the operations of set union and set intersection are binary.

Intersection.   We can take any two sets A and B and form a third set that contains only those members that are in both A and B. The intersection operation on two sets directs us to find a set that includes only the common members of both sets.

Note the difference between intersecting sets and intersection of two sets. *Intersecting sets* are sets that have some members in common. The *intersection* of two sets is another set consisting of the common members from the two sets. The symbol used for intersection is $\cap$. Just as 3×4 is a numeral for 12, so $A \cap B$ is a symbol for a set. The notation $A \cap B$ is read "A intersection B."

As an example, let us use a situation common to many classrooms. Assume that you have two committees composed of students in the class. You wish to form a coordinating committee composed of students who are members of both the other committees. Let the first committee be set $A = \{$Mary, Tom, Chuck, Barbara, Bill, Alice$\}$. Let the second committee be set $B = \{$Sam, Barbara, Tom, Bill, June, Ned$\}$. The students who are members of both sets are Tom, Barbara, and Bill. We can then say that $A \cap B = \{$Tom, Barbara, Bill$\}$.

In the following example we use names of numbers instead of names of people. If $A = \{3, 4, 5, 6\}$ and $B = \{4, 6, 8, 10\}$, then $A \cap B = \{3, 4, 5, 6\} \cap \{4, 6, 8, 10\} = \{4, 6\}$. The intersection of set A and set B gives us the set $\{4, 6\}$ because 4 and 6 are the only two members that are in both A and B. Let us reverse the order of the two sets under consideration and see if it affects the intersection set. $B \cap A = \{4, 6, 8, 10\} \cap \{3, 4, 5, 6\} = \{4, 6\}$. We find that in each case the new set formed by the intersection operation on sets A and B is the same set, $\{4, 6\}$. This result is due to the fact that the intersection operation of sets is commutative. We say for any two sets A and B that $A \cap B = B \cap A$.

For two sets to be intersecting sets, the two sets must have at least one member in common. Intersecting sets also may have all common members. For example, if set $A = \{a, b, c, d\}$ and set $B = \{c, d, a, b\}$, then $A \cap B = \{a, b, c, d\}$. In this case, if we wish, we can say that $A \cap B = A$, or $A \cap B = B$ because A and B are equal sets. We can also say that $A = B$.

Sometimes the two sets under consideration have no members in common and, therefore, are not intersecting sets. If set A and set B contain no common members, the sets are called *disjoint sets*. The set of your feet and the set of your hands are disjoint sets. If set $A = \{1, 3, 5, 7\}$ and set $B = \{2, 4, 6, 8\}$, the set that is their intersection is the empty set or null set. This example would be written $A \cap B = \{\ \}$. Let us consider one more example. If $A = \{\ \}$ and $B = \{6, 7, 8\}$, then $A \cap B = \{\ \}$.

Earlier addition and intersection were defined as binary operations. What happens, then, when confronted with the addition of more than two numbers or the intersection of more than two sets? In adding 3, 4, and 5, we are dealing with three numbers. We add two of the numbers $(3 + 4)$, which will give us a new number. Then we add this new number and the third number: $(3 + 4) + 5 = 7 + 5 = 12$. Of course a different grouping could have been used, $3 + (4 + 5) = 3 + 9 = 12$. The result is the same in both cases, therefore $(3 + 4) + 5 = 3 + (4 + 5)$.

We use the same idea in dealing with the intersection of three sets. For example, let us consider the intersection of three sets, $X \cap Y \cap Z$. We shall first take the intersection of X and Y, which will give us a new set. Then we shall intersect the new set with Z. We write this as $(X \cap Y) \cap Z$. If we let $X = \{2, 3, 4, 5\}$, $Y = \{4, 5, 6, 7\}$, and $Z = \{3, 5, 7, 9\}$, then $(X \cap Y) \cap Z = (\{2, 3, 4, 5\} \cap \{4, 5, 6, 7\}) \cap \{3, 5, 7, 9\} = \{5\}$.

The intersection of the first two sets enclosed in parentheses produces a new set, $\{4, 5\}$. The intersection of this new set with the third set produces the set $\{5\}$. Would the answer have been the same if we had started with the intersection of Y and Z and then had taken the intersection of the new set and X? When you perform the operation, you will see that the result is the same. When intersecting three sets, the result is the same whether you start with the first and second set or with the second and third set because the intersection operation on sets is associative. For any three sets A, B, and C, we can say $(A \cap B) \cap C = A \cap (B \cap C)$.

Union. We can take any two sets A and B and form a third set that contains all the members in either A or B or both A and B. Union is denoted by the symbol $\cup$. The union of sets A and B would be denoted by $A \cup B$ and would be read "A union B."

To distinguish between intersection of sets and union of sets, it might be helpful to consider again the definitions for the two operations. By the operation called *intersection*, given two sets A and B, a new set is formed that contains *only* those members in *both* A *and* B. By the operation called *union*, given any two sets A and B, a new set is formed that contains *all* the members in either A or B or both A and B. The set A ∪ B may contain members that are in both A and B, but they would be listed only once in the new set formed by the union.

As an example let us consider two of the sets that were used to illustrate intersection of sets.

$$A = \{\text{Mary, Tom, Chuck, Barbara, Bill, Alice}\}$$
$$B = \{\text{Sam, Barbara, Tom, Bill, June, Ned}\}$$

The intersection set, A ∩ B, was {Tom, Barbara, Bill}. What will be the union set A ∪ B? It will contain all the members of A or B or both. Then A ∪ B = {Mary, Tom, Chuck, Barbara, Bill, Alice, Sam, June, Ned}.

As another example consider set A consisting of all students in the class who are at least $4\frac{1}{2}$ feet tall and set B all students in class who have freckles on the nose. A ∪ B would be the set consisting of those students in class who are at least $4\frac{1}{2}$ feet tall or who have freckles on the nose. It does not matter if some members of A ∪ B possess both these characteristics.

Bob's pets are represented by B = {dog, snail, bird} and Jim's pets are J = {birds, goldfish, dog, hampster}. B ∪ J = {dog, snail, bird, goldfish, hampster}. J ∪ B = {bird, goldfish, dog, hampster, snail}. Because the union set resulting from B ∪ J or J ∪ B contains exactly the same members, we say that B ∪ J = J ∪ B. In performing the union operation on any two sets, it does not matter if we begin with the first set or the second set because the *union operation is a commutative operation.*

We found that we could form the intersection of three sets. We can also form the union of three sets. If we let A, B, and C represent any three sets, we can first form the union of A and B, A ∪ B; then we can form the union of this new set with C. We would write the notation for this as (A ∪ B) ∪ C. Let A = {1, 2, 3}, B = {2, 3, 4}, and C = {4, 5, 6}. Then (A ∪ B) ∪ C = ({1, 2, 3} ∪ {2, 3, 4}) ∪ {4, 5, 6} = {1, 2, 3, 4, 5, 6}. If we wish, we can first form the union of B and C, B ∪ C, and then form the union of this result with A. A ∪ (B ∪ C) = {1, 2, 3} ∪ ({2, 3, 4} ∪ {4, 5, 6}) = {1, 2, 3, 4, 5, 6}. Although we used different groupings in the two union operations, the resulting union set is $\{1, 2, 3, 4, 5, 6\}$. By working several similar examples, it becomes evident that the new set formed by the union of three sets is the same whether you start with the first and second set or with the second and third set because the *union operation* on sets is an *associative operation*. This should lead to the generalization that for any three sets A, B, and C, $(A \cup B) \cup C = A \cup (B \cup C)$. Some other examples of union sets are as follows:

1. $A = \{\text{orange, apple, pear}\}$ and $B = \{\text{candy, apple, gum}\}$
    $A \cup B = \{\text{orange, apple, pear, candy, gum}\}$
2. $A = \{1, 2, 3, 4\}$ and $B = \{0, 1, 3, 5\}$
    $A \cup B = \{0, 1, 2, 3, 4, 5\}$
3. $A = \{0\}$, $B = \{0, 2, 4, 6\}$, and $C = \{0, 1, 3, 5\}$
    $(A \cup B) \cup C = \{0, 1, 2, 3, 4, 5, 6\}$

Write the union set for the following:

4. $A = \{a, c, e\}$, $B = \{d, e, f\}$, and $C = \{b, e, a\}$
    $(A \cup B) \cup C =$
5. $A = \{1, 2, 3\}$, $B = \{\ \ \}$, and $C = \{o, z, 4\}$
    $(A \cup B) \cup C =$

Sets and Venn diagrams

Sometimes drawings or diagrams are very helpful in understanding mathematical concepts. Venn diagrams are frequently employed to aid the visualization of set concepts. "A Venn diagram is a plane figure in which sets can be represented geometrically by letting points of the plane represent the members of the universe (U). The region bounded by any plane figure can be used for such symbolic representation of a set, but it is customary to use the region bounded by a rectangle. Subsets are usually represented by disks within the rectangle."[1]

For example, $U =$ the set of all dogs is illustrated in the Venn diagram in Figure 1.

---

[1] Everson, A. B., *Modern Mathematics.* Glenview, Ill.: Scott, Foresman and Company, 1962, p. 12.

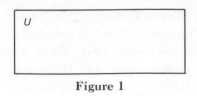

Figure 1

If U = the set of all dogs and A = the set of all cocker spaniel dogs, this relationship is diagrammed in Figure 2. In Figure 2 it is rather easy to visualize that A, the set of all cocker spaniels, is a subset of U, the set of all dogs.

subset of U [handwritten]

Figure 2

A subset of A can be shown by drawing another circle or disk within the circle or disk that represents A. If we let B = the set of all brown cocker spaniels, then B would be included in A. Every member of B is a member of A and every member of A is a member of U. This relationship is diagrammed in Figure 3.

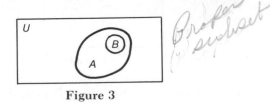

Proper subset [handwritten]

Figure 3

If A = the set of all registered cocker spaniel dogs and C = the set of all registered collie dogs, we think of A and C as being disjoint sets because no dog is a member of both sets. Figure 4 pictures A and C as being two separate or disjoint sets within a universal set.

disjointed sets [handwritten]

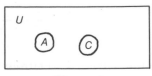

Figure 4

U = the set of all automobiles, T = the set of all automobile taxicabs, and W = the set of all white automobiles. If some taxicabs are white, there are some members of T that are also members of W. Sets T and W are intersecting sets. This relationship is illustrated in Figure 5. The shaded area is composed of those members that belong to both sets T and W, or, in this particular case, the white taxicabs.

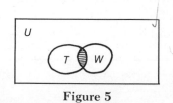

Figure 5

Suppose we use the same sets, where U = all automobiles, T = all automobile taxicabs, and W = all white automobiles, and consider some possible situations. If none of the taxicabs are white, then the relationship would be diagrammed as in Figure 6. In this case set T and set W are disjoint sets.

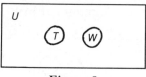

Figure 6

If all automobiles are white and all taxicabs are white, then T and W contain exactly the same members and are called equal sets. Equal sets are usually shown in Venn diagrams as in Figures 7a and 7b.

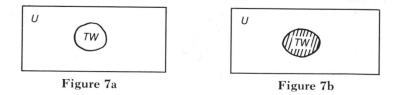

Figure 7a   **Figure 7b**

If all taxicabs are white cars, this relationship can be expressed as in Figure 8a. If all white cars are taxicabs, Figure 8b expresses the relationship.

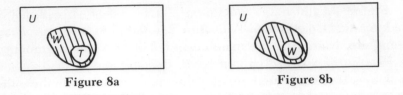

Figure 8a   Figure 8b

The "union of sets" means we pull together into a new set all members that are in A or B or both A and B. We shall use Venn diagrams to illustrate four different situations as they relate to union of sets. Figure 9a illustrates the union of two sets; if $A = \{3, 4, 5, 6\}$

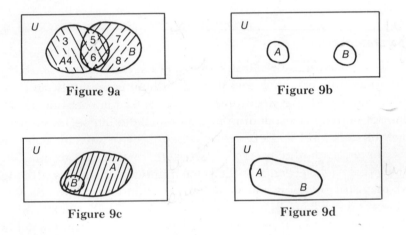

Figure 9a   Figure 9b

Figure 9c   Figure 9d

and $B = \{5, 6, 7, 8\}$, then $A \cup B = \{3, 4, 5, 6, 7, 8\}$. Sets A and B also intersect because they have common members. Notice that 5 and 6 are members of both original sets but are listed only once in the union set.

Figure 9b shows the union of two sets; if $A = \{3, 4, 5\}$ and $B = \{6, 7, 8\}$, then $A \cup B = \{3, 4, 5, 6, 7, 8\}$. Sets A and B are disjoint sets because no member of one set is a member of the other. Because the original sets are disjoint, we simply combine all the members in one set with all the members of the other set to form the union set.

Figure 9c pictures the union of two sets; if $A = \{3, 4, 5, 6\}$ and $B = \{4, 6\}$, then $A \cup B = \{3, 4, 5, 6\}$. B is a proper subset of A because A contains all the members of B, but B does not contain all the members of A. In this case the union set consists only of the members of A.

Figure 9d illustrates the union of two sets; if $A = \{2, 4, 6, 8\}$ and $B = \{2, 4, 6, 8\}$, then $A \cup B = \{2, 4, 6, 8\}$. Sets A and B are equal sets. Notice that the space occupied in the Venn diagram by A is exactly the space occupied by B. Because the membership in both sets is exactly the same, this membership will form the union set.

Make Venn diagrams to illustrate the following set concepts.

1. $A \cap B$, when $A = \{0, 1, 2, 3\}$ and $B = \{2, 3, 4\}$
2. $A \subseteq B$, when $A = \{2, 3\}$ and $B = \{1, 2, 3, 4\}$
3. $A \cup B$, when $A = \{1, 3, 5\}$ and $B = \{2, 4, 6\}$
4. $A = B$, when $A = \{1, 3, 4, 2\}$ and $B = \{3, 2, 1, 4\}$

Matching sets

If we wish to determine if two sets have the same number of members, this can be accomplished without counting the number of members. All we need do is to pair or match each member of one set with a corresponding member of the other set. If no members of either set are left over, we say the two sets are matching sets or equivalent sets. If the two sets "match one to one," we know that each set contains the same number of members, although we may still not know how many members either set contains. Consider set $A = \{\text{Tom, Bill, Charles}\}$ and set $B = \{\text{ball, truck, wagon}\}$. We can determine if each boy can have a toy by simply matching the members in each set in a one-to-one correspondence in the following manner:

$$A = \{\text{Tom, Bill, Charles}\}$$
$$\updownarrow \quad \updownarrow \quad \updownarrow$$
$$B = \{\text{ball, truck, wagon}\}$$

There are exactly enough toys in set B for each boy in set A to have one. The two sets contain the same number of members and are considered equivalent sets. This set concept of equivalence or one-to-one correspondence as it relates to number will be discussed in more detail in following chapters.

Utilizing concepts of sets

The terminology, definitions, symbolism, notation, and diagrammatic illustrations of sets could be taught as an isolated topic to young children in a very abstract way involving a great deal of rote memorization. However, this method of including sets in modern programs of elementary mathematics would hardly be more appropriate than the content and instructional procedures of traditional programs of several decades ago. Therefore, as set concepts were developed in this chapter, an attempt has been made to utilize illustrations in terms of their applicability for the elementary school.

Concepts of sets should be taught to children in a meaningful way, not necessarily as a separate topic, and should be utilized as an integral part of the total program to develop concepts of number, operations, geometry, and problem solving. Procedures for introducing and utilizing set concepts in this manner are discussed or implied in following chapters.

Some of the areas in which set concepts can be introduced and used include the following:

1. Developing the concepts of cardinality of number and number names through the use of equivalent sets and one-to-one correspondence
2. Developing an understanding of the structure of our system of numeration through the classification of types of numbers and Venn diagrams of the subsets of numbers in the set of real numbers
3. Developing an understanding of our number system through emphasizing the concept of "base" or collecting numbers into subsets of 10
4. Developing the concept of equality through renaming numbers in problem-solving situations requiring the operations of counting, addition, and multiplication
5. Classifying geometric ideas or figures
6. Improving children's problem-solving abilities by using Venn diagrams to illustrate the problems and an approach that uses the combining of sets, comparison of sets, and separation of sets in the process of analysis of the problem situation

Ideas, in the above list, for utilizing set concepts are developed and illustrated in later chapters.

Suggested activities

1. Most of the current elementary mathematics programs devote attention to the basic ideas of sets, particularly in the primary grades. What does the set concept offer to justify its inclusions?

2. Do you believe that too much emphasis is given in elementary school mathematics textbooks to set terminology, symbolism, and notation? Justify your answer.

3. Distinguish between intersection of sets and union of sets. Give illustrations of the two operations that would be within elementary age children's experience.

4. List the significant ideas you want children to understand about sets. Why did you choose these particular ideas?

5. What is the justification for the relatively heavy emphasis given to equivalent sets in most programs?

Selected references

Botts, Truman, "Numbers, Sets, and Counting," *The Arithmetic Teacher,* 8:281–286, Oct. 1961.

Dubisch, Ray, "Set Equality," *The Arithmetic Teacher,* 13:388–391, May 1966.

Fehr, H. F., "In Answer to Your Questions: What Is a Set," *The Arithmetic Teacher,* 12:203, March 1965.

Geddes, Dorothy, and S. I. Lipsey, "Set-Natural, Necessary, (k)nowable?," *The Arithmetic Teacher,* 15:537–540, April 1968.

National Council of Teachers of Mathematics, *Topics in Mathematics.* Twenty-ninth Yearbook. Washington, D.C.: The National Council of Teachers of Mathematics, Inc., 1964, pp. 1–47.

Paul, J. S., "Sets and Numbers," *The Arithmetic Teacher,* 10:411, Nov. 1963.

Saunders, W. J., "Cardinal Numbers and Sets," *The Arithmetic Teacher,* 13:26–29, Feb. 1966.

Tassone, A. D., " 'Sets': A Unifying Factor," *Catholic School Journal,* 66:79–81, Sept. 1966.

3

Teaching concepts of number and numeration

Children, during their preschool years, are exposed to a variety of quantitative problem situations and explore many ways of solving them. As this search continues through the years, each person should continue to improve and refine his ideas about number and should find more effective and efficient means of solving his mathematical problems.

The child of today is fortunate indeed in that he grows up in a culture that has a well-established and functional numeration system. At an early age children hear people using number names often and observe their older brothers and sisters or their parents perform various number operations.

Growing up so closely with a numeration system, children may take for granted or give little thought to why we happen to have the system we do. However, our experience has been that many children do ask such questions as "Why do we have a number system?", "Have we always used the system we are now using?", "Did people long ago count as we do?", "Have people always been able to count?" Children should be encouraged to ask such questions and should be helped to find sensible answers to them.

Our numeration system has evolved over many centuries and many civilizations. The history of mathematics is clearly interwoven with the history of mankind. The importance of studying the historical struggles of man has been long argued in order that we may better understand and appreciate the social, economic, and political structure of our country. Enjoyment and reward can likewise be found from learning about the history and development of number and numeration.

What is number?

To understand the concept of number, it is helpful to study its origin. One of the first ideas usually associated with number today is that of counting—to find the answer to the question "How many?" or "Which one?" Yet, there was a time when man did not know how to count at all, at least not in the sense that we count today.

Primitive man's need for number was rather simple. He generally did not need to deal with large numbers or with computation. Early man soon discovered, however, that he needed a means of keeping track of things—his family, herd of animals, tribe, and so forth. For instance, he may have wished to know if all his animals had returned from grazing or if all the warriors in his tribe had returned safely from battle.

The early history of man's development tells us that many centuries ago man could not tell "how many" possessions he had but that he could distinguish between one and many. He could probably tell if he had "a few" or "a lot" and he could determine if some of his possessions were missing.

Number and sets

Before man could count, he relied heavily upon objects and employed some form of tallying or comparing to get an idea of how many of anything he had. By comparing one set of objects with another, early man was able to recognize whether two sets contained the same or different numbers of objects long before he could tell how many objects were in a particular set. Today children still develop many number ideas much the same way as did early man. Long before a child can actually count, he can determine whether one set contains the same number of objects as another set or whether one set contains more or less objects than another set.

Distinctions described in the preceding paragraph are made by comparing two sets. In fact, given any two sets, a person can compare the number of objects that are in the sets without knowing anything about the concept of number. This is done by finding out if there is a one-to-one correspondence between the members of the two sets. If it is possible to match or pair each member of one set to a member of another set so that there is a one-to-one correspondence between the members of the two sets, we say the two sets contain the same number of elements.

An ancient herdsman likely used this one-to-one correspondence method of comparing sets in keeping track of his sheep. For example, the herdsman may have stood beside a narrow passageway through which the sheep must pass. As the sheep went out to graze, he would drop a pebble for each sheep that passed him. If we let S = the set of sheep and P = the set of pebbles, there would be exactly one sheep in set S for each pebble in set P and exactly one pebble in set P for each sheep in set S. In other words, the pile of pebbles contained the same number of pebbles as there were sheep. As the sheep returned from grazing, the herdsman would remove from the pile of pebbles one pebble for each sheep that returned to determine if as many sheep came back as went out to graze. Today, we use this principle in the modern concept of mapping. Suppose we wish to match or pair a set of capital cities with a set of states or vice versa; the mapping could be as follows:

$$\text{set } C = \{\text{Columbus, Lansing, } \quad \text{Austin, Nashville}\}$$
$$\updownarrow \qquad\qquad \updownarrow \qquad\quad \updownarrow \qquad\quad \updownarrow$$
$$\text{set } S = \{\text{Ohio, } \qquad \text{Michigan, Texas, Tennessee}\}$$

Sets C and S are in a one-to-one correspondence because it is possible to assign to each member in set C one, and only one, member of set S and vice versa. When such a correspondence can be established between two sets through a reversable mapping procedure, the two sets are said to contain the same number of objects or to possess the same number.

However, before we can utilize this method of determining how many things are in a group (cardinal number), there must exist some organized, systematic means of expressing numbers with words and/or number symbols. Therefore, throughout history man has developed many systems of numeration in his effort to find an effective means of using number symbols to represent numbers. Teachers need to be familiar with this historical development to help youngsters develop a deeper appreciation of the beauty and relative simplicity of the Hindu-Arabic numeration system.

Other numeration systems

Lack of historical records makes it difficult to describe accurately early man's efforts to express and record number ideas. Archeological remains and sketchy records, however, do show that different civilizations have invented different ways of expressing and recording numbers with symbols. Man has apparently always tried to make whatever number system he used simple and convenient.

A study of the history of number development in various societies and civilizations shows that many things have been used to stand for different quantities but that they all served a particular need of man. For instance, the Egyptians used pictures, the Babylonians used wedge-shaped marks, and the Romans and Greeks used letters.

A general belief is that the first mathematical systems were developed by the people who lived in the ancient civilizations clustered around the Mediterranean Sea. Remains from these civilizations give us some ideas as to the way people living thousands of years ago used symbols individually and in combination to represent numbers. Surprisingly, they had many advanced ideas about mathematics. The earliest of these peoples used crude pictures or drawings to represent number, for instance,

for one warrior

for two warriors

The Egyptian system.   Even though the Egyptian numeration system is one of the oldest and its number symbols were hieroglyphs, it is quite remarkable for its simplicity and usefulness.

The Egyptians used simple marks or strokes to represent the numbers from 1 through 9. Inasmuch as a symbol could be repeated up to nine times, the Egyptians found it easier to read a numeral if the symbols were grouped in two or more rows, as:

1	2	3	4	5	6	7	8	9
/	//	///	////	/////	///	////	////	///
					///	///	////	///
								///

In addition to the marks or strokes, the Egyptians had symbols representing powers of ten, up to one million:

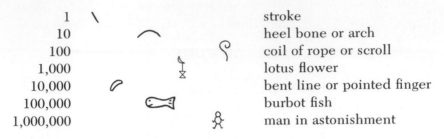

1	\		stroke
10	⌒		heel bone or arch
100		⟲	coil of rope or scroll
1,000		⚱	lotus flower
10,000	⌒		bent line or pointed finger
100,000	⊂⊐		burbot fish
1,000,000		𝓀	man in astonishment

History does not reveal to us why the Egyptians chose these symbols to represent number. However, it is rather easy to imagine why the number one million might be represented by a man in astonishment. Trying to comprehend such a large number was, undoubtedly, a shocking experience.

The Egyptian numeration system was basically decimal; however, it did not utilize the concept of place value. Therefore a symbol always had the same value regardless of the position it occupied. The principles of repetition and addition were used in the Egyptian system. No particular pattern of arrangement was required when two or more symbols were to represent a number. For instance, 128 could be written as ⟲∩∩//// or ////∩∩⟲ or ∩∩////⟲ or ∩∩////⟲//// , and so forth. To determine the number represented in this system, you simply need to add the amounts represented by the various symbols representing the number. Following are some examples of representative numbers formed by combining Egyptian symbols:

Our number	Egyptian numbers	
18	∩ //// ////	//// //// ∩
48	∩∩ //// ∩∩ ////	//// ∩∩ //// ∩∩
111	⟲∩/	/∩⟲
2,169	⚱⚱ ⟲ ∩∩∩ /// ∩∩∩ ///	/// ∩∩∩ /// ∩∩∩ ⟲ ⚱⚱
1,200,003	𝓀 ⊂⊐ ⊂⊐ ///	/// ⊂⊐ ⊂⊐ 𝓀

Try writing the Egyptian number symbol for each of the following Hindu-Arabic numerals:

18	372
56	22,361
79	2,131,425

Try writing Hindu-Arabic numerals for each of the following Egyptian numerals:

The Babylonian system.   Some 2000 B.C. the Babylonians used a stylus to press into wet clay tablets wedge-shaped characters, called cuneiforms, to represent number. Babylonians utilized only two basic characters or numerals to express numbers, ⋎ for one and ⟨ for ten.

In notating number the Babylonians used two base systems, the decimal (10) and the sexagesimal (60). Also, two principles were utilized, the additive and the multiplicative.

In notating numbers up to 60, a simple additive decimal grouping system was used.

Babylonian	Hindu-Arabic
	3
	7
	12
	33
	56

In the notation of numbers 60 and greater, a system based on 60 and the multiplicative principle was used. Instead of the basic character having one meaning or value, its value was dependent upon its position or place in the numeral. The Babylonians are thought to have been the first to use the place or positional value concept. For a long time the Babylonians had no symbol to indicate an empty place; therefore it was difficult to interpret the meaning of a numeral made up of several symbols. For example, the numeral ∀ ∀ ∀ might be interpreted as meaning 3, or 62, or 3,602. The practice was soon adopted of leaving a wider space between symbols to indicate an empty place or the absence of a certain size group. Later a special symbol was used to indicate an absence of value in a particular place. However, the symbol was apparently never used at the end of a number. The Babylonian sexagesimal numeration system utilized the place-value concept; however, the system suffered the disadvantage of not having a definite symbol for zero. Because of difficulty in interpreting and computing, history indicates that people employing this system rarely used large numbers.

Babylonian Place-Value Chart

$(60 \times 60 \times 60 \text{ or } 60^3)$ 216,000's	$(60 \times 60 \text{ or } 60^2)$ 3,600's	$(60 \times 1 \text{ or } 60^1)$ 60's	(60^0) 1's
			⟨ ∀∀∀ / ⟨ ∀∀∀∀
		∀	⟨ ∀
		∀	⟨ ∀∀∀∀ / ⟨ ∀∀∀∀
	∀	∀	⟨ ∀ ∀

The four numerals shown on the chart translated into Hindu-Arabic numerals are 27, 71, 88, and 3,672. In comparison to our system, the Babylonian system causes us to think in groups of 60 and the ones column or place includes numerals usually thought of as having two places, 1–59. The Babylonian system did not utilize a two place numeral until 60 was reached. This system is of special interest because today we still measure and record certain aspects of time and angles based on the number 60.

Translate each of the Babylonian numerals in the following chart to equivalent Hindu-Arabic numerals.

Babylonian Place-Value Chart

60^3	60^2	60^1	60^0	Hindu-Arabic equivalent
			⧉⧉ᐯᐯᐯ	
		ᐯᐯ		
	ᐯ			
ᐯ		ᐯᐯᐯ	⧉ ᐯᐯ	

How would the following Hindu-Arabic numerals be written using Babylonian numerals?

6 = _____   18 = _____   72 = _____

3703 = _____   229,830 = _____

The Greek system.   The ancient Greeks used the 24 letters of their alphabet plus three obsolete forms as symbols to denote numbers. The last column in the chart shows accented letters representing multiplication by 1000. The Greek system of numera-

Greek numerals and the Hindu-Arabic equivalents

1	α	alpha	10	ι	iota	100	ρ	rho	1,000	α'	
2	β	beta	20	κ	kappa	200	σ	sigma	2,000	β'	
3	γ	gamma	30	λ	lambda	300	τ	tau	3,000	γ'	
4	δ	delta	40	μ	mu	400	υ	upsilon	4,000	δ'	
5	ε	epsilon	50	ν	nu	500	φ	phi	5,000	ε'	
6	F	vau°	60	ξ	xi	600	χ	chi	6,000	F'	
7	ζ	zeta	70	o	omicron	700	ψ	psi	7,000	ζ'	
8	η	eta	80	π	pi	800	ω	omega	8,000	η'	
9	θ	theta	90	ϙ	koppa°	900	ϡ	sampi°	9,000	θ'	

°Denotes obsolete symbols.

tion did not utilize the place-value concept; therefore the quantity represented by any of the basic symbols was independent of position or sequence. The additive principle was applied in giving value to Greek numbers smaller than 10,000. For example, the number 555 would be written $\phi\nu\epsilon$, or $500 + 50 + 5$.

In expressing numbers 10,000 or larger, the multiplicative as well as the additive principle was used. The letter M written directly under one of the basic symbols indicated multiplication by 10,000. The number 30,000 would be written $\overset{\gamma}{M}$. 50,259 would be written $\overset{\epsilon}{M}\beta\epsilon\theta$.

The Greek system of numeration could become very confusing when written in narrative context. The Greeks devised various methods to distinguish the numerals from the letters of the alphabet. For instance, if the letters representing a number also represented a Greek word, a line may have been drawn above the letters to indicate a number rather than a word.

In terms of counting, the Greek system was satisfactory, but calculation was clumsy and difficult. The early Greeks drew marks or lines in sand or dust to calculate. Also, the Greeks were one of the early users of some form of abacus in performing calculations. The word abacus is derived from the Greek word for dust.

Write Hindu-Arabic numerals for each of the following Greek numerals.

$$\nu F \qquad \chi\pi\eta \qquad \overset{\epsilon}{M}\alpha'\phi o\beta$$

$$\vartheta\lambda\epsilon \qquad \beta'\tau\mu\theta \qquad \varphi\theta$$

The Roman system.   The Roman system is very old and once again the hand apparently influenced the numerals used. It is thought that the I was used to represent a finger, the V to represent a hand , and the X to represent two hands (two V's). Roman numerals are still used enough in our culture to warrant helping children understand their meaning. Roman numerals are used today in books to denote chapter numbers, in sections of an outline, on clock faces, as dates of films and public buildings, and more recently as the names of space vehicles such as the "Saturn V."

The Roman numerals are written with the use of seven basic symbols. These symbols and their decimal equivalents are $I = 1$, $V = 5$, $X = 10$, $L = 50$, $C = 100$, $D = 500$, and $M = 1,000$. The system represents a simple grouping process to base 10 and until modern times operated on the principles of addition and repetition. At first only four symbols, I, X, C, and M were used in this system. To lessen the necessity of repeating symbols so many times to write certain numbers, the Romans invented the symbols V, L, and D. Due to the fact that the symbols for 10, 100, and 1,000 were available, the symbols V, L, and D are not repeated in writing a number. The only symbols that are repeated are

I equal to 1   C equal to 100

X equal to 10   M equal to 1,000

In the Roman system, whenever adjacent symbols in a numeral represent the same number or the symbol to the right represents a smaller number, the numbers are added. The following are examples of the additive and repetitive principles:

$$VII = (5 + 1 + 1) = 7$$
$$XIII = (10 + 1 + 1 + 1) = 13$$
$$LXXV = (50 + 10 + 10 + 5) = 75$$
$$CCLXII = (100 + 100 + 10 + 1 + 1) = 262$$
$$DCXXV = (500 + 100 + 10 + 10 + 5) = 625$$
$$MDCLX = (1,000 + 500 + 100 + 50 + 10) = 1,660$$

In an effort to make notation less cumbersome, the Romans improved their system by using the principle of subtraction. However, the principle of subtraction can be used only when the following conditions are observed:

1. Only the symbols I, X, and C are used in a subtractive sense.
2. The value of I is subtracted only when it appears immediately before either V or X in a numeral.
3. The value of X is subtracted from the value of L or C only when it appears immediately before L or C in a numeral.
4. The value of C is subtracted from the value of D or M only when it appears immediately before D or M in a numeral.

The following are examples of the subtractive principle:

$$IV = 5 - 1 = 4$$
$$IX = 10 - 1 = 9$$
$$XL = 50 - 10 = 40$$
$$XC = 100 - 10 = 90$$
$$CD = 500 - 100 = 400$$
$$CM = 1,000 - 100 = 900$$
$$XIV = 10 + (5 - 1) = 14$$
$$LIX = 50 + (10 - 1) = 59$$
$$CDXIV = (500 - 100) + 10 + (5 - 1) = 414$$
$$XLIX = (50 - 10) + (10 - 1) = 49$$
$$CMLIV = (1,000 - 100) + 50 + (5 - 1) = 954$$
$$MDXLV = 1,000 + 500 + (50 - 10) + 5 = 1,545$$

Whenever the Romans wished to write 1,000 times a given number, they drew a bar over the particular symbol to indicate it had been multiplied by 1,000. Thus they used the multiplicative principle in writing large numbers:

5,000 is written $\overline{V}$
50,000 is written $\overline{L}$
500,000 is written $\overline{D}$
101,256 is written $\overline{C}MCCLVI$
20,014 is written $\overline{XXX}IV$

Notice that only the symbols immediately under the bar are multiplied by 1,000.

The Roman system was an improvement over previous systems as far as notation was concerned, but computation was still very difficult. In fact, to compute in this system, it was necessary to use some mechanical computational device such as the Roman counting board or reckoning board.

Translate the following Roman numerals to Hindu-Arabic numerals:

LXIV   MMCXLIV
MDCXX $\overline{X}DCCXXIX$
DCLXXVII $\overline{MDCL}CCXCVII$

Write a Roman numeral for each of the following:

$$88 \qquad 1,965$$
$$947 \qquad 22,544$$

Mayan system.   Uncovered early records clearly reveal the Mayan Indians of Central America developed, apparently all on their own, a numeration system complete with the place-value concept and a symbol for zero. The first incorporation of these two concepts into a highly functional numeral system is generally credited to the Mayans.

A study of the records of the Mayan civilization indicates that their numeration system, with the exception of the third place in a numeral, is vegesimal, operating on a base of twenty. In addition to the symbol of zero, they used a system of dots and dashes to notate numbers. A dot meant one and a dash meant five. The first 20 numbers in the Mayan system were:

In this system the principle of place value was used for the first time in writing the numeral for twenty, ⵔ. The symbol for zero indicates no kins (1's) and the dot over the symbol for zero indicates one uinal (20), or one of the base. The first five place values in the Mayan system are:

kins   = 1's
20 kins   = 1 unal (base) = 20
18 unials = 1 tun   = 360^2
20 tuns   = 1 katun   = 7,200
20 katuns = 1 cycle   = 144,000

_____

[2] The only position (place value) not consistent with base twenty.

When numerals were written to express numbers greater than 20, the symbols constituting the numerals were arranged in vertical order starting with the lowest place value at the bottom. For example, the following Mayan numeral represents 349,216:

••	= (2	144,000's) = 288,000	
•••	= (8	7,200's) = 57,600	
══	= (10	360's) = 3,600	= 349,216
⬭	= (0	20's) = 0	
⩦	= (16	1's) = 16	

Why study early numeration systems?

If the study of earlier numeration systems is included in an elementary school mathematics program, the purpose must be understood by all concerned. The main objective of such study should be to help children appreciate and understand the fundamental characteristics of the Hindu-Arabic system of numeration. The realization of this objective likely would be enhanced by studying the struggles mankind has made in attempting to find more efficient means of recording and communicating number concepts.

When approached from a comparative viewpoint, the study of ancient systems in present mathematical programs of instruction should reveal that the structure and characteristics of our current system is the result of man's advancement in notating number: utilization of objects, tally marks, grouping, basic numerals, additive property, place value. When viewed from this perspective, the beauty, simplicity, and efficiency of the Hindu-Arabic system as compared to other numeration systems should be more apparent to elemenetary school pupils.

Suggested activities

1. Outline some activities appropriate for helping elementary children to understand better and appreciate the history and development of the Hindu-Arabic numeration system.

2. Choose a grade level and outline three possibilities for encouraging children to dramatize early man's efforts to keep records and to represent numbers.

3. Explain why it was so difficult to interpret the meaning of a numeral containing several symbols after the place or positional-value concept was in use.

4. How do you justify spending time on Roman numerals in a modern mathematics program?

Selected references

Bidwell, J. K., "Mayan Arithmetic," *The Mathematics Teacher*, 60:762–768, Nov. 1967.

Dubisch, Ray, *The Nature of Number*. New York: The Ronald Press Company, 1952.

Eves, Howard, *An Introduction to the History of Mathematics*. New York: Holt, Rinehart and Winston, Inc., 1953.

Johnson, D. A., and W. H. Glenn, *Understanding Numeration Systems*. Manchester, Mo.: Webster Publishing Division of McGraw-Hill, Inc., 1960.

Lerch, H. H., *Numbers in the Land of Hand*. Carbondale, Ill.: Southern Illinois University Press, 1966.

National Council of Teachers of Mathematics, *Topics in Mathematics*. Twenty-ninth Yearbook. Washington, D.C.: The National Council of Teachers of Mathematics, Inc., 1964, pp. 102–132.

O'Donnell, J. R., "Number, Numeral, and Plato," *The Arithmetic Teacher*, 13:401–402, May 1966.

Smith, D. E., *History of Mathematics*. New York: Dover Publications, Inc., 1958.

Smith, D. E., and J. Ginsburg, *Number and Numerals*. New York: Teachers College, Columbia University, 1937.

Teaching

4

our numeration system

The elementary school has an obligation to help pupils gain a good understanding of the basic principles of our numeration system. The numeration is "ours" only in the sense that we have adopted it for our usage. This remarkable system that now serves as a communications media for number ideas throughout the civilized world is really quite old. It is generally conceded that the Hindus invented the system and that the Arabs introduced it to the Western world. This is why we often refer to "our" numeration system as the Hindu-Arabic or decimal system. The term *decimal* comes from the Latin word decem, meaning ten, and again, as noted in Chapter 3, there appears to be a direct relationship between the development of a numeration system and the fact that man has 10 fingers.

What do we mean when we speak of a numeration system?

To have a system of any kind, there must be some form of regular interaction and interdependence. This is certainly true of a numeration system. The term *numeration system* is used, then, to indicate a well-organized, orderly, systematic scheme for expressing quantity with symbols. The symbols used to express quantity are *numerals*. The quantity expressed is *number*. In other words, number is an abstract idea—a mental concept. A numeral is not the concept; it only names or stands for the concept. The symbol

47

⚧ is not a boy, but it may be used to stand for, represent, or name a boy. Similarly, the symbol 5 is not five, but it may be used to name or represent five of something. We read, write, or erase numerals. We think, add, subtract, multiply, and divide numbers. Elementary teachers need to recognize the distinct difference between a numeral and a number. Teachers must also make the decision as to the most appropriate level or stage to begin helping the pupils in their classrooms recognize whether a number or the name of a number is being discussed. This distinction can be developed by discussing various objects in the classroom. Use such objects as a desk, eraser, chalk, map, book, and so forth, to establish the concept that everything including an idea has a name; however, that name is not the thing, but the name for it.

There are many times when we wish to talk and write about numbers. Obviously we must use names or number symbols (numerals) to express number ideas, whether written or spoken. Neither the appearance (form) of the symbols nor the name is significant as long as the quantity or number they represent is agreed upon by people using the numeration system. In the history of numeration, as pointed out in Chapter 3, many types of numerals have been used. In any numeration system, including the Hindu-Arabic, there first had to be an arbitrary assignment of a given quantity to a mutually agreed upon symbol. Any symbol may be used but its use must be consistent after it is selected. If a numeration system is to function effectively as a means of communication over a period of time, the system must be simple, convenient, and consistent.

The Hindu-Arabic or decimal numeration system has been in existence for many centuries. In fact, the system was known in Europe as early as the thirteenth century. Several centuries later, developments in science and trade made its computational simplicity advantageous over the older existing systems, and the Hindu-Arabic system came into extensive use. Let us explore some of the characteristics that have made our system preferred over older systems.

Numerals or digits.   Ten separate and distinct one-place numerals are employed to represent the whole numbers zero through nine, or zero up to the base. This set of basic numerals, sometimes called digits, consists of the symbols 0, 1, 2, 3, 4, 5, 6, 7, 8, 9. Each of the 10 numerals has a face value all its own. The numeral 0 always indicates an absence of value or the number of the empty set. The numerals 1 through 9 always indicate value. The face value of an individual numeral is determined by the set whose cardinal number corresponds to the particular digit under consideration. The following chart illustrates the face value of each of our 10 basic numerals.

0	1	2	3	4	5	6	7	8	9
zero	one	two	three	four	five	six	seven	eight	nine

We use the term "10 basic numerals" because these numerals may be used individually or in some combination to express any number we wish to represent. Peoples of various nationalities use different names for these symbols or numerals, but the number symbols are written in much the same form throughout the world; therefore they serve as a common language for expressing number ideas among many nations.

The learning of numerals and names for number should be closely related to usage. Numbers are used to express two basic ideas. A number may be used in the *cardinal* sense to indicate *how many* or the total quantity. Or, a number may be used in the *ordinal* sense to indicate *which one*, or a particular location or position. A number, itself, is neither cardinal nor ordinal; it only becomes cardinal or ordinal in terms of the way it is used. For example 25 is neither cardinal nor ordinal. But, if the statement is made, "There are 25 rooms in this school", then 25 is used as a cardinal number. In the statement "My room is 25" the 25 is used as an ordinal number. If the child hears, "Read 25 pages in this book" he should recognize that 25 is used to express a cardinal idea, and that the statement "Turn to page 25" uses 25 to express an ordinal idea. In most programs the cardinal meaning of number is emphasized first, but more teachers than formerly are introducing children to the ordinal meaning of number as soon as they have some idea of cardinality.

Number concepts become more meaningful when they are developed as properties of sets. Children's first activities, however, with the manipulation of sets of objects should not involve number names or number symbols. The major purpose of these early activities is not to help children answer the question "How many?", but to introduce concepts of equivalence, nonequivalence, equality, and inequality. The readiness program for effectively dealing with numbers should provide the child with the ability to determine if two sets are equivalent—if one set contains exactly as many members as the other.

In helping children build the equivalence concept, sets of objects familiar to youngsters should be utilized. For example, pupils in the early primary grades might be asked to determine if sets A and B contain exactly the same number of objects when set $A = \{\ominus, \ominus, \ominus\}$ and set $B = \{\text{♟}, \text{♟}, \text{♟}, \text{♟}, \text{♟}\}$. Children can find an answer to this question by attempting to match the objects in set A with the objects in set B.

$$\text{Set } A = \{\ominus, \ominus, \ominus\}$$
$$\updownarrow \quad \updownarrow \quad \updownarrow$$
$$\text{Set } B = \{\text{♟}, \text{♟}, \text{♟}, \text{♟}, \text{♟}\}$$

When each object in set A is paired or matched with an object in set B, the child can easily see that there are not enough baseballs for each boy to have one. Set B contains more members than set A, or set A contains fewer members than set B; therefore the two sets are nonequivalent or do not have the same cardinal number or contain the same number of objects.

Many experiences such as

$$\text{set } A = \{\text{♀}, \text{♀}, \text{♀}\}$$
$$\updownarrow \quad \updownarrow \quad \updownarrow$$
$$\text{set } B = \{\text{♟}, \text{♟}, \text{♟}\}$$

in which every member of a set can be placed in a one-to-one (matching) relationship with every member of another set are needed in building the concept of equivalent sets—a prerequisite for understanding numbers.

When the major purpose of instruction does become that of helping children to learn the numerals or number names for a group of objects or to answer the question "How many?," a teaching procedure utilizing set approach has proved to be very effective.

Sets may have little or nothing in common as far as the physical characteristics or properties of the members is concerned. Yet, if it is possible to establish a one-to-one correspondence between the members of two sets, we say the sets possess a common property—that of having the same number of members. This idea is basic to counting.

Counting, then, involves matching through one-to-one correspondence the members of a set of objects to be counted with the members of a set of counting numbers. If we let $S = \{$ ⊖, ▽, ⚹ $\}$ and $N = \{1, 2, 3\}$, we can, by pairing or matching, place in one-to-one correspondence the objects in set S with the numerals in set N.

$$S = \{ \; ①, \; ▽, \; ⚹ \; \}$$
$$\updownarrow \quad \updownarrow \quad \updownarrow$$
$$N = \{ \; 1, \quad 2, \quad 3 \; \}$$

Because these are equivalent sets, the last numeral in set N matched with the last object in set S tells us "how many" things are in the set or group; therefore we say set S contains three objects.

Consider for a moment a set of baseballs, a set of gloves, and a set of boys.

set $X = \{$ 👦, 👦, 👦, 👦, 👦 $\}$

set $Y = \{$ ⊖, ⊖, ⊖, ⊖, ⊖ $\}$

set $Z = \{$ 🧤, 🧤, 🧤, 🧤, 🧤 $\}$

The members of sets, X, Y, and Z can be placed in one-to-one correspondence so that each boy has one baseball and one glove with none left over. Each set contains precisely the same number of members and therefore they all have the common number property of five. By working through several similar situations, children develop the concept of fiveness or 5. Similar procedures should be used in developing number concepts for all the basic number symbols $0, 1, 2, 3, \ldots, 10$. When utilizing a set approach, number names for first small and then larger sets of objects are brought out by beginning with small collections and their number properties and successively including one more element in the sets. Not only will pupils learn the meaning of each of the basic numerals through this procedure, but the relationship among numbers and the idea of order should evolve. For example, the idea that 3 is one more than 2 and one less than 4, or that 2 comes after 1; 3 after 2; 4 after

3, or that 3 comes between 2 and 4. "Zero", 0, is taught as the cardinal number name for the empty set. During the early elementary school years, children also need experiences that will help them recognize that 0 serves as a reference point on a scale such as a thermometer, a numberline, a speedometer, and so forth.

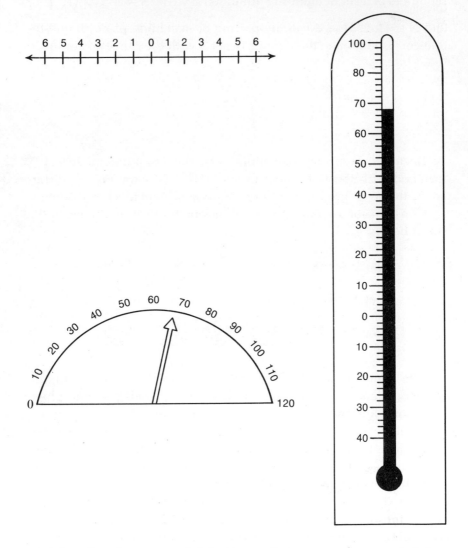

The idea that a set of objects may have several names is introduced early in the program. For example, a teacher might begin with a set containing one element illustrated on a flannel board. The number name for this set of objects could be brought out by asking the children if any of them know the number name to describe this set. In the most unusual case in which no child in the class will know, the teacher will tell. (Names cannot be discovered.) Some child might be asked to make another set containing one element on the flannel board. Then the teacher might ask the children to identify other sets in the room that contain one element or object. The responses could include one teacher, one clock, one pencil sharpener, and so forth. In succeeding activities an additional element will be put in the set previously under discussion, and the question concerning the number name for the set will be repeated. If the new set contains two or more elements, several number names might be given, but one of those names will be emphasized.

Consider this set: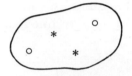

The number names given for the set might include "three and one" and "two and two," but the name that is to be emphasized would be "four." In addition to working with sets of objects, the utilization of pictures such as the four ice cream cones illustrated can help children progress toward a generalized idea of number.

When collections of more than 10 objects are being considered, children should be encouraged to collect the objects into subsets of 10 in order to find the number more easily. For example, the group of counting sticks on the desk may be regrouped into two subsets of 1 ten and 2 ones or 12.

///////////

///////////P //

Base. The Hindu-Arabic system has 10 as its radix or number base. Ten was probably chosen as the base or a way of grouping because man had long used the 10 digits on his hands as a model group for counting. When he had counted nine and one more (10), he had used all his fingers (digits) and would make some record of this size group before starting to count another group of 10. This first collection in a number series has become the established base of our number system. The base is equal to the set of basic one-digit numerals employed to notate number in the system; thus the decimal system uses only 10 number symbols. The numeral nine (9) expresses the largest value we can write with one digit; therefore, we use a two-digit numeral, 10, to express the base. We call this numeral ten (10); the 1 means one unified group of ten, or one of the base, and the 0 means no ones. The progression of number in the base ten system uses the principle of grouping by tens. This principle is used both in our idea of counting and in our scheme of notation.

After pupils learn to understand, read, and write the basic numerals, $0, 1, 2, \ldots, 9$, they should learn to count in sets of ten and to associate the sets of ten with the numerals $10, 20, 30, \ldots, 90$.

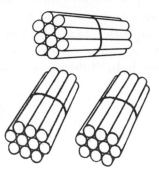

For example, when we get one more than nine (9), we collect or regroup, give the new group the name ten, and write it 10. When we get another set of nine and one more, we have two groups of 10 and the numeral 20 would express the number of counters. Children should have similar experience of collecting or bundling 10 counters through nine sets of ten, or 90. When we get 10 groups of ten, we again collect or regroup, call the new group hundred, and write 100. In this way, children can see that the group of objects represents 1 hundred, 0 tens, and 0 ones.

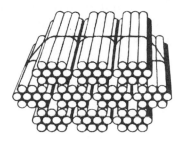

Young children would find it very difficult to count the tally marks below one by one.

/ /

A simpler means of determining the number of tally marks is to group them into sets of ten:

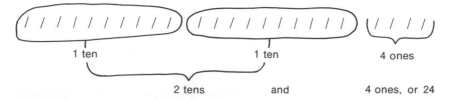

It is not important that all children use the same kind of counters, but a cheap, colorful aid can be supplied. A number of boxes of colored toothpicks can offer children as much experience as they need in grouping objects into sets of 1, 10, 100, and so forth. An understanding of how the base or model group functions in our numeration system is fundamental to the development of confidence and competence in counting, notation, and computation.

The following chart shows how our number system progresses in terms of the base ten grouping principle.

one	= 1 ones	= 1
ten	= 10 ones	= 10
hundred	= 10 tens	= 100
thousand	= 10 hundreds	= 1,000
ten-thousand	= 10 thousands	= 10,000
hundred-thousand	= 10 ten-thousands	= 100,000
million	= 10 hundred-thousands	= 1,000,000

This chart illustrates the function of base in terms of Taylor and Mills' description, "The base of a number system is the number of units of a group that make one unit of the next higher group."[1]

Place Value.   Without the concept of place value our numeration system would have little advantage over many of the earlier systems discussed in Chapter 3. Place value, then, is the big distinguishing characteristic of the Hindu-Arabic system of numeration.

[1] Taylor, E. H., and C. N. Mills, *Arithmetic for Teacher-Training Classes.* New York: Holt, Rinehart and Winston, Inc., 1955, p. 13.

The value of a digit in our numeration system is determined by the place or position it occupies in a numeral. Each of our 10 digits (0–9) really has two values: a face or cardinal value that makes it equivalent to a set of three objects. Thus, whenever we see the symbol 3, we think three of something. When the 3 is written as a one-place numeral, it means 3 ones, because it holds the ones place in the numeral. In other words, the digit 3 occupies one's place and it also tells us how many ones we are considering; therefore we say the value is 3 ones.

Until the invention of a special symbol to always represent the empty set or an absence of value, we were not able to assign a digit a value according to the place it occupied in a numeral. Zero (0) is the digit we use to represent the empty place or to hold the place when there is an absence of value in a particular place in a numeral. Many books describe zero as the numeral we use for a placeholder. Indeed it does serve the important function of a placeholder, but it is also important to recognize that each of our 10 basic numerals or digits serve as a placeholder.

Let us go back to the numeral 3, which we said meant 3 ones. If we place the 3 in another position and write 30, we use the 3 in ten's place and it means 3 tens. The 0 occupies one's place and means no ones. Therefore, we say the numeral 30 represents 3 tens plus 0 ones, or thirty.

The numeral 444 is a three-place numeral, using the same digit (4) in three different place-value positions. The first 4 starting on the right occupies the place assigned the value of one; the next 4 to the left occupies the place assigned the value of ten; the 4 on the far left occupies the place assigned the value of hundred. Thus, we have used the same digit (4) to stand for three different amounts, 4, 40, 400, depending upon its place in the numeral. Children enjoy this, too, especially using the same numeral up to millions or more, for example, 9,999,999,999.

In our numeration system with a base of ten, the value of a place or position in a numeral is 10 times the place immediately to the right. The value of each digit in a numeral is the product of its face value times its place value. For instance, 444 can be expressed as $(4 \times 100) + (4 \times 10) + (4 \times 1) = 444$. We call this an expanded form of notation.

Pupils' understanding of place value may be checked by having them express selected numerals in expanded notation. For example,

$$11 = (1 \times 10) + (1 \times 1) \qquad \text{or } 10 + 1 = 11$$
$$12 = (1 \times 10) + (2 \times 1) \qquad \text{or } 10 + 2 = 12$$
$$17 = (1 \times 10) + (7 \times 1) \qquad \text{or } 10 + 7 = 17$$
$$24 = (2 \times 10) + (4 \times 1) \qquad \text{or } 20 + 4 = 24$$
$$66 = (6 \times 10) + (6 \times 1) \qquad \text{or } 60 + 6 = 66$$
$$89 = (8 \times 10) + (9 \times 1) \qquad \text{or } 80 + 9 = 89$$
$$135 = (1 \times 100) + (3 \times 10) \qquad \text{or } 100 + 30 + 5 = 135$$
$$+ (5 \times 1)$$
$$350 = (3 \times 100) + (5 \times 10) \qquad \text{or } 300 + 50 + 0 = 350$$
$$+ (0 \times 1)$$
$$1{,}247 = (1 \times 1{,}000) + (2 \times 100) \qquad \text{or } 1{,}000 + 200 + 40 + 7$$
$$+ (4 \times 10) + (7 \times 1) \qquad = 1{,}247$$
$$5{,}306 = (5 \times 1{,}000) + (3 \times 100) \qquad \text{or } 5{,}000 + 300 + 0 + 6$$
$$+ (0 \times 10) + (6 \times 1) \qquad = 5{,}360$$
$$20{,}020 = (2 \times 10{,}000) + (0 \times 1{,}000) \qquad \text{or } 20{,}000 + 0 + 0 + 20 + 0$$
$$+ (0 \times 100) + (2 \times 10) \qquad = 20{,}020$$
$$+ (0 \times 1)$$

PLACE-VALUE AIDS.   Place-value pocket charts often are an effective means of helping pupils to develop an understanding of the place-value concept and to helping learn names associated with positional notation. Heavy paper can be cut and stapled to make three pockets labeled from right to left "ones," "tens," and "hundreds."

Hundreds	Tens	Ones
		/ / // /// / / /

First, 10 counters are placed in the one's pocket. These counters are then removed and bundled into a group of ten. A counter representing one group of ten is then placed in the tens pocket.

Hundreds	Tens	Ones
	/	

Children can see that the chart now shows one ten and no ones. Showing only one counter in the tens place instead of the bundle of ten will help children see the relationship of "base ten" to place value — that one ten is another name for ten ones.

Labeled frozen juice cans may be used instead of an oaktag pocket chart to illustrate place value. Children may be asked, "What value is represented by each can?" Starting with the can on the right, what value is represented by the counters in each can? If we think of *all* the counters in the three cans, what number is represented? 3 hundreds and 1 ten and 2 ones is 312.

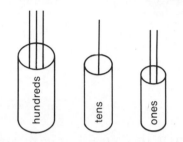

A chart similar to the following one has been useful in helping children understand how our *base ten* and *place-value* concepts are used in writing numerals. The chart should help pupils to see that each place has a value 10 times that of the place to the immediate right, or that each place has a value $\frac{1}{10}$ that of the place to the immediate left.

Place-value chart

Name of place	Thousand	Hundred	Ten	One
Meaning of place	$10 \times 10 \times 10$	10×10	10×1	1
Number represented by each place	1,000	100	10	1

After studying and understanding this chart, children can be asked to place small cards with basic numerals on them, [0] [1] [2] [3] [4] [5] [6] [7] [8] [9]   , in the correct position to represent various numbers on a chart without labels, [| | |]. For instance, show a number containing:

3 tens and 4 ones

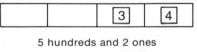

5 hundreds and 2 ones

1 thousand and 2 tens and 6 ones

1	0	2	6

A numeral that contains 43 tens and 7 ones

	4	3	7

The abacus was used at least as early as the sixth century B.C. and has been utilized in nearly every country to assist man's counting and computation. Presently, teachers are finding the abacus to be a valuable tool to illustrate and interpret place value. It is particularly effective in helping children understand the concept of zero as a placeholder. There are many forms of the abacus. Probably the four most popular forms currently found in the classroom are pictured here.

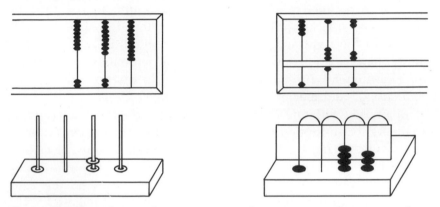

Basically the abacus has a series of wires or rods arranged in parallel columns. Beginning at the far right, each column represents a place value of ones, tens, hundreds, and so forth. The number of columns used to represent decimal positions will depend upon the level of the children in the class. Beads or counters in each column are used to represent the frequency count of a particular positional value. Zero is indicated by an absence of counters in a column.

Grouping in terms of the base may be illustrated by placing 10 counters in the ones column, then renaming the 10 ones (regrouping), and placing one counter in the tens column.

Similarly, regroupings can be made to illustrate 10 tens = 1 hundred or 10 hundreds = 1 thousand.

Another utilization of the abacus is to arrange the counters to represent a number and then to ask the pupils if they can name the number and explain why they believe it is the number they name. Still another good teaching technique is to read a numeral and ask a pupil to represent the number on an abacus. Individual differences can be met by gearing the number of digits in the numeral to the needs of the particular child.

Exponential notation.   The values of each position in a two-place or larger numeral are successive powers of ten (base). A power of the base means 10 is used one or more times as a factor. In our number system, hundred means 10×10 and thousand means $10 \times 10 \times 10$. A shortened form of expanded notation using exponents is an effective means of interpreting numerals in terms of this power structure. 10×10 can be written 10^2. The small 2 written to the right and above the 10 is called an *exponent* and shows the repetitious multiplication of the same number, namely, 10. The numeral 10^3 can be read as "ten to the third power" or "ten cubed" and means $10 \times 10 \times 10$, or 1,000.

Beginning with one's place and moving to the left, each digit in a numeral is multiplied by 10 raised to some power. One's place can be symbolized by 10^0, indicating there are no tens, or factors of the base (we are still dealing with ones). By definition, universally accepted, any number (except zero) raised to the zero power is 1. For example, the 7 in the numeral 347 means $7 \times 10^0 = 7 \times 1 = 7$. The following chart shows the value of each digit in the numeral 33,333 in terms of the power of base ten.

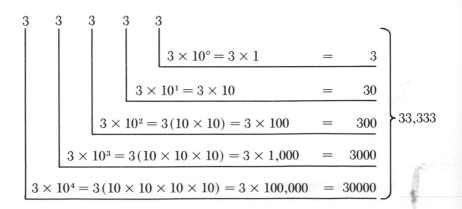

Observation of a chart similar to this one should enable pupils to see how the use of exponents provides a simplified form for showing the number of times ten (base) is used as a factor in each place to the left of the decimal point. Study of the chart also helps one to see a pattern for determining the value of each position in a numeral expressed in a system that uses place value as powers of the base.

The additive characteristic.   Many systems have employed the additive principle in expressing number. For example, the Romans write XVII for 17, meaning $10 + 5 + 1 + 1$. They simply found the sum of the face values of the symbols used to represent the number. We utilize the additive principle along with the concept of place value. In arriving at the numerical meaning of a two place or larger numeral, we find the sum of the products of the face value of the digits and the value of the places occupied by the digits.

The numeral 325 represents the sum of 3 hundreds, 2 tens, and 5 ones or $300 + 20 + 5 = 325$. The numeral 5,386 may be illustrated in many ways. The method used in the classroom should depend mainly on the mental and mathematical maturity of the youngster. From early elementary school years to later elementary school years, the sequence might be as follows:

1. $5,286 =$ the sum of 5 thousands, 2 hundreds, 8 tens, and 6 ones or $5,000 + 200 + 80 + 6 = 5,286$
2. $5,286 = 5(10 \times 10 \times 10) + 2(10 \times 10) + 8(10) + 6(1)$
   $= 5(1,000) + 2(100) + 8(10) + 6(1)$
   $= 5,000 + 200 + 80 + 6 = 5,286$
3. $5,286 = 5(10^3) + 2(10^2) + 8(10^1) + 6(10^0)$
   $= 5(1,000) + 2(100) + 8(10) + 6(1)$
   $= 5,000 + 200 + 80 + 6$
   $= 5,286$

All these expressions of number meaning for the numeral 5,286 are known as *expanded notation*. Thus we see that a number may be named in many ways. Expressing number in standard form and expanded form helps one to understand the four important characteristics of our number system — basic numerals, base, place value, and the additive principle. Portraying the meaning of a numeral in expanded form also contributes to the foundation necessary for the grouping processes involved in the operation on number. Use expanded notations to show three different names for the following numbers.

49	235,178
236	30,409
8,764	

Systems of numeration with bases other than ten

We have discussed the characteristics of the decimal system and have shown that it is possible to symbolize any quantity with the use of only 10 basic numerals. However, it is possible to have a numeration system that employs all the characteristics of our system, yet the model group or base could be some number other than ten. In fact, any number other than 0 or 1 can be used as the base of a number system, and such numbers as 2, 8, 12, 20, and 60 have been used as a base.

The Hindu-Arabic or decimal system is so deeply entrenched in our society that undoubtedly few people would seriously argue for a change to another base. However, there are at least two good reasons we should explore systems with bases other than ten. First, a careful exploration of systems with other bases will help us to understand better the basic characteristics of our decimal system. Second, we are presently using systems with bases other than ten, such as base two in mathematical operations with electronic computers and base sixty and base twelve in various aspects of measurement.

Teachers have found that counting is a good starting point for children in the study of systems using a base other than ten. Many teachers find a brief review of counting in the decimal system a beneficial practice before launching a study of nondecimal base systems. In our system, when we have counted nine and one more, we utilize numerals, base, and place value in recording the quantity as 10. The 1 occupies ten's place, indicating one of the base (10) and the 0 indicates no ones. The numeral 10 is called ten. If a numeration system employs the concept of place value and uses the numeral 1 as the first counting number and the numeral 0 to hold an empty place, the first two-place numeral indicating one of the base in the system will always be written 10, whatever the base may be. However, the name of the numeral 10 in a nondecimal base would not be ten.

Have children examine tally marks or counting sticks such as those illustrated to see how they would be counted using different bases.

Base
Ten $\quad$ / / / / / / / / / / / / / / /
$\qquad$ 1 2 3 4 5 6 7 8 9 10 11 12 13 14 15 $= 15_{\text{ten}}$

Base
Eight $\quad$ / / / / / / / / / / / / / / /
$\qquad$ 1 2 3 4 5 6 7 10 11 12 13 14 15 16 17 $= 17_{\text{eight}}$

Base
Six $\quad$ / / / / / / / / / / / / / / /
$\qquad$ 1 2 3 4 5 10 11 12 13 14 15 20 21 22 23 $= 23_{\text{six}}$

Base
Four $\quad$ / / / / / / / / / / / / / / /
$\qquad$ 1 2 3 10 11 12 13 20 21 22 23 30 31 32 33 $= 33_{\text{four}}$

This counting exercise should make clearer to pupils the fact that a number may be expressed by different numerals. The same number of tally marks were represented as 15_{ten}, 17_{eight}, 23_{six}, and 33_{four}. To identify a numeral in a base other than a decimal, either the word or number symbol indicating the base is written as a subscript. For example, 17_{eight} or 17_8.

Also, to distinguish two-place numerals in other bases from those in base ten, we shall call the numeral 10, one zero base two; 11, one one base four; 12, one two base six; . . .; 20, two zero base five; 21, two one base nine; and so forth. This is necessary because the values of these numerals are not the same as they are in base ten.

Why does it take a larger numeral in bases smaller than ten to represent the same number of tally marks? Because it takes fewer of the tally marks to constitute one group of the base and a lesser number of this size group to make a group of the next higher value. Therefore, it requires a numeral with a greater number of digits in base eight than in base ten, to express the same quantity.

From such counting experiences, pupils should form the generalization that the smaller the base, the larger the numeral, or the larger the base, the smaller the numeral required to represent the same quantity. The counting examples should also lead to the generalization that the base a particular system employs determines the number of basic numerals. For example, in base ten we have the basic numerals 0, 1, 2, . . ., 9. In base 6, we have the basic numerals 0, 1, 2, . . ., 5, and in base four we have 0, 1, 2, 3. In each case the numeral 0 indicates an absence of value in the place it holds.

Nondecimal place value: base eight. The value of each position in a two-place or larger numeral is determined as powers of the base. No matter in which base it is written, each digit has a value for the place in which it stands. With the exception of one's place, the values and names for the values in a nondecimal numeral will be different than those in a base ten numeral. For example, in base eight we have ones, eights, sixty-fours, and five-hundred twelves instead of ones, tens, hundreds, and thousands in base ten. The following chart shows how a base eight system progresses in powers of the base and the numerals for the first four places compared with equivalent base ten numerals.

Base eight number system

	Base eight values	Base eight numeral	Equivalent base ten numeral
4th place	$8 \times 8 \times 8$ or 8^3	1,000	512
3rd place	8×8 or 8^2	100	64
2nd place	8 or 8^1	10	8
1st place	1 or 8^0	1	1

Let us compare the same numeral written in base ten and in base eight (6352_{eight}, 6352_{ten}). The digits forming the numeral in the two bases are the same. Notice, however, that the values assigned to each position occupied by a digit in the two numerals are different, due to the fact that one numeral has a base eight and the other a base ten. (Refer to above chart.) The two numerals, although the same, represent a different number. The number expressed by a numeral represents the sum of the products of the digits and the value assigned to the position of the digits. For example, the value or quantity represented by the base ten numeral 6352 is

$$6(10^3) + 3(10^2) + 5(10^1) + 2(10^0)$$
$$= 6(1000) + 3(100) + 5(10) + 2(1)$$
$$= 6000 + 300 + 50 + 2$$
$$= 6352$$

Let us determine what the numeral would be in base ten for a number expressed by the numeral 6352 in base eight. Multiply each digit by the values assigned to its position. Remember the positional value is in terms of powers of eight. The derived products will be expressed in base ten and the sum of the products will be the base ten numeral equivalent to 6352_{eight}. The chart below shows the value of each digit in the numeral 6352 in terms of the power of base 8.

$$
\begin{array}{cccc}
6 & 3 & 5 & 2
\end{array}
$$

$$
\left.
\begin{array}{lcr}
2 \times 8^0 = 2 \times 1 & = & 2 \\
5 \times 8^1 = 5 \times 8 & = & 40 \\
3 \times 8^2 = 3(8 \times 8) = 3 \times 64 & = & 192 \\
6 \times 8^3 = 6(8 \times 8 \times 8) = 6 \times 512 & = & 3072
\end{array}
\right\} 3306
$$

The principle of place value applied through the use of expanded notation can also be used to convert the numeral 6352 in base eight to a numeral expressing the same number in base ten.

$$6\,3\,5\,2_{eight} = \boxed{}_{ten}$$

$6(8^3) + 3(8^2) + 5(8^1) + 2(8^0)$
$$= 6(512) + 3(64) + 5(8) + 2(1)$$
$$= 3072 + 192 + 40 + 2$$
$$= 3306_{ten}$$

We find that $6\,3\,5\,2_{eight} = 3\,3\,0\,6_{ten}$. In other words, the two numerals express the same quantity supporting the statement made earlier that any number can have many names.

If children understand place value and expanding notations, any number written in a nondecimal base can be converted to an equivalent base ten number by expressing each digit in base ten and finding the sum.

Now let us rewrite $2\,4\,1\,3_{six}$ as a base ten numeral.

$2(6^3) + 4(6^2) + 1(6^1) + 3(6^0)$
$$= 2(216) + 4(36) + 1(6) + 3(1)$$
$$= 432 + 144 + 6 + 3$$
$$= 585$$

$2\,4\,1\,3$ base six is written as 585 base ten.

In translating a base ten numeral to a numeral in another base, start by establishing the positional values for the numeral in the given base. Then determine the number of groups in each position.

Consider the base six numeral 2 4 1 3 that we just converted to the base ten numeral 585. The positional values for $2\,4\,1\,3_{six}$ were

6^3	6^2	6^1	6^0
216	36	6	1

Examine 585 to see if it would contain the place value (216) of the base six numeral. Because it does a four place numeral should be the answer. The procedure is to determine how many groups of the base six place values can be renamed from 585.

$$
\begin{array}{cccc}
2 & 4 & 1 & 3 \\
216\overline{)585} & 36\overline{)153} & 6\overline{)9} & 1\overline{)3} \\
\underline{432} & \underline{144} & \underline{6} & \underline{3} \\
153 & 9 & 3 &
\end{array}
$$

There are 2 groups of 216's, 4 groups of 36's, 1 group of 6's, and 3 groups of 1's, therefore $585_{ten} = 2\,4\,1\,3_{six}$.

A similar procedure for making the conversion of 585_{ten} to $\square_{six}$ is to determine place values for base six. The first four place values are 1, 6, 36, 216. Compare with 585. The largest place value in 585 is 216, therefore the answer in base six will be a four place numeral. First subtract the largest number of 216's in 585. Then subtract the largest number of 36's in the remainder. Next subtract the largest number of 6's in the remainder. Lastly, subtract the largest number of 1's in the remainder.

$$585 \quad = \quad 2 \qquad\qquad 4 \qquad\qquad 1 \qquad\qquad 3$$

$$
\begin{array}{cccc}
585 & \rightarrow 153 & \rightarrow 9 & \rightarrow 3 \\
-432\,(2 \times 216) & -144\,(4 \times 36) & -6\,(1 \times 6) & -3\,(3 \times 1) \\
\hline
153 & 9 & 3 & 0
\end{array}
$$

$$585_{ten} = 2413_{six}$$

Base two. A place value system with two as its base is called a *binary* system. In the binary system only two basic numerals are used, 0 and 1. Grouping in this system is on powers of two. The following place value chart shows how the binary system progresses in terms of powers of the base and the numerals for the first eight places compared with equivalent base ten numerals.

Place value chart

	Base two values	Base two numeral	Equivalent base ten numeral
8th place	$2 \times 2 \times 2 \times 2 \times 2 \times 2 \times 2$ or 2^7	10,000,000	128
7th place	$2 \times 2 \times 2 \times 2 \times 2 \times 2$ or 2^6	1,000,000	64
6th place	$2 \times 2 \times 2 \times 2 \times 2$ or 2^5	100,000	32
5th place	$2 \times 2 \times 2 \times 2$ or 2^4	10,000	16
4th place	$2 \times 2 \times 2$ or 2^3	1,000	8
3rd place	2×2 or 2^2	100	4
2nd place	2 or 2^1	10	2
1st place	1 or 2^0	1	1

Binary numerals are based on groups of two; therefore a numeral with several digits is required to express a relatively small quantity. For example, 1011_{two} and 11_{ten} represent the same number of objects.

Base	Number	Objects represented										
ten	12	1	2	3	4	5	6	7	8	9	10	11
		↓	↓	↓	↓	↓	↓	↓	↓	↓	↓	↓
		×	×	×	×	×	×	×	×	×	×	×
		↑	↑	↑	↑	↑	↑	↑	↑	↑	↑	↑
two	1100	1	10	11	100	101	110	111	1000	1001	1010	1011

The inconvenience of working with numerals of many digits is overcome now by the terrific speed with which modern electronic digital computers operate, and most of their work is based on the binary system. A closed electric circuit corresponds to one and causes the computer machine to punch a hole in the record kept by the machine, meaning 1. An open electric circuit corresponds to zero, and no hole in a space on the machine's record means 0. The binary numeral 101011 would be indicated in a computer machine record as the following example ▮ 0 ▮ 0 ▮ ▮ . (The shaded symbol in a square indicates a punched hole representing one of that place value.) Write the binary numerals indicated by the following computer machine records.

(1) | ● | ● | O | O | ● | O | =
(2) | ● | O | ● | O | ● | ● | O | ● | =

Write the binary numerals to represent the following number of dots

(1) ● ● ● ● ● ● ●

(2) ● ● ● ● ● ● ● ● ● ● ● ● ● ●

Base twelve.   A place value system with twelve as its base is known as a duodecimal system. In the duodecimal system 12 basic numerals are used, therefore we need two new one-digit numerals. When discussing the duodecimal system, most authorities accept T (dec) to represent ten and E (elf) to represent eleven. The 12 one-digit numerals in this system are:

$$0, 1, 2, 3, 4, 5, 6, 7, 8, 9, T, E.$$

In the duodecimal system we group in twelves for example:

> one = one
> twelve = one dozen
> twelve × twelve = one gross
> twelve × twelve × twelve = one great gross

The most frequently used arguments in favor of the duodecimal system of numeration are (1) twelve has more factors than ten, therefore division would be easier; (2) work with fractions would be easier; and (3) we use many units of measure based on twelve.

Duodecimal counting chart

1	2	3	4	5	6	7	8	9	T
E	10	11	12	13	14	15	16	17	18
19	1T	1E	20	21	22	23	24	25	26
27	28	29	2T	2E	30	31	32	33	34
35	36	37	38	39	3T	3E	40	41	42
43	44	45	46	47	48	49	4T	4E	50
51	52	53	54	55	56	57	58	59	5T
5E	60	61	62	63	64	65	66	67	68
69	6T	6E	70	71	72	73	74	75	76
77	78	79	7T	7E	80	81	82	83	84

The duodecimal numerals that would correspond to the decimal numerals in a 100's chart are shown above. Notice that T replaces 10, E replaces 11, 4E replaces 59, 5T replaces 70, etc. The duodecimal numeral 84 corresponds to 100 in the decimal system.

Write duodecimal numerals for each of these decimal numerals:

35   120

58   131

Write decimal numerals for each of these duodecimal numerals:

3T   TE

83   1TE

Inventing a numeration system

With the exception of base 12, our discussions of nondecimal bases have dealt with numeration systems that utilize numerals that are a part of the decimal system. After several years of experience with the decimal system it is difficult for children to associate any meaning for 10 other than ten or for that matter any other numeral composed of the same basic number symbols as we employ in our system.

An increasing number of teachers in the middle and upper levels or the grades of the elementary school encourage children to apply their knowledge and understanding of the characteristics of the decimal system — number symbols, base, place value, and additive property — to formulating a numeration system with the four properties upon which the decimal system functions, but with a non decimal base, and with new basic numerals and names.

Suppose we wish to invent a numeration system with a base equivalent to the set { ◊, ◊, ◊, ◊, ◊ }. If we wish to count in order to communicate number ideas, it is necessary to have an agreed upon set of symbols and names to express the desired ideas. A set of basic synbols equivalent to the base is needed. Let us agree to use

ack,   eck,   ick,   ock,   unk

Understand that ☆ = Ack is the symbol and name we shall use to indicate an absence of quantity or value. With a set of { ◊ } use

\ = Eck, a set of { ◊◊ } is ⊘ = Ick, a set of { ◊◊◊ } is △ = Ock, and a set of { ◊◊◊◊ } is □ = Unk. When another member is added to the set { ◊◊◊◊◊ }, we have a group of the base and no more. The numeral for this set is \ ☆ meaning Eck number of units of the base and Ack number of individual objects. By utilizing the concept of number symbols, base, and place value, the set { ◊◊◊◊◊ } can be expressed with a numeral composed of a combination of Ick basic number symbols. But we have no name for this collection {\ ☆} constituting the base. Call it Ecky and put a ring around the objects (◊◊◊◊◊) to signify Eck of the base.

The largest set of objects which could be expressed by an Ick-place numeral is (◊◊◊◊◊◊◊◊◊◊◊◊◊◊◊◊◊◊◊◊◊◊◊◊◊) = □ □ , Unky Unk. If another object is added to the above set, an Ock-place numeral would be needed to express the quantity and another name would need to be invented for this new collection. The new group represents another power of the base because we have as many groups of the base as the number required to make a group of the base — Ecky number of objects for a group of the base and Ecky groups of the base. One way to illustrate the concept is:

(◊◊◊◊◊)(◊◊◊◊◊)(◊◊◊◊◊)(◊◊◊◊◊)(◊◊◊◊◊) = \☆☆   Fen

Ecky number of objects = group representing base	Ecky groups of the base = next power of the base or place value of base times base.	Ock place numeral	New name

Some numerals in the newly formulated system and their corresponding decimal numerals are shown below:

New System	Decimal System
△	3
\□	9
⊘\	11
□\	23
\⊘☆	35
△✷□	79
\□⊘△	238

Ask children to utilize the new system to express the quantities represented by these sets of objects:

$\{\varphi\varphi\}$

$\{\varphi\varphi\varphi\}$

$\{\varphi\varphi\varphi\varphi\varphi\varphi\varphi\}$

$\{\varphi\varphi\,\varphi\varphi\,\varphi\varphi\varphi\,\varphi\varphi\varphi\,\varphi\varphi\,\varphi\varphi\varphi\}$

$\{\varphi\varphi\varphi\,\varphi\varphi\varphi\,\varphi\varphi\varphi\varphi\varphi\varphi\varphi\varphi\varphi\,\varphi\varphi\varphi\,\varphi\varphi\varphi\varphi\,\varphi\,\varphi\varphi\,\varphi\varphi\varphi\}$

Ask children to express the following decimal numerals in the new system:

$$2, \ 12, \ 23, \ 28, \ 47, \ 88, \ 203$$

A very profitable experience, both for teacher and pupils, is to have children utilize what they know about the decimal numeration system to construct their very own numeration system using number symbols, names, and a base different than in our own system. This requires children to concentrate on the characteristics that make our numeration system function as it does rather than simply using symbols and terminology they may have memorized or perhaps known since early childhood. Experiences such as those described not only contribute to meaning and understanding but also provide a fresh approach to needed practice in utilizing the decimal numeration system.

Suggested activities

1. Describe and illustrate the characteristics of the decimal numeration system.
2. What approach will you use with pupils in distinguishing between number and numeral?
3. List the understandings you would want children to have for the numerals 7, 49, 602. What would you do to assist the pupils?
4. Could we have a numeration system that employs all the characteristics of the Hindu-Arabic system and yet has as its base a number other than ten? Illustrate.

5. Formulate a numeration system employing the four decimal-system characteristics discussed in this chapter, but use a nondecimal base and new basic numerals and names.

Selected references

Ashlock, R. B., "What Mathematics for Fours and Fives," *Childhood Education*, 43:469–473, April 1967.

Bradfield, D. L., "Majesty of Numbers," *The Mathematics Teacher*, 60: 588–592, Oct. 1967.

Ginther, J. L., "Applications of Base-Three Numeration," *The Mathematics Teacher*, 60:858–859, Dec. 1967.

Gray, E. H., "How to Give Mathematics More Meaning," *Grade Teacher*, 84:121–123, April 1967.

Killea, A. R., "Developing Number Ideas in the Kindergarten," *The Arithmetic Teacher*, 14:396, May 1967.

Mehl, W. G., "Grids, Integers, and Number Bases," *The Mathematics Teacher*, 60:843–847, Dec. 1967.

Monsour, N., "Largest Number That Can Be Written in Any Base," *The Arithmetic Teacher*, 14:218, March 1967.

Muente, G., "Where Do I Start Teaching Numerals?", *The Arithmetic Teacher*, 14:575–576, Nov. 1967.

Teaching 5
addition of whole
numbers

The nature of the addition operation

Addition is an operation to be performed upon number that is very closely related to the operation of union of disjoint sets. In the union of disjoint sets, we are concerned with tabulating or defining the elements in the combined sets. With the operation of addition, we are concerned with the number properties of each of the disjoint sets and with the number property of the union of the sets. To perform the operation of addition upon numbers, we use numerals to describe number properties of the sets involved.

For example, consider disjoint sets A and B.

$$A = \{\text{Mary, Paul, John, Jane}\}$$
$$B = \{\text{dog, cat, wagon, bicycle, ball}\}$$

The union of the two sets, set C, might be tabulated as

$$C = \{\text{Mary, Paul, John, Jane, dog, cat, wagon, bicycle, ball}\}$$

The number property of set A is described by the numeral 4, $n(A) = 4$. The number property of set B is described by the numeral 5, $n(B) = 5$. The number property of set C is described by the numeral 9, $n(C) = 9$. The number property of set C could have been ascertained by counting, but it is more appropriate to think of the operation of addition as the process of determining a single number name equal in value to the combined value of two number names without counting.

The teacher of some years ago was correct in stating that we cannot add pigs and horses. Sets of objects cannot be added; they can be joined, combined, or put into union. However, numbers can be added, and the number property of the set of pigs and of the set of horses could each be ascertained and these numbers could be added. Getting children to think of addition as an operation performed upon numbers may be difficult because in their development of language they may have been using the terms add and adding in reference to combining sets of objects, such as in adding milk to cereal.

Just as the union of sets is a binary operation because only two sets can be combined at a time and other sets are combined one by one with the resulting unions, addition is also called a binary operation. Only two numbers can be added at one time. If the total or sum of more than two numbers is to be found, two of the numbers are added and the remaining numbers are added one at a time to the resulting sums.

Our method of performing the operation of addition is somewhat misleading in that it appears as though we are adding three or more numbers at one time. However, in reality, we are performing the operation in a binary fashion. Consider the example:

$$62 + 13 + 54 = \Box.$$

or
$$
\begin{array}{r}
62. \\
13 \\
+54 \\
\hline
\end{array}
$$

In performing the addition operation, we might first add 3 ones and 4 ones; to that sum we add 2 ones; to that sum we add 5 tens; to that sum we add 1 ten; and to that sum we add 6 tens. Of course, there are other ways in which these numbers might be added, but in every instance the operation will be binary. In the process of teaching the addition operation to children, little emphasis need be placed upon the binary nature of addition because in the instructional procedure the nature of addition as a binary operation seems to be a natural development.

Note that the operation of addition may also be used to determine the number of elements in the union of intersecting sets. When this is done, the number property of one of the sets is added to the number property of the elements of the second set that are not shared with the first set. For example, consider intersecting sets M and N and the corresponding Venn diagram.

$$M = \{\text{bread, fruit, butter, cereal, milk}\}$$
$$N = \{\text{meat, bread, vegetable, milk}\}$$

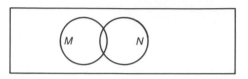

The number property of set M is five. The number property of set N is four. But the number property of the elements of set N not shared with set M is two. Therefore, the number property of the union of these two sets is seven: $5 + (4 - 2) = 7$.

The number names denoting the number properties of the disjoint sets are called *addends*, and the number name determined by the addition operation is called the *sum*. Emphasizing the addend, addend, sum relationship will be helpful in developing the idea that addition is an operation performed upon numbers and in developing the relationship between addition and its inverse operation, subtraction.

In the process of developing understanding and mastery of the addition operation, teachers and children will find it necessary to use certain prerequisite learnings concerning sets of objects and the number properties of sets and concerning characteristics of our system of numeration. At an early level, they will have to establish the basic facts of addition that are to be used in the operation. These facts will have to be established in a meaningful way and to the point at which recall will be accurate and rapid. Principles or properties of the operation will be utilized to develop an abstract procedure for performing the operation and for verifying the results of the operation.

Prerequisite learnings for the operation of addition

The concept of readiness for learning elementary mathematics insofar as children are concerned is a continuous procedure in which new concepts and understandings are built upon old learnings at all levels in the educational process. For each new concept or understanding that is to be introduced and developed, there are certain prerequisite learnings. By using these preceding learnings, children will be able to discover new facts and principles and to verify the newly discovered ideas. They will be encouraged to attack and to solve new problem situations by bringing to bear previously acquired and pertinent knowledge. Such backgrounds of learning will also be used to develop understandings of the arithmetic operations, relationships between the operations, and relationships between other concepts.

In general, the prerequisite learnings for the formal study of addition involve certain primary concepts concerning sets and some elementary but basic concepts concerning number. Before beginning such study, children should have had experiences involving (1) matching the elements of one set in one-to-one correspondence with the elements of another set, (2) making sets equal in number to other sets, (3) comparing sets through one-to-one correspondence to determine which set has the larger or smaller number of elements, (4) combining two sets to make a new set, and (5) separating the elements in one set to make two subsets.

Through activities concerning the development of concepts of number, children should acquire those prerequisite learnings and skills necessary for success in the formal study of the addition operation. These skills are easily discernable and teachers should ascertain that children have acquired the necessary understandings, skills, and abilities. Before the addition facts are formally introduced, children should be able to

1. Ascertain whether or not two sets of objects are equal in number
2. Count the objects in sets containing up to 20 elements and preferably sets containing greater quantities
3. Recognize and give the number names for small collections (up to five objects) without counting
4. Combine two sets that are small in number to make a new set
5. Collect the objects in a large set (between 10 and 50 elements) and tell how many in the set by stating □ sets of ten and □ ones.

Before beginning the study of the addition of two-digit numerals and the addition operation or *algorithm*, children should have mastered the addition facts that are contained in the examples and be able to express two-digit numerals in expanded notation. For example, before children are asked to solve problems involving the addition of such numerals as $24 + 43 = \square$, they need to know the addition facts $4 + 3 = 7$ and 2 tens + 4 tens = 6 tens. To understand the addition algorithm, they will also need to be able to express 24 as $20 + 4$ and 43 as $40 + 3$.

$$
\begin{array}{ccc}
24 & \text{2 tens} + \text{4 ones} & 20 + 4 \\
+43 & +\text{4 tens} + \text{3 ones} & +40 + 3
\end{array}
$$

Properties of addition to be taught and utilized

One of the characteristics of modern programs in elementary mathematics is an emphasis upon the properties of numbers. There are 11 properties or laws that may be used to describe how numbers behave when the operations of addition or multiplication are performed upon them. With reference to the operations, these properties may be listed or named as:

ADDITION

1. Closure property of addition
2. Identity element of addition
3. Commutative property of addition
4. Associative property of addition
5. Additive inverse

MULTIPLICATION

6. Closure property of multiplication
7. Identity element of multiplication
8. Commutative property of multiplication
9. Associative property of multiplication
10. Multiplicative inverse

MULTIPLICATION AND ADDITION

11. Distributive property

Rather than review all of the properties and their application to other subsets of the real number system at this point, it seems more reasonable to review only those properties of addition. An understanding of the properties of number can best be developed through a study of them in relation to whole numbers, and the understanding can later be extended to include rational numbers and negative integers.

The identity element.   Choose from the set of whole numbers, $\{0, 1, 2, 3, 4, . . .\}$, any one element that is to be used as an addend. Now try to select a second element that is to be used as an addend and added to the first, with the condition that the result or sum is to be the same as the first chosen element. This is similar to completing the following number sentences:

$$9 + \square = 9 \qquad 37 + \square = 37 \qquad 264 + \square = 264$$

Or, to generalize, if a represents any whole number, $a + \square = a$.

What number or element was chosen to complete the sentences?

When zero (0) is added to any number, the sum is the same as or identical to that number. Therefore, zero (0) is called the *identity element* for addition.

The commutative property.   From the set of whole numbers, select any two elements to be used as addends. Write the possible number sentences that indicate the operation of addition is to be performed with these addends. For example,

$$7 + 9 = \square \qquad \text{and} \qquad 9 + 7 = \square$$
$$34 + 15 = \square \qquad \text{and} \qquad 15 + 34 = \square$$

What can be said about the sums of the addition examples? Did changing the order of the two whole-number addends change the sum? The property that allows changing the order of two addends without a change in the associated sum is called the *commutative property* of addition.

The associative property.   The associative property of addition is concerned with three or more addends and the fact that addition is a binary operation (only two numbers can be added at one time). Suppose that three whole numbers $(3, 5, 7)$ are involved as addends in an addition example. Only two of these numbers can be added at a time, and the resulting sum is added to the third number. Insofar as the final sum is concerned, does it matter which two numbers are added first? What are the possibilities for grouping the addends?

$$(3 + 5) + 7 = \square \qquad (3 + 7) + 5 = \square \qquad (5 + 7) + 3 = \square$$
$$8 + 7 = \square \qquad\qquad 10 + 5 = \square \qquad\qquad 12 + 3 = \square$$

The property that allows changing the grouping of addends, when three or more addends are involved, without affecting the final result or sum is the *associative property* of addition.

The closure property. Consider the set of whole numbers, $\{0, 1, 2, 3, 4, \ldots\}$, and select any two of the elements to serve as addends. What class of number will the sum be?

$$9 + 0 = \square \qquad 17 + 3 = \square \qquad 1{,}896 + 2{,}332 = \square$$

When any two whole numbers are added, the sum will always be a whole number. Thus the set of whole numbers is *closed* under the operation of addition, and this property is referred to as the *closure property.*

This property is not developed as thoroughly as it might be in most elementary mathematics programs. It is not as useful in helping pupils to establish facts, to verify solutions, or to understand the addition agorithm. However, children should be helped to establish this idea and, in turn, to find that the set of whole numbers *is not* closed under the operation of subtraction, *is* closed under the operation of multiplication, and *is not* closed under the operation of division.

The additive inverse. Although this property is not directly involved when teaching children the operation of addition on whole numbers, it should be reviewed here because it is a property or law of addition, and because of its pertinence in later discussions in this chapter and Chapter 6. Addition was previously described as an operation performed upon numbers (*addends*) to produce a result called a *sum*. An operation that undoes another operation is called an *inverse* operation.

Subtraction is the operation that undoes addition and that is used for finding the missing addend when one addend and the sum are known. This situation exists in problems such as "John has 4 cents. He needs 10 cents. How much more does he need?" The number sentence that describes this situation is $4 + \square = 10$. In the problem, one addend and the sum are known. One addend is miss-ing. To find the missing addend, we might undo the addition by restating the number sentence as $10 - 4 = \square$.

Addition and subtraction are *inverse* operations. One undoes the other. The relationship between addition and subtraction can be clearly illustrated with whole numbers:

7 addend	12 sum	12 sum
+5 addend	−5 addend	−7 addend
□ sum	□ missing addend	□ missing addend

Soon after children begin working with negative numbers, they may discover an important idea that is related to this concept but that is not exactly the same. Beginning at zero (0) on the number line, the man takes five positive steps (+5).

He then takes five backward steps (⁻5) of the same size. Describe his location on the number line: $(+5) + (^-5) = \square$.

Suppose the little man on the number line began at zero (0) and took three backward steps (−3) and then took three forward steps (+3) of the same size. Where would he be on the number line? $(^-3) + (+3) = \square$.

The idea being developed is that for every positive whole number there is a corresponding negative number such that when the two numbers are added, the sum is zero. The corresponding negative numbers are not whole numbers but are elements of the set of integers. How would you complete these number sentences to make them true?

$$26 + \square = 0 \qquad 83 + \square = 0 \qquad 1{,}763 + \square = 0$$
$$-13 + \square = 0 \qquad -41 + \square = 0$$

When this idea is extended to include all classes of numbers in the set of real numbers, the property is called the *additive inverse*.

All recent commercially published textual materials contain content dealing with these properties. However, the nature of the presentation of this content in commercial materials may be very dissimilar. In some materials the presentation is quite concrete, meaningful, and understandable for children; in others, it is very abstract. The same may be said for the procedures or methods of presentation used by classroom teachers.

Another characteristic of modern programs in elementary mathematics is that the structure of mathematics is to be emphasized and that patterns and relationships are to be stressed. Too often, content concerning the properties appears in textual materials or in classroom programs as fragmented bits of mathematical information not apparently related to the rest of the mathematics curricula. In too many instances the names of the properties and the generalizations stated in algebraic form become the content that elementary pupils are expected to master.

If pupils are to understand the structure of mathematics through seeing patterns and understanding relationships, the study of these properties should become an integral part of the elementary mathematics program and should be utilized in helping children to (1) learn the basic facts of addition and multiplication, (2) understand the operations or algorithms, (3) understand the relationships between the operations, (4) improve abilities to do mental calculations, and (5) verify ideas and computational solutions.

Establishing and mastering the facts of addition

Nature of addition facts. The facts of addition, sometimes called the *basic addition facts* or the *key addition facts*, consist of all the possible pairs of two one-digit numbers together with their associated sum. Consider set A, which includes all the one-digit whole numbers, and set B, which is identical or equal to set A.

$$\text{set } A = \{0, 1, 2, 3, 4, 5, 6, 7, 8, 9\}$$
$$\text{set } B = \{0, 1, 2, 3, 4, 5, 6, 7, 8, 9\}$$

All the possible combinations that can exist by taking one element from set A and one element from set B together with the proper sum comprise the addition facts. If the number of facts are to be counted in a singular fashion, there are 100 facts of addition for pupils to learn. In arithmetic programs of years ago, that is the way in which the addition facts were counted and taught—in tables or sets of ten in which one of the addends in each fact was identical. The facts in the "two table" consisted of

$$2 + 0 = 2 \qquad 2 + 5 = 7$$
$$2 + 1 = 3 \qquad 2 + 6 = 8$$
$$2 + 2 = 4 \qquad 2 + 7 = 9$$
$$2 + 3 = 5 \qquad 2 + 8 = 10$$
$$2 + 4 = 6 \qquad 2 + 9 = 11$$

The 100 addition facts thus taught are illustrated in the following chart. Each of the rows or columns includes the 10 facts that were taught in a set of facts having one identical addend.

+	0	1	2	3	4	5	6	7	8	9
0	0	1	2	3	4	5	6	7	8	9
1	1	2	3	4	5	6	7	8	9	10
2	2	3	4	5	6	7	8	9	10	11
3	3	4	5	6	7	8	9	10	11	12
4	4	5	6	7	8	9	10	11	12	13
5	5	6	7	8	9	10	11	12	13	14
6	6	7	8	9	10	11	12	13	14	15
7	7	8	9	10	11	12	13	14	15	16
8	8	9	10	11	12	13	14	15	16	17
9	9	10	11	12	13	14	15	16	17	18

In modern programs the addition facts are generally not considered in a singular fashion or taught in isolation. If the teaching-learning procedure takes advantage of the properties of addition of whole numbers that were previously described, there are only 46 related ideas or facts for pupils to understand and to master. In the following chart and legend, these 46 related ideas are illustrated.

+	0	1	2	3	4	5	6	7	8	9
0										
1		2	a	b	c	d	e	f	g	h
2		a'	4	i	j	k	l	m	n	o
3		b'	i'	6	p	q	r	s	t	u
4		c'	j'	p'	8	v	w	x	y	z
5		d'	k'	q'	v'	10	A'	B	C	D
6		e'	l'	r'	w'	A	12	E	F	G
7		f'	m'	s'	x'	B'	E'	14	H	I
8		g'	n'	t'	y'	C'	F'	H'	16	J
9		h'	o'	u'	z'	D'	G'	I'	J'	18

⬛ · · ·	Zero (0) is an addend in the combination (identity element of addition)	1 major idea
$\{2, 4, 6, \ldots, 18\}$	Two addends that are the same (doubles in the addition facts)	9 facts or ideas
$\{(a, a'), (b, b'), (c, c'), \ldots, (J, J')\}$	Facts in which the addends are the same but in different order and that have the same sum (commutative property)	36 related facts or ideas

When pupils are asked to respond to examples such as

$$4 + 3 = \square \qquad 5 + 4 = \square$$

$$8 + 6 = \square \qquad 7 + 7 = \square$$

or

$$\begin{array}{cccc} 3 & 2 & 9 & 6 \\ +2 & +6 & +3 & +5 \\ \hline \end{array}$$

it can hardly be said that the operation or procedure they will employ will be addition. If we expect their responses to be immediate and accurate, we are asking them merely to recall the sum of the combination or the fact. Recalling facts is only one aspect of performing the addition operation. If we do not expect an immediate response, but are asking them to determine the appropriate sums, the pupils will undoubtedly use some form of a rational counting operation.

Recommendations for teaching addition facts. The facts of addition are used in performing the operation of addition upon numbers together with the rules or principles of the operation. Establishing and mastering the facts of addition are prerequisites for learning to perform the operation of addition. The following recommendations and discussions are offered as procedures to be followed when teaching the addition facts to children.

The addition combinations should be introduced orally with meaningful problem situations. Inasmuch as children come to school from quite varied experiential backgrounds, teachers should not depend primarily upon out-of-school experiences for problem situations. Neither should they depend upon the introductory problems used in textbooks, because textbooks are directed toward larger populations and such problems may be far removed from pupils' interests. Textbooks and teachers' manuals may be used to suggest the general order and pattern for introducing the facts, to suggest the instructional materials and the teaching procedures to be used, and to provide reference, review, and practice materials for pupils.

Introductory problem situations involving the addition combinations should stem directly from the classroom environment and commonly shared pupil experiences. Problems should be presented orally and discussed thoroughly with pupils. There are many natural additive situations (disjoint sets that can be combined) existing in the primary grade classroom. There are sets of boys, sets of girls, sets of desks, sets of books, and sets of many other objects. From these sets, two sets can be selected, the number properties of the sets can be ascertained, the sets can be combined, and then the number property of the new set can be determined. When the sets of objects from which the addition combinations to be introduced do not exist naturally in the room, the teacher can contrive the situations in many, many ways.

The original emphasis in these introductory experiences should be upon the manipulation of the sets of objects with a great deal of pupil participation in oral discussion of the situation and the manipulation. Children should not be required to read or to write sums or facts either in number sentences or in computational form until they have had practical concrete experiences with the combinations. Too often, teachers assume that children have the ability to read and to write the symbols used in the language of elementary mathematics before sufficient emphasis and opportunity have been given to the development of those skills. Developing children's abilities to read and to write the symbols of elementary mathematics (both word symbols and sign symbols) is of such importance that special efforts similar to those used in teaching them to read and to write the English language should be an integral part of the mathematics program.

One introductory problem situation for a combination is generally not sufficient. A number of different problems should be used in the introduction of a combination or pair of combinations, $3 + 2$ and $2 + 3$, so that all pupils can see and understand the situation and can begin to generalize the fact. Although the primary objective of using introductory problems may appear to be the establishment of the facts of addition, developing pupils' abilities to recognize the additive situation in which sets are to be combined when it occurs in a real problem situation stated orally should also be regarded as a major objective.

A *set approach using manipulative materials should be employed.* This teaching approach is implied in the preceding paragraphs. The introductory problem situations should involve two disjoint sets that are to be combined. The number properties of each of the disjoint sets are to be ascertained before the sets are combined. After the sets are combined, the number property of the newly formed set is to be determined.

Introductory problem situations should involve sets of objects in which the elements in the sets can actually be manipulated or moved around by the pupils. Whenever possible, each pupil should have his own sets of objects so that he can actively participate in the manipulation. These objects may be ice cream sticks, cardboard disks, or any other small inexpensive objects that are easy to use and easy to store. The physical combining of the sets will help pupils to better understand the additive situation.

Consider the following two problems.

1. John has some pencils in one hand and some pencils in his other hand. How many pencils is John holding?
2. There are some windows in our classroom and some windows in Miss Smith's classroom. How many windows are in the two classrooms?

In one of the problems, the sets of objects can physically be combined and children can see the combination. In the other problem the actual combination is not possible and must be imagined. Of course, children must eventually learn to solve problems in which the sets cannot be physically combined. Their initial work with such problems will involve substituting equivalent sets of manipulative objects for the original sets and performing the combination. But the introductory problems with addition combinations should be concerned with sets of objects that can be physically combined.

In addition to the objects in the possession of individual pupils, there are other instructional aids very appropriate for the further development of concepts of addition. These include the usually present flannel board and materials, counting frames both large and small, play money, pocket charts, and number lines.

Children should be allowed to discover the sums associated with the addition combinations. They should also be allowed to discover similarities and to form their own generalizations. The meaning of discovery and the nature of a discovery approach in teaching elementary mathematics are frequently discussed in the literature dealing with modern programs in elementary mathematics. Although opinions vary as to the best means of invoking pupil discovery, there seems to be agreement in that (1) discovery involves active pupil participation in the learning process; (2) discovery involves pupil completion of a learning without help from the teacher or the text; (3) the pupil process used in discovery is as important as the result. Because very few printed materials allow active pupil participation in discovery procedures, it is the responsibility of the classroom teacher to establish and maintain learning situations and experiences that provide pupils with such opportunities. The teacher's role is one of structuring, questioning, and guiding instead of demonstrating, telling, and giving directions. The role involves establishing problem situations, providing manipulative materials and time to explore with them, and stimulating pupil thinking and inquiry.

Allowing pupils to find and develop the procedure or procedures to be used in the process of discovering facts or principles is as important as arriving at the correct solution. In discovering the addition facts, this process involves combining sets, rational counting, and, with the harder facts, regrouping into subsets of ten. Pupils should see the rationale of the procedure as well as the correctness of the solution. If they do, they will be able to apply the general principles, ideas, or procedures more readily to other similar problem situations.

In arithmetic programs of the past, children were told or given the addition facts, usually in the form of tables, and required to memorize them. In most instances, meaningful problem situations and manipulative objects were not employed. Counting to find sums was so frowned upon or forbidden that pupils learned *not* to use it or to feel guilty if they used it as a procedure for determining sums of the combinations. They were expected to memorize the facts to the point of instant accuracy, to use these facts with rules memorized by rote to perform computations, and then to apply computational skills to solution of word problems. As a result, when children forgot a sum or a fact, they were either stymied or forced to guess. Only those exceptional children, who had on their own, figured out the relationships among putting sets of objects together, counting, and addition facts, were able to ascertain the forgotten sum.

Of course we still want children to memorize the facts, but only after they have been involved in a meaningful process of discovery in which verification of sums by counting has been emphasized and guessing has been discouraged. Thus, if and when sums or facts are forgotten, they can reemploy the discovery process and reestablish the facts.

Addition combinations or facts should be introduced and developed in an order from easier to more difficult. Most modern programs classify those combinations that have sums less than 10 as the easier facts. Those facts having sums of 10 and greater than 10 are classified as more difficult. This ordering of presentation and classification is not completely dependent upon the difficulty that children may have in ascertaining the sums through a process of rational counting or that they may have in remembering the sums.

The categorization of easier and more difficult addition facts is based upon the process of regrouping or the emphasis upon the concepts of base and positional value that should occur when the facts with sums of 10 and more than 10 are introduced and developed. In arithmetic programs of the past, when the facts were presented in sequential tables and memorized by children, the regrouping process, or "carrying" as it was called, was not introduced until children became involved with two-digit addends. When it was introduced, the process was mechanically performed.

In modern programs of elementary mathematics, both the easier and the more difficult facts of addition are studied in families or groups having the same sum. Emphasis is placed upon the idea that the number of the sum can be renamed with a combination of addends or *vice versa*. When problem situations are used to introduce new facts, the combination of the addends is the name of the number known to children and the discovery procedure involves finding a new name for the number – the sum. Then other problems with other combinations having the same sum are used to complete the family.

Another approach, which is probably just as effective and which may be used in conjunction with the problem situations, is to help children discover the possible combinations of two addends that may be used to rename the number of the sum through the manipulation of a set of objects that has the number property of the sum. As they find the new number names, they may write down or record their discoveries. When the possibilities of combinations are exhausted, the recorded discoveries may be rearranged into an order in which the patterns can be seen.

For example, the family of facts with a sum of 6 may emerge in the following way for one pupil:

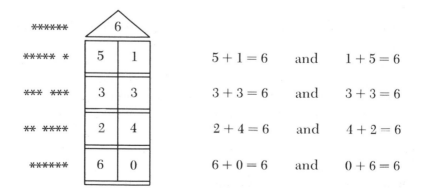

******	6			
***** *	5	1	$5 + 1 = 6$ and $1 + 5 = 6$
*** ***	3	3	$3 + 3 = 6$ and $3 + 3 = 6$
** ****	2	4	$2 + 4 = 6$ and $4 + 2 = 6$
******	6	0	$6 + 0 = 6$ and $0 + 6 = 6$

and may be arranged by all pupils as

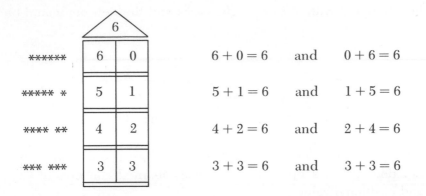

******	6	0	$6 + 0 = 6$ and $0 + 6 = 6$
***** *	5	1	$5 + 1 = 6$ and $1 + 5 = 6$
**** **	4	2	$4 + 2 = 6$ and $2 + 4 = 6$
*** ***	3	3	$3 + 3 = 6$ and $3 + 3 = 6$

The use of the commutative property to facilitate pupil learning of the facts when they are thus grouped and introduced is apparent. It is easy for pupils to see and to understand that the new set formed by combining a set of two objects with a set of four objects has the same number property as the set formed by combining a set of four objects with a set of two objects. They learn that the additive expressions $2 + 4$ and $4 + 2$ are names for the same number and that another name for that number is 6. They will also learn that when 2 and 4 are the addends, regardless of their order, the sum is 6. As they continue to study addition, they will develop this generalization by using it with other pairs of addends.

Introducing and emphasizing the regrouping procedure when the more difficult facts of addition are being studied not only further relates the operation of addition to the characteristics of our system of numeration, but also helps children to begin to develop a firm understanding of the regrouping procedures necessary in future operations with addition, multiplication, subtraction, and division. The fact family with a sum of 10 will have to be mastered by pupils if the regrouping process is to be utilized in pupil discovery of the other more difficult facts. When the facts with sums of 10 are mastered, children will be better able to make the necessary groupings and, to use the renaming of numbers and the associative property of addition in ascertaining sums.

Consider ice cream sticks as the manipulative materials to be used in helping children to learn the addition facts with sums of 15. The sticks are used to represent the numbers in the problems to be solved. Rational counting could be used to ascertain the total number in the union of the two disjoint sets. If the problem required finding the sum of $8 + 7$ or $7 + 8$, a set of seven sticks would be combined with a set of eight sticks and the new set would be counted.

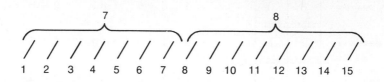

This procedure does not emphasize the process of regrouping, nor does it build upon the previously learned concepts of base and positional value.

When regrouping is utilized, the procedure is one of collecting the sticks into sets of ten and determining the number of sets of ten and the number of single sticks. The concept of ten as the base of our system of numeration is further developed or strengthened through this manipulation. When the numeral describing the number of regrouped sticks is written, the emphasis is upon positional value.

Thus, in a sequential illustration in which the sticks in a, b, and c are the same sticks being regrouped, the collection is visible and the numeral describes the result.

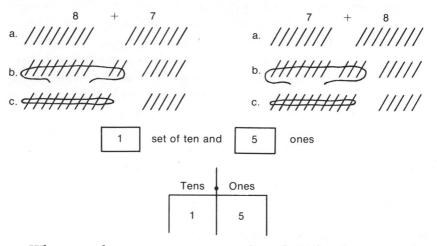

When number sentences are used to describe the manipulations of the sticks, the renaming of one addend into an additive expression and the use of the associative property to help children to discover sums and to understand the regrouping procedure of addition becomes more obvious. Describing the manipulations with number sentences should lead pupils to use number sentences without counters to find sums of the harder combinations. They should proceed from examples such as a to those similar to b.

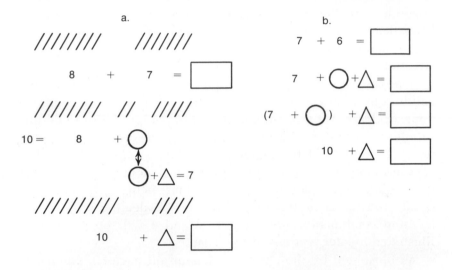

This procedure is a means for increasing pupil understandings and competencies with addition combinations and it should not be regarded as an end. Eventually, pupils should be able to recall immediately the sums of the harder combinations. This implies that other forms of practice will be necessary. If the associative property is used in teaching the harder facts of addition, pupils will have at their disposal another means (in addition to counting) of ascertaining or of verifying specific sums when they cannot recall them or have doubt as to their correctness.

The regrouping procedure used at this elementary level is basically the same procedure that children will be using at higher levels of difficulty in the addition operation when they will be collecting 10 sets of ten to make a set of one hundred or 10 sets of one hundred to make a set of one thousand.

The pertinent properties of number should be utilized to make the addition facts and the addition operation easier for children to learn and to understand. Most pertinent to the study of addition of whole numbers at the elementary level are the commutative, associative, and additive identity properties. If these properties are properly employed, teaching and learning will become more efficient in terms of time and energy spent by teachers and pupils and more effective in terms of pupil mastery and retention of content.

The use of the commutative property to relate addition facts and thus reduce the major ideas of addition that are to be memorized has previously been discussed. The goal is to have children know that the order of two addends does not affect the sum, to know and be able to show why it does not, and to ignore or pay little attention to the order of addends when finding sums.

The associative property of addition should be used to help children to (a) discover the sums of the harder addition combinations, (b) learn that renaming numbers sometimes helps in finding solutions, (c) understand the regrouping procedure used in addition, (d) understand the general procedure or *algorithm* used in adding numbers described by multidigit numerals, and (e) verify their solutions to addition examples. Statements a, b, and c are briefly illustrated in the preceding section dealing with harder addition combinations. Statements d and e will be graphically illustrated in later sections of this chapter.

As illustrated by the chart and legend on page 83, emphasizing the identity element as one major idea when the addition facts are being established will reduce the number of ideas to be memorized from 19 to 1. If problem situations and manipulative materials are used to introduce addition combinations, helping children to develop the idea that "when zero is added to any number, the sum is the same as or identical to that number" will be relatively easy. The teaching procedure for developing this generalization will proceed from adding zero to small numbers to adding zero to larger numbers to adding zero to any number.

Subtraction, the inverse operation of addition, will be discussed in detail in Chapter 6. The inverse idea is mentioned here because most modern programs introduce and develop some of the addition and subtraction facts simultaneously. The suggested advantages of simultaneous development are that pupils will better understand the nature of the addition and subtraction operations and the relationship between them and that they will be aided in remembering the sums and differences (missing addends). One of the practice exercises often employed after meaning has been established through the use of problems and manipulative materials is to ask children to write four true number sentences using three given numerals such as 3, 6, and 9. The pupil is expected to respond with some form of:

$$3 + 6 = 9 \qquad 6 + 3 = 9 \qquad 9 - 3 = 6 \qquad 9 - 6 = 3$$

When developing pupil understanding of the properties of whole numbers, the idea and the utilization of the idea (meaning and understanding) should precede the name of the idea or property. Adding the names of the properties to the vocabularies of children should be a natural process of adding the word to their listening vocabularies through use of the word by the teacher, then helping them to add the word to their speaking vocabularies through participation in classroom discussions, and, finally, adding the word to their reading vocabularies and developing a more or less formal definition.

Practice on facts should come only after understanding and should involve a variety of interesting and fascinating additive situations as well as the traditional computational examples. In modern programs the term practice is not synonymous with the term drill. *Drill* has generally been used to refer to a situation in which the learner is repeatedly presented with a stimulus to which he is to make the correct response. In drill situations the learning is primarily of a mechanical nature — immediate correct response to a presented stimulus. It has often been erroneously implied that drill connotes rote memorization without meaning or understanding. More specifically, drill on the arithmetic facts has been most often associated with "flash cards" or pages of example after example in computational form to which the pupil was to respond mechanically and understanding was not a necessary prerequisite.

Flash Cards   **Page of Examples**

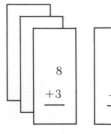

		Add:						
8	4	2	5	6	3	7	4	8
+3	+5	+4	+3	+5	+7	+2	+5	+3

If properly used, drill can be one aspect of practice in a modern elementary mathematics program. The skills or learnings achieved through drill do not have to be rote or meaningless. The term practice implies that the learner understands the underlying concepts of what is being practiced and that the situation has meaning for him. He knows what he is practicing and why he is practicing. Practice also implies that the goal of the activity may be other than immediate recall or mechanical manipulation. The purpose of practice may be the development of deeper or broader understanding or to encourage pupil thinking. In all instances, practice activities are to be preceded by experiences that have given real meaning

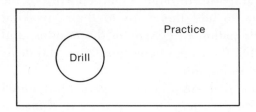

to the concept or skill to be practiced. All drill in modern programs should be practice, but all practice activities will not be drill.

In addition to the use of problem situations and manipulative materials that have been cited as concrete means of introducing, developing, and practicing the addition facts, there are other more abstract activities that are quite useful as practice experiences. Some of the means through which concepts of addition may be developed, broadened, or strengthened include number lines, number sentences, number houses and squares, and games. Games in which addition facts may be practiced are too varied and numerous to cite, but a few examples of other devices follow.

Number lines

1. What addition idea is shown on this number line?

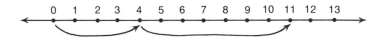

2. On this number line, find the sum of 3 and 6.

3. What addition idea is shown on this number line?

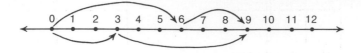

Number sentences

1. Find the missing sums.
   a. $3 + 4 = \square$ b. $6 + 6 = \square$ c. $8 + 9 = \square$
2. Which of these number sentences are true?
   a. $5 + 3 < 7$ b. $5 + 8 = 13$ c. $6 + 5 > 10$
3. Fill in the missing numerals.
   a. $\triangle + 5 = 9$ d. $\square + 3 = 8$
   b. $3 + \bigcirc = 10$ $\triangle + \square = 11$
   c. $\square + \square = 8$ $7 + \triangle = \bigcirc$

Number houses and squares

1. Fill in the missing numerals. The sum in each row should be the number described at the top of the house.

a.
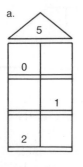

b.
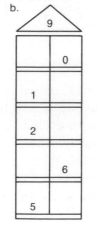

c.

d.
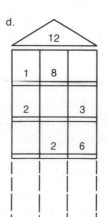

2. Fill in the missing numerals so that the sums in the number squares are as described.

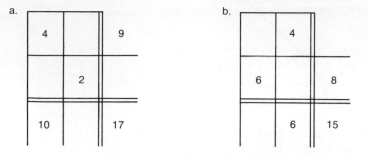

3. Use only the numerals 0, 1, 2, 3, 4, 5, 6, 7, 8, 9 to complete the triangle and the square. Each numeral can be used only once in each figure. Be sure the sums in all directions are as described.

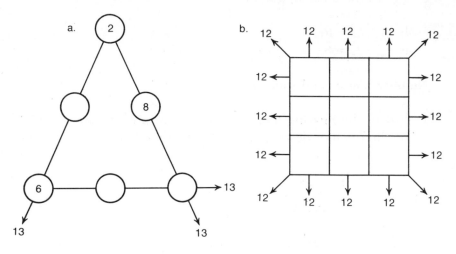

Practicing ideas and skills in a variety of contexts will be productive for most elementary pupils. Some pupils will benefit greatly from the widest variety of practice exercises. That is, they will continue to grow in understandings and skills. However, unless each approach or context is made meaningful, there are some pupils who may become confused by the variety. They may see the approaches or contexts as unrelated ideas and their learning will be hindered. Others who understand well the mathematical ideas involved may see the variety of approaches as repetitious and lose interest. The goal of teachers should not be to use as many means of practice as possible, but to help each child at his own level develop understandings and skills. The selection and use of practice activities and exercises appropriate to the needs of individual pupils is one of the major challenges of teaching elementary mathematics.

Pupil mastery of the addition facts should be regarded as something more than the ability to make the correct sum response to an addition combination stimulus. The pupil who has really mastered an addition fact can do more than immediately recall the sum. He understands the elementary nature of addition and the addition fact and he can demonstrate his understanding in several ways. He recognizes additive or combining situations in problems as distinct from other problem situations. In other words, he could tell which of the following problems could be solved by addition and which could not. He might also be able to write a number sentence that describes the addition problem situation.

1. Mary has some dolls and Jane has some dolls. How many dolls do the two girls have?
2. Eight birds were in a tree. A few flew away. How many were left?
3. Tom, Jack, and Bill each have two pencils. How many pencils do they have?
4. Bill has six cookies. If he shares them with his sister, how many will he then have?

The pupil who understands the addition fact will be able to respond to the question "How do you know?" in regard to the particular combination and sum by using manipulative materials in a combining of sets approach to illustrate that his sum is correct. He should also be able to illustrate the fact with a number line diagram. Accepting this comprehensive definition of mastery has implications for the developmental procedures used in helping children learn and for the evaluative procedures used in determining what and how well they have learned.

Elementary mathematics programs are currently contained in several kinds of organizational patterns: continuous individual progress, the nongraded school, heterogeneously grouped self-contained classrooms, and various other types of instructional units based on grouping techniques. Instructional procedures in contemporary elementary mathematics programs in all organizational patterns are concerned with providing for pupil differences in abilities and understandings and with diagnosing pupil difficulties and directing corrective experiences. Teachers must select and structure content, learning experiences, materials to be used, and evaluative techniques suitable for helping each child progress at an appropriate level and rate. Teacher knowledge of the sequence in which concepts and ideas of the operation of addition are generally developed is a major factor in effectively adjusting instruction to pupil differences.

Summary schema for sequence of concepts

Level	Examples*	New ideas and generalizations
Combining sets		Additive idea of disjoint sets to be combined to make a new set. Can count to find "How many objects in the new set?" Commutative idea concretely introduced.
Easier facts of addition	a. $4 + 2 = \bigcirc$ $2 + 4 = \bigcirc$ b. $\begin{array}{r} 6 \\ +3 \\ \hline \end{array}$ $\begin{array}{r} 3 \\ +6 \\ \hline \end{array}$	Twenty-one related facts to be established and mastered. Commutative idea stressed. Zero in addition introduced. Addition families grouped according to sums. Counting used as a means of verification.
Harder facts of addition	a. $6 + 4 = \bigcirc$ $4 + 6 = \bigcirc$ b. $\begin{array}{r} 8 \\ +7 \\ \hline \end{array}$ $\begin{array}{r} 7 \\ +8 \\ \hline \end{array}$	Twenty-five related facts to be established and mastered. Regrouping introduced. Set of ten made by collecting ones. Relate to positional value of number system. Commutative idea continued. Addition families grouped according to sums. Subtraction facts taught simultaneously. Counting used as a means of verification.
Three one-digit addends	a. $3 + 2 + 4 = \bigcirc$ b. $4 + 3 + 5 = \bigcirc$	Partial sum must be remembered. Associative idea of addition is introduced. First sums are less than ten as in a. Later sums are greater than 9 but less than 20 as in b. Subtraction introduced as a means of verification.

* Examples are also in an order of difficulty

Summary schema for sequence of concepts

Level	Examples*	New ideas and generalizations

Adding tens	a. 30 20
	    +20 +30
	
	b. 34 25
	    +25 +34
	
	c. Three or more addends so long as regrouping of ones or tens is not involved
		Only like units can be added. Ones are added to ones; tens are added to tens. Tens are added just like ones. Commutative idea continued. Renaming addends used in b. When three addends are used, associative idea is continued. Subtraction and associative idea used as means of verification.

Adding hundreds	a. 400 300
	   300 100
	   100 400
	
	b. 324 112
	   203 324
	   112 203
		Only like units can be added. Hundreds are added just like tens and ones. Renaming of addends to develop understanding continued. Commutative and associative ideas continued. No regrouping involved. Subtraction and associative idea used as means of verification.

Regrouping ones with two-digit addends	a. 14 8
	    +8 14
	
	b. 35 29
	    +29 35
	
	c. 16 34
	   27 16
	   34 27
	
	d. 28 9
	   37 37
	    9 28
		Set of ten made by collecting ones. That set is added to already existing tens. Later, as in d, more than one set of ten may be collected and added to the existing tens. Renaming of addends used. Relate to positional value characteristic of our number system. Verification by means of subtraction and associative idea.

Three or more one-digit addends	a. $6 + 4 + 7 = \bigcirc$ b. $7 + 8 + 6 = \bigcirc$	Regrouping involved in first combination. Partial sum to be remembered includes tens. In b regrouping is involved in first and second combinations and addition of tens is involved.

* Examples are also in an order of difficulty

Summary schema for sequence of concepts

Level	Examples*		New ideas and generalizations
Regrouping tens with two- and three-digit addends	a. 74 +62	b. 30 84 51	Ten sets of ten collected to make one set of one hundred. Renaming of addends continued. Relate to positional value characteristic of our number system. Collected sets of one hundred are added to existing sets of hundreds. Verification primarily by associative idea.
	c. 182 +360	d. 176 281 190	
Regrouping ones and tens with two- and three-digit addends	a. 65 +39	b. 34 45 56	There are no new ideas or generalizations to be established with these examples. They are merely a combination of the two preceding difficulty levels.
	c. 285 +349	d. 254 89 193	
Regrouping hundreds	a. 300 542 617	b. 1670 1605 2513	Collecting ten hundreds to make a set of one thousand. New collections of one thousand are added to existing thousands. Collecting hundreds and regrouping to thousands is similar to regrouping ones and tens.
Regrouping ones, tens, and hundreds	a. 584 +458	b. 356 238 440	No new ideas or generalizations. Combination of all ideas previously learned.
	c. 2864 1968 2727 2090		

* Examples are also in an order of difficulty

Developing understanding and mastery of the operation

The teaching procedures recommended for establishing and mastering the facts of addition are to be continued, whenever possible, as the higher order of difficulty or more complex aspects of the addition operation are developed. Pupils' development of understanding of the procedural operation or algorithm of addition and of accuracy in the computation is dependent upon the prerequisites of (1) mastery of the addition facts, (2) understanding of the base and positional value characteristics of our system of numeration, and (3) ability to rename numbers with expanded notation. Unless these prerequisites are met, we can expect pupil difficulties in understanding the step-by-step procedure in which only like units are added (ones are added to ones, tens are added to tens, and so forth) and in understanding the regrouping procedure.

Addition with three or more one-digit addends is introduced soon after the facts or combinations involved have been presented. Some addition with three one-digit addends is undertaken before all the facts have been ascertained. For example, an addition problem involving $3 + 4 + 2 = \bigcirc$ would be appropriate after children have had sufficient learning experiences with the combinations $3 + 4$, $4 + 2$, $3 + 2$, $6 + 3$, $7 + 2$, and $5 + 4$; but perhaps before they have established the sums of such combinations as $8 + 7$ and $6 + 9$.

As illustrated by the schema for sequence of concepts, beginning work with three one-digit addends will not involve regrouping. In later study, regrouping will be required in the second step and then in both the first and second steps. When children are solving problems and working examples with three one-digit addends, the binary nature of addition should become evident. Teachers should encourage pupils to do their calculations mentally, without recording on paper the sum of each addition and without counting. Pupils should also be guided toward learning that the grouping of addends does not affect the sum (associative idea) and that this idea can be used in making mental calculations easier and in verifying sums. The following exercises constitute one form of practicing the associative idea.

"Here are *two* sets of addition examples for you to complete."

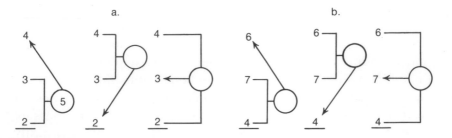

"What can you say about the sums in each set of examples?"

Pupils should have had some exeriences in renaming numbers described by two-digit numerals in expanded notation when they were establishing the harder facts of addition. However, it will be necessary for teachers to help pupils extend this learning to renaming other numbers described by two-digit, three-digit, and other multidigit numerals through such exercises as:

a.

$$\text{///////} \text{///////} \text{//////} = \underline{\quad} \text{ sets of ten and } \underline{\quad} \text{ ones}$$

$$\text{///////} \text{///////} \text{///////} \text{///} = \underline{\quad} \text{ tens } \underline{\quad} \text{ ones}$$

b.

$$\text{///////} \text{///////} \text{////////} = \underline{20} + \underline{\quad}$$

$$\text{///////} \text{///////} \text{///////} \text{///////} = \underline{\quad} + \underline{7}$$

c. $63 = \underline{\quad}$ tens $\underline{\quad}$ ones $63 = \underline{\quad} + \underline{\quad}$

$386 = \underline{\quad}$ hundreds $\underline{\quad}$ tens $\underline{\quad}$ ones

$386 = \underline{\quad} + \underline{\quad} + \underline{\quad}$

$6,705 = \underline{\quad}$ thousands $\underline{\quad}$ hundreds $\underline{\quad}$ tens

$\underline{\quad}$ ones

$6,705 = \underline{\quad} + \underline{\quad} + \underline{\quad} + \underline{\quad}$

d. $493 = 4(100) + \bigcirc (10) + \bigcirc (1)$

$819 = 8(\quad) + 1(\quad) + 9(\quad)$

Number names written in expanded form will be used to help children understand the step-by-step procedure in the algorithm (that only like units can be added) and further understand the regrouping process in the abstractness of the algorithm.

Teachers will have to be more selective in their use of manipulative materials and other instructional aids to develop pupil understanding of the addition of numbers described by two- and three-digit numerals than they were when establishing the addition facts. The teaching procedure is to move from the concreteness of combining sets of manipulative objects to the abstractness of computing sums with the algorithm. This sequence may be easily illustrated when the numbers to be added are described by two-digit numerals. Consider a problem or problems that involve addition combinations such as $25 + 17$:

Ice Cream Sticks

Play Money

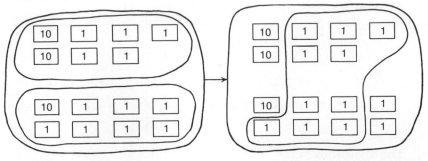

Place-Value Chart

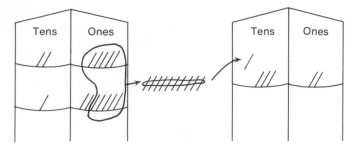

Renaming numbers. As the above concrete and semiconcrete aids and procedures are used, the manipulations should be described with numerical expressions involving the renaming of numbers with expanded notation. In other words, a record is made of the activity. The manipulation with ice cream sticks might best be described as in a below. The activities with play money might be successively recorded as in a, b, and c. Continuing the development of understanding through the use of a place-value chart should involve recording the manipulation as in d. Note the transition from a through d to the conventional algorithm.

a. 2 tens   5 ones

   1 ten   7 ones

   3 tens (12) ones

   1 ten   2 ones

   4 tens   2 ones   or 42

b. $20 + 5$

  $10 + 7$

  $30 + 12$ 30

             $+12$

              42

c. $2(10) + 5(1)$

  $1(10) + 7(1)$

  $3(10) + (12(1))$

  $1(10) + 2(1)$

  $4(10) + 2(1) = 40 + 2$ or 42

d.

T.	O.	
2	5	
1	7	
1	2	sum of the ones
3		sum of the tens
4	2	

The algorithm

a. $25 + 17 = (20 + 5) + (10 + 7)$

or

     Ones   Tens

  $(5 + 7) + (20 + 10)$

     12   +   30 $= 42$

b.   25

   $+17$

    12 sum of ones

    30 sum of tens

    42

c. (1) ten regrouped

    25

  $+17$

    42

Note that certain instructional materials, although suggested by some authorities in mathematics education and some current textual materials as aids for teaching addition of multidigit numerals, are not mentioned here. Although the number line is appropriate for earlier work with addition, finding sums of several multidigit numbers by counting and drawing on a number line does not contribute much to pupils' understandings of the operation. The abacus is not recommended as an aid because the manipulation of the beads often appears to be more magical than meaningful for children. This is especially true in the exchange of ones beads for a ten bead or the exchange of tens beads for a hundreds bead. The use of colored markers in the place-value chart is not suggested because the color becomes another factor to be remembered by pupils, one that is to be discarded later. Use of the abacus or colored markers as aids to teaching regrouping hardly seems necessary if the concept is properly developed with manipulative objects and play money.

Care should be taken that children do not become completely dependent upon using one device for finding sums. They should be encouraged through the use of several aids to make generalizations and to develop rules based upon their understandings for performing the operation. The teaching aids that are suggested here are similar to or extensions of the materials that have been used and that will be used to develop understanding of number and of the other operations.

The teacher's decisions as to what instructional aids to use and as to which form of notation is to be used will depend upon the level of understanding and abilities of the individual pupil and the nature of the numbers to be added. Children should not be asked to perform operational tasks in addition that are unsuited to their levels of understanding and skill. They should not be required to continue to work with manipulative devices or to use one form of notation when they have acquired sufficient understanding to proceed to higher levels of abstraction. Nor should they be required to work at levels for which they have insufficient backgrounds.

When children are ready to study the addition of numbers described by three-digit numerals, it is impractical to use manipulative objects such as ice cream sticks to represent the numbers. The addition of hundreds could be introduced more appropriately with play money or markers in the place-value chart. It is not unusual for some children to acquire sufficient understanding of the nature of addition when working with the addition of tens and ones to make the application in the addition of hundreds and of thousands when it is introduced through the use of expanded notation.

Accuracy in computation with the addition algorithm was a goal of arithmetic programs of the past and is a goal of modern elementary mathematics programs. However, in modern programs, mechanical performance is not the complete objective. We want children to know the when, why, and how of it.

Processes of verification

As indicated in the Summary Schema for Sequence of Concepts, children should learn to verify or to ascertain the correctness of sums at every level of work with the addition operation. To be more general, processes of verification should be developed as an integral part of the instructional procedure for all the operations with all the subsets of the set of real numbers. The nature of the instructional procedure, including pupil practice exercises and assignments, will determine whether children learn to view processes of verification as useful learnings or whether they will see verification processes as extra tasks with little or no useful purposes.

Pupils are more likely to view verification procedures as useful learnings or techniques if (1) they are guided to understand that their ability to verify solutions will aid them by giving them a personal knowledge of their accuracy and thus make them less dependent upon the teacher or textbook to know when they have a correct idea or solution; (2) the processes of verification are integrated throughout the activities and experiences used in introducing, developing, and practicing the operations, thus broadening understanding of the operations; and (3) better pupil self-actualization and self-realization are achieved through using verification techniques. These statements imply that verification is to be used as pupil self-reinforcement in the learning procedure.

On the other hand, if verification techniques are delayed until pupils have acquired some degree of mastery of the operational algorithm, and if practice on verification is assigned intermittently as "extra" work, pupils are likely to deemphasize its importance and interpret the exercise of verification techniques as extra busy work of no importance. Little will be gained in pupil self-realization, and they may even short-cut or avoid the actual procedure of verification by simply rewriting the original solution as the solution of the verification process.

The procedures or forms of verifying solutions in the addition operation may be classified as to the degree of accuracy required. In the early study of addition, verification should involve the correctness of the exact number of the sum. Later, pupils may be satisfied with determining the reasonableness of the solution. If the correctness of the exact number of the sum is to be ascertained, the processes used will involve other operations on number or some property of the same operation. If only the reasonableness of the solution is of concern, the procedure used will involve estimation or the use of concrete or semiconcrete materials to indicate relationships.

The operation of *counting* is the first process that children will use to verify sums. Although all sums could be verified by counting, this procedure is generally utilized only when the sums of the basic facts of addition are to be verified and when the addition of three one-digit addends is introduced.

Subtraction may be introduced as a verification of the sums of the basic combinations with the use of manipulative objects.

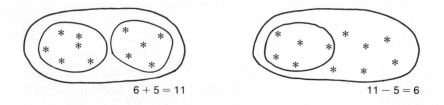

$$6 + 5 = 11 \qquad\qquad 11 - 5 = 6$$

The basic facts of subtraction and the subtraction algorithm are appropriately used to verify sums of three one-digit addends and sums of two or more two-digit addends.

a.			b.					c.		
	4	12		addend	42	95	sum		34	79
	3	−4		addend	53	−53	addend		27	−27
	5	8			95	42	other		18	52
	12	−3					addend		79	−34
		5								18
		−5								−18
		0								0

Subtraction, the inverse operation of addition, may be used to undo any addition operation or to verify any sum. However, pupils should be guided to generalize that it is most appropriate to use subtraction only when two addends are involved. Using subtraction to verify long addition examples involves the use of many facts and calculations and more opportunities to make mistakes exist.

```
a.   5 2 8 0     1 0 0 4 2       b. 1 3 7 6      9 1 2 4
    + 4 7 6 2    − 5 2 8 0          2 0 2 7   − 1 3 7 6
     1 0 0 4 2      4 7 6 2          3 2 0 8      7 7 4 8
                                     2 5 1 3   − 2 0 2 7
                                     9 1 2 4      5 7 2 1
                                              − 3 2 0 8
                                                 2 5 1 3
                                              − 2 5 1 3
                                                      0
```

The regrouping of addends and re-adding, application of the *associative property*, is also introduced as a means of verifying sums when three one-digit addends are involved. Use of the associative property is continued as a form of verification through-out the remainder of study of addition of whole numbers. (It will also be used to verify addition of other numbers in the subsets of the set of real numbers, as will counting and subtraction.) Finding the sum of large numbers described by multidigit numerals by adding in one direction and verifying that sum by re-adding in the other direction is an application of the associative property. The process is actually one of regrouping addends. If we regard the commutative idea as involving only two addends (the order of the two addends does not affect the sum), the commutative property of addition cannot be used to verify sums. Children who mistakenly believe the sum of $8 + 5$ to be 14 will also have the same idea of the sum of $5 + 8$.

Examples of verification using the associative property:

$$a.\quad 7 + 6 + 5 = \bigcirc$$

$$(7 + 6) + 5 = \bigcirc \qquad 7 + (6 + 5) = \bigcirc$$

$$13 + 5 = 18 \qquad 7 + 11 = 18$$

```
       6              6
       3              3
       5              5
```

```
b.    3 8        3 8        3 8
      4 7      + 4 7      + 2 9
      2 9        8 5        6 7
sum of ones   2 4
sum of tens   9 0        8 5        6 7
            1 1 4      + 2 9      + 4 7
                       1 1 4      1 1 4
```

c.
```
    ① ③ ①              1  1  6  1  5  adding up
    3  4  6  3          3  4  6  3
    2  1  9  7          2  1  9  7
    3  0  8  0          3  0  8  0
    2  8  7  5          2  8  7  5
  ─────────── adding    ① ③ ①
    1  1  6  1  5  down
```

As pupils develop skills in addition, there will be many occasions when it will be necessary to ascertain only the reasonableness of a sum. Estimation of the sum can be based upon general information about the addends. For example, a sum less than 3 tens, or 30, would be a reasonable answer for $8 + 9 + 7 = \bigcirc$ because each of the addends is less than ten. In an example such as $37 + 38 = \bigcirc$ or in computational form (solved incorrectly),

$$
\begin{array}{r}
3\,7 \\
+3\,8 \\
\hline
6\,1\,5
\end{array}
$$

615 would not be a reasonable sum because 3 tens + 3 tens are only 6 tens, or 60.

When pupils are confronted with problems that they doubt they have solved correctly or suspect that they have used the wrong operation, they may wish to verify their method of solution by using manipulation of concrete objects or by drawing diagrams. This experience may help them to see the relationships of the numbers involved in the problem and verify the correctness of their procedure.

Children should be guided to select verification procedures most suitable to the nature of the addition example. They should also learn that if the process results in nonverification, the mistake is not necessarily in the original computation. It may be either in the first computation or the verification process.

Suggested activities

1. Construct an inventory to be used to determine whether primary pupils possess the necessary prerequisite knowledge and skills for the systematic or formal study of the addition facts.

2. Compare the approaches used in two contemporary textbook series for developing understanding of the regrouping procedure used in addition.

3. Develop a set of practice exercises for the addition facts that differ from the traditional forms of $\begin{array}{r} 8 \\ +7 \\ \hline \end{array}$ and $4 + 9 = \Box$.

4. Estimate the sum of the following example. Then compute the sum and verify it by using subtraction and by using the associative property.

$$675 + 1{,}683 + 2{,}098 + 1{,}477 = \Box$$

5. Collect from children in one of the early elementary grades a set of problems which they have "made up" and that require addition for solution. How might you use such problems in teaching?

Selected references

Bouwsma, W. D., C. G. Corle, and D. F. Clemson, Jr., *Basic Mathematics for Elementary Teachers*. New York: The Ronald Press Company, 1967, Chapter 3, "Addition," pp. 26–48.

Buckingham, B. R., *Elementary Arithmetic—Its Meaning and Practice*. Boston: Ginn & Company, 1953, Chapter 5, "Addition of Whole Numbers," pp. 89–129.

Flournoy, F., "A Consideration of the Ways Children Think when Performing Higher-Decade Addition," *The Elementary School Journal*, 57:204–208, Jan. 1957.

Mueller, F. J., *Arithmetic—Its Structure and Concepts*. Englewood Cliffs, N.J.: Prentice-Hall, Inc., 1964, Unit 6, "Operation of Addition," and Unit 7, "Addition Algorithms," pp. 55–81.

Smith, L. B., "Venn Diagrams Strengthen Children's Mathematical Understanding," *The Arithmetic Teacher*, 13:92–99, Feb. 1966.

Teaching 6

subtraction of whole

numbers

Subtraction of whole numbers is one of the fundamental operations of arithmetic—*fundamental* in the sense that all operations in arithmetic can be reduced to procedures of counting, adding, subtracting, multiplying, or dividing whole numbers. In many mathematics textbooks and content courses, subtraction is defined by its relation to addition and treated or studied in that respect. In this volume the relationship is stressed, but for purposes of organization and emphasis, a separate chapter is directed to the teaching of the operation.

The nature of the subtraction operation

Like addition, subtraction is an operation to be performed upon number that is related to and that can be thought of in terms of sets and subsets. The addition operation is primarily concerned with finding the number property of the union of two or more disjoint sets. The operation of subtraction is related to the *separation* of a set into two distinct subsets and to the *comparison* of two disjoint sets. In other words, the subtraction operation is used to find the missing number properties in several different "set" situations.

Consider the situation in which B is a subset of set A. The elements of set A are separated into two distinct subsets: those elements that are in subset B and those elements that are in set A but that are not in subset B. Number properties may be associated with set A, with subset B, and with the subset of elements that are in A but not in B. If the number property of the subset of elements that are in A but not in B is missing, that number property could be found by counting or by the operation of subtraction:

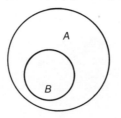

$$n(A) - n(B) = n(\text{elements in } A \text{ but not in } B)$$

If the number property of subset B is missing, that number property could also be found by counting or by the operation of subtraction:

$$n(A) - n(\text{elements in } A \text{ but not in } B) = n(B)$$

Note that if the number property of set A is missing that number property would be found by counting or by addition:

$$n(B) + n(\text{elements in } A \text{ but not in } B) = n(A)$$

If more than one number property is missing in this situation, a unique solution could not be found but an infinite number of possible solutions could be determined.

Other situations in which subtraction is the operation to be used to find missing number properties involve the comparison of sets. Suppose that we know the number properties of two disjoint sets (set C and set D) and from this knowledge we know that set D has a greater number than set C: $n(D) > n(C)$.

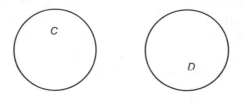

We could ascertain the difference in the number of elements in set C and the number of elements in set D by matching the elements of set C with the elements of set D in one-to-one correspondence and by then counting the difference in set D. We could also use the operation of subtraction to find the number property of the difference by subtracting the number property of set C from the number property of set D:

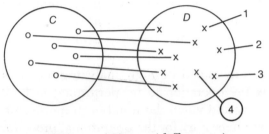

$$n(D) - n(C) = n(\text{difference})$$

A more abstract and complex comparison situation exists when we know the number properties of set M and of set N and that set M and set N are equal in number: $n(M) = n(N)$. We also know that set N contains subset P and the number property of subset P. The missing number property which we are seeking is the number of elements in set N that are not in subset P.

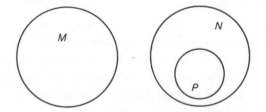

Matching and counting could be used to determine the number of elements in set N that are not in subset P. The elements in P could be matched with elements in M. The number property of the elements in M that are not matched with elements of P would be the number property of the elements in N that are not in subset P.

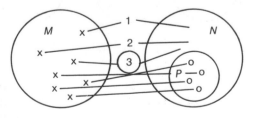

The following sentences that describe the situation indicate that the operation of subtraction could be used to ascertain the missing number property of the elements in set N that are not in subset P.

$$n(M) = n(N)$$
$$n(P) + n(\text{elements of } N \text{ not in } P) = n(N)$$
$$n(N) - n(P) = n(\text{elements of } N \text{ not in } P)$$
$$n(P) + n(\text{elements of } N \text{ not in } P) = n(M)$$
$$n(M) - n(P) = n(\text{elements of } N \text{ not in } P)$$

When it is understood through analyzing the set situation that subtraction is the operation to be performed to find the missing number property and when the number properties of the sets and subsets that are necessary for the operational procedure have been ascertained, subtraction can be considered as an arithmetic operation. Sets or their elements cannot be subtracted; they can be separated or compared. However, the number properties of sets and subsets can be ascertained, and these numbers can be subtracted to find their difference. Subtraction, like addition, is a binary operation in that it can be performed on only two numbers at a time. Only one number can be subtracted from one other number in any single instance.

The process used in the arithmetical operation of subtraction to find the difference of two whole numbers will be the same regardless of the set situations previously described. As an arithmetical operation, subtraction may be defined as the inverse of addition. The process is one of finding the missing addend when one addend and the sum are known. This relationship may be shown with the separation situation and with the comparison situations. For clarification, number properties have been arbitrarily assigned.

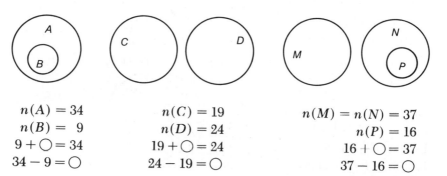

$n(A) = 34$
$n(B) = 9$
$9 + \bigcirc = 34$
$34 - 9 = \bigcirc$

$n(C) = 19$
$n(D) = 24$
$19 + \bigcirc = 24$
$24 - 19 = \bigcirc$

$n(M) = n(N) = 37$
$n(P) = 16$
$16 + \bigcirc = 37$
$37 - 16 = \bigcirc$

For purposes of communication, the numerals used in the subtraction operation are called the *minuend,* the *subtrahend*, and the *difference.* Some references prefer to call the result of the subtraction operation the *remainder.* However, because the term remainder is also used to name a part of the result in the division operation, it is suggested that to avoid confusion and to be consistent with elementary pupils the term difference be used to name the result of the subtraction operation. Although it may be considered important for pupils to learn the terminology for the parts of a subtraction example, it is more important for teachers to stress with their pupils the relationship of the addend, addend, sum of addition to the sum (minuend), addend (subtrahend), and missing addend (difference) of subtraction.

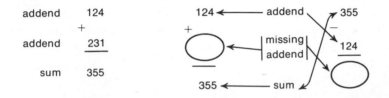

Prerequisite learnings for the operation of subtraction

Before children begin the formal study of subtraction, that is, establishing for themselves or discovering the basic subtraction facts, they should have acquired certain concepts, ideas, or understandings that will not only serve as foundations for new learnings but that will allow them to discover the facts and to verify their discoveries and ideas. Children's understandings and mastery of the subtraction facts and the subtraction operation will be built upon learnings pertaining to sets of objects and the manipulation of sets of objects and to the characteristics of our system of numeration. The early learning experiences or activities that are used to introduce these important elementary but basic concepts should involve an intuitive or "premathematics" approach in which children *see* the idea in a physical representation.

The necessary prerequisite learnings for the formal study of subtraction are nearly identical to those cited as necessary for the formal study of addition. However, because subtraction is being discussed as a distinct operation to be performed when the situation calls for a set to be separated or for two sets to be compared, some brief description of desired early learning experiences seems appropriate.

Prior to establishing or discovering the subtraction facts, children should have acquired the understanding that a set of objects can be separated into two disjoint subsets and should be able to ascertain the number properties of the set and the subsets. Activities in which children are asked to separate a set into two disjoint subsets should come early in the primary mathematics program. At first they may be asked to separate a set on the basis of some characteristic of elements in the set without regard to number properties or names. For example, separate the set of balloons into a subset of balloons with strings and a subset of balloons without strings. Later, when counting has become one of the children's accomplishments, ascertaining the number properties of the set and of the subsets should be included in the activity: There are _____ balloons in the set. There are _____ balloons with strings. There are _____ balloons without strings.

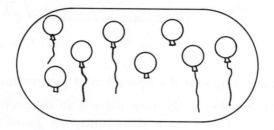

Activities in which children are asked to match the elements of one set in one-to-one correspondence with the elements of a disjoint set to determine whether the sets are equivalent or equal in number should also come early in the primary program. Such activities are often used to have children find out which sets have the same number property as a given set.

Which sets have the same number as set *A*?

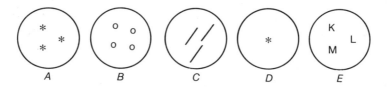

Children's experiences with comparing sets should not be limited to ascertaining which sets can be given the same number names. They should be expanded and extended toward answering such questions as:

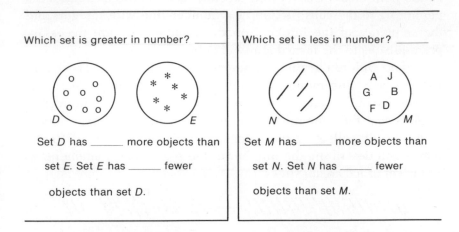

Which set is greater in number? _____

Set D has _____ more objects than set E. Set E has _____ fewer objects than set D.

Which set is less in number? _____

Set M has _____ more objects than set N. Set N has _____ fewer objects than set M.

Combining a set of objects with a given set to make a new set of n elements and removing some elements from a set to make a set of n elements are also good foundational experiences for developing children's understanding of the application of the subtraction operation. Beginning activities of this type should involve manipulation of objects. Later, pupils might be asked to complete worksheet exercises such as:

A. Draw enough X's to make the number of X's in set B equal to 7.

Make $n(B) = 7$

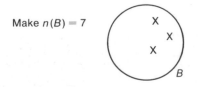

B. Cross out (remove) 0's from set R to make the number of 0's in set R equal to 5.

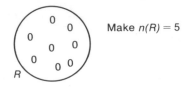

Make $n(R) = 5$

If the number line is to be used as an instructional device to help children develop understanding of the subtraction operation and to help them discover and practice facts, learning experiences pertaining to the construction of a number line with integers and the sequence of the integers on the number line are necessary prerequisites to the formal study of subtraction.

Before children begin to systematically establish any of the subtraction facts with minuends of 10 to 18, they should have a basic knowledge of the concept of base in our system of numeration. This implies that they should have a good background of experiences in physically collecting the objects in a set into subsets of 10 elements and describing the number of the set by such statements as "This set of ice cream sticks

////////////////////////——▸ ⫽⫽⫽⫽⫽ ⫽⫽⫽⫽⫽ ///

can be described as _____ sets of ten and _____ ones."

Children's experiences should also include the reverse procedure of beginning with a certain number of collections of ten and ungrouping to single units. Learning activities directed toward developing an understanding of the concept of base should begin with very concrete representations of number and proceed to more abstract representations.

Ice Cream Sticks

//////////////// ⟶ ⫽⫽⫽⫽⫽ //////

Money (Dimes and Pennies)

Place-Value Chart

Tens	Ones
/	///

⟶ ⫽⫽⫽⫽⫽ /// ⟶ ////////////

Numerals

23 = _____ tens and __3__ ones   or   __1__ ten and _____ ones

Establishing and mastering the facts of subtraction

The subtraction facts consist of all the possible inverse statements that can be made of the addition facts. This includes all the situations in which the known sum (minuend) is a number from the set $\{0, 1, 2, \ldots, 18\}$; the known addend (subtrahend) is a number from the set $\{0, 1, 2, \ldots, 9\}$; and the missing addend (difference) is also a number from the set $\{0, 1, 2, \ldots, 9\}$. There is only one major idea or fact to be learned from all instances when zero is the known addend. The difference between any number and zero is that known number: $N - 0 = N$. (Refer to the table illustrating related addition facts in Chapter 5.) There are nine subtraction facts in which the missing addend (difference) is the same as the known addend. These are the inverse statements of the doubles in the addition facts: $N - b = b$. For each of the remaining 36 related addition facts, two corresponding subtraction facts exist: If $a + c = N$, then $N - a = c$ and $N - c = a$. Thus, there are 82 subtraction facts to be mastered by pupils as prerequisites to their success in performing the formal subtraction operation. These facts are the same facts that pupils will use in the subtraction of rational numbers, both common fractions and decimal fractions.

There is some difference in authoritative opinion presented in "methods of teaching" textbooks and in pupils' textural materials as to whether the subtraction facts are to be introduced to pupils simultaneously with the corresponding addition facts or whether children ought to know some of the addition facts before the formal development of the subtraction facts is begun. Claims for both methods of introductory instructional procedures include better pupil understanding of the addition and subtraction operations and their inverse relationship and the facilitation of pupil mastery of the facts. The success of either procedure is dependent upon a solid foundation of experiences such as those described in the preceding section.

The formal development of the subtraction facts after pupils have had some basic experiences and knowledge of some of the easier addition facts would seem to lessen pupil confusion concerning the oral vocabulary, the reading vocabulary, and the symbolism that is to be developed. The major advantages of introducing addition and subtraction facts simultaneously are the emphasis upon the relationship of the two operations and the possibility of teaching the facts in "families" involving three numbers. Such advantages are not lost in a procedure that develops understanding of the easier addition facts first if we consider that the inverse relationship of

Fact family for 9, 4, 5	
$4 + 5 = 9$	$9 - 4 = 5$
$5 + 4 = 9$	$9 - 5 = 4$

subtraction to addition could then be built upon the pupil's knowledge and understanding of addition and that facts can be classified and practiced as families after both the addition and subtraction facts have been introduced and the relationship of facts has been ascertained by pupils. If such distinct emphasis is given, pupils will be less likely to confuse problem situations in which sets are to be combined, a set is to be separated, or sets are to be compared.

In some contemporary textbook programs, the implication is that pupils are to be led to think of subtraction situations in an "additive" way. The difference is to be regarded as a missing addend, and the thinking procedure is to involve "What is to be added to the known addend to arrive at the known sum?" The underlying arguments for this implied instructional procedure are that pupils could then use the same thinking procedure for examples such as $3 + 4 = N$ and $4 + N = 9$, that the relationship between addition and subtraction is more completely developed through this procedure, that pupils will be able to use their knowledge of addition facts to answer subtractive problem situations, and that *perhaps* children will learn the subtraction facts incidentally through this procedure. Another implication is that pupils will continue to use this thinking process in their further study of the subtraction algorithm or operational procedure.

There is little or no evidence to indicate that children who are initially taught to think of subtraction in an "additive" way develop a better understanding of the relationship between addition and subtraction or that the procedure is more effective in helping children to learn the subtraction facts. The major criticisms of elementary teachers involved in such programs are that children *do not* learn the subtraction facts and that later in the program when the subtraction operation is taught by a *decomposition* method (described in a later section of this chapter), they use a different thinking process in which mastery of the subtraction facts is a prerequisite.

Pupils should be helped to establish the subtraction facts in such a way that the facts will be applicable, together with pertinent rules or principles, in their operation with the subtraction algorithm. The inverse relationship of subtraction to addition is to be developed from a general idea based on the manipulation of objects to the use of one operation as a process of verification of the other.

The teacher's role in helping each child establish the subtraction facts for himself in such a way that each is building an individual but consistent structure of knowledge of number and operation will be one of selecting and organizing content and materials and organizing and guiding learning experiences. The role will involve structuring problem situations, providing manipulative instructional aids and materials, posing guiding questions and suggestions, encouraging pupil discussion and participation, giving order and sequence to the learning situations, ascertaining that each child sees the important patterns and relationships, and encouraging him to keep a record of his own discoveries.

In general, the recommendations made for teaching the addition facts are also applicable to introducing and developing the facts of subtraction. Meaningful problem situations, preferably centered on the common classroom environment of pupils, are to be used to orally introduce the subtraction combinations. A better pupil understanding of the subtraction situation and combinations will probably be developed if the initial formal work with establishing subtraction facts involves the separation of a set or the "take-away" idea. Problem situations in which the subtraction facts are applied to situations involving the comparison of the number properties of two sets would be introduced after children have some knowledge and understanding of subtraction facts.

Activities and experiences involving the use of subtraction facts to compare the number properties of two sets should precede "additive type" problems in which subtraction is the operation to be used for solution. In additive type problems, the total number required and the number possessed are known and the additional number needed is sought. A simple illustration of an additive type problem is

"Jill wants to buy an item that costs $9. She has $4.
How much more does she need?"

$$4 + \square = 9 \rightarrow 9 - 4 = \square$$

The number of dollars Jill has is to be compared to the number of dollars required in order to find the addition number needed. The following diagram might be used to illustrate the problem situation.

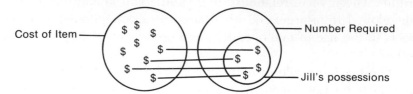

The use of subtraction in comparison situations of additive type problems may be more difficult for children to understand than other comparisons of the number properties of two sets because the required number is often only stated and not concretely illustrated.

Pupil knowledge and understanding of the subtraction facts and the operation or algorithm of subtraction are to be built upon basic concepts of number and numeration. The number property of sets, one-to-one correspondence, base, positional value, and naming number through the use of additive and subtractive expressions are both foundation concepts and concepts that can be further developed as the operation of subtraction is formally studied.

Children should be allowed to discover the differences associated with the subtraction combinations presented in the problems through their own individual approaches, which will basically involve the *manipulation of* the *objects* described in problems or objects such as "counters" representing the described objects and *counting.* A pupil's observance of a difference with a particular number combination in a single introductory problem should lead to his establishment of this observation as a fact through his experiences with other problems including the same combination and his processes of verification. Dependent upon the teacher's knowledge of the capabilities of the pupils in an instructional group, one subtraction fact or several subtraction facts can be introduced in a single problem situation.

As pupils establish facts, they should make a personal record of their discoveries. The symbolism used in reading and writing facts $(8 - 5 = 3; \begin{array}{r} 8 \\ -5 \\ \hline 3 \end{array})$ must be taught to pupils as communication skills. As facts are accumulated, they can be classified according to the known sum (minuend). This record becomes a personal reference for the pupil and a record of pupil progress for the teacher. Pupils are to be encouraged to view such expressions as $9 - 4$, $8 - 3$, and $10 - 5$ along with $3 + 2$ and $4 + 1$ as names for the same number. Some pupils and teachers may want to keep the facts recorded in a table that combines the addition facts and the subtraction facts. Such a record would look like the table of addition facts, and pupils would need to learn to read the table correctly to obtain the inverse subtraction facts. Others may want to keep separate records of the subtraction facts. A completed record of established subtraction facts may look like the accompanying table, Subtraction Facts I Know.

The easier subtraction facts, those in which the known sum is less than 10, are to be established first. As they are established, their inverse relationship to the easier addition facts is to be developed through learning experiences that call attention to "fact families." The emphasis on the inverse relationship is continued as the harder facts of subtraction, those with known sums (minuends) greater than 10, are introduced and developed. The regrouping process used in the subtraction algorithm should be introduced with the harder subtraction facts. Lack of understanding of this process is probably the greatest cause of pupil difficulty with the operation of subtraction. Developing pupil understanding of the subtraction facts and the regrouping procedure involves the appropriate selection of instructional materials and encouraging, guiding, or directing pupil thinking.

A sequence in the use of manipulative materials or instructional aids and instructional procedures is implied by the preceding statements:

EASIER FACTS

Separation

Counters

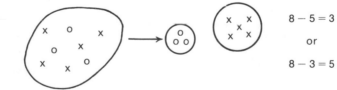

$8 - 5 = 3$

or

$8 - 3 = 5$

Number line

$8 - 3 = 5$

Subtraction facts I know

"Known sum"

Difference or number named	1	2	3	4	5	6	7	8	9	10	11	12	13	14	15	16	17	18
1	1—0	2—1	3—2	4—3	5—4	6—5	7—6	8—7	9—8	10—9								
2		2—0	3—1	4—2	5—3	6—4	7—5	8—6	9—7	10—8	11—9							
3			3—0	4—1	5—2	6—3	7—4	8—5	9—6	10—7	11—8	12—9						
4				4—0	5—1	6—2	7—3	8—4	9—5	10—6	11—7	12—8	13—9					
5					5—0	6—1	7—2	8—3	9—4	10—5	11—6	12—7	13—8	14—9				
6						6—0	7—1	8—2	9—3	10—4	11—5	12—6	13—7	14—8	15—9			
7							7—0	8—1	9—2	10—3	11—4	12—5	13—6	14—7	15—8	16—9		
8								8—0	9—1	10—2	11—3	12—4	13—5	14—6	15—7	16—8	17—9	
9									9—0	10—1	11—2	12—3	13—4	14—5	15—6	16—7	17—8	18—9

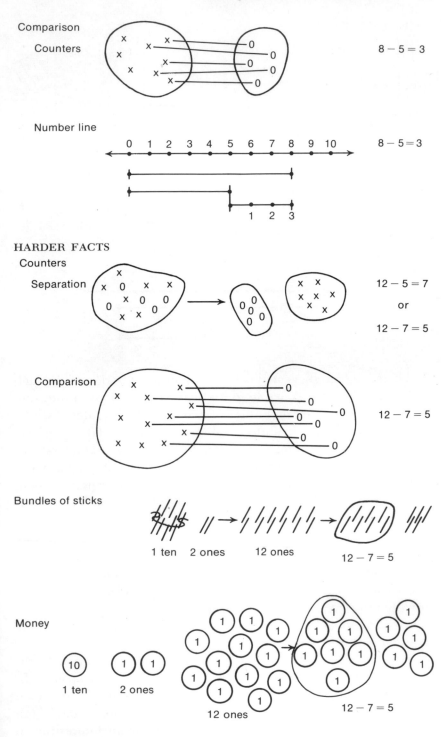

Comparison

Counters

$8 - 5 = 3$

Number line

0 1 2 3 4 5 6 7 8 9 10 $8 - 5 = 3$

1 2 3

HARDER FACTS

Counters

Separation

$12 - 5 = 7$

or

$12 - 7 = 5$

Comparison

$12 - 7 = 5$

Bundles of sticks

1 ten   2 ones   12 ones

$12 - 7 = 5$

Money

10   1 1

1 ten   2 ones

12 ones

$12 - 7 = 5$

Place-value chart

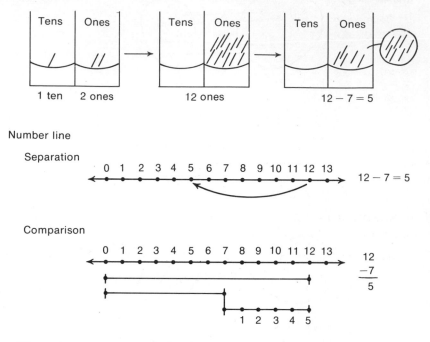

Number line

Separation

12 − 7 = 5

Comparison

$$\begin{array}{r} 12 \\ -7 \\ \hline 5 \end{array}$$

　　The sequence suggested is based upon the criterion of abstractness, from the most concrete to the least. Illustrations of the comparison of the number properties of two sets with bundles of sticks, money, and counters in a place-value chart are not shown because of the recommended emphasis upon developing pupil understanding of the regrouping process with the harder subtraction facts. Note that the number line is used to help develop or practice both the easier facts and the harder facts, but that the regrouping process is not evident, visible, or even necessary when the number line is used to illustrate a harder fact. Using the number line to illustrate the comparison of the number properties of two sets at this level makes the comparison situation more meaningful. Such experiences will also serve as foundation for later comparison situations in which the operations of division with whole numbers, subtraction with rational numbers, and/or division with rational numbers will be employed.

　　The described aids also suggest a variety of practice-type learning activities that are directed toward a pupil mastery of the subtraction facts that includes understanding as well as immediate recall of the difference of a subtraction combination. Other more abstract types of practice exercises that are more interesting to children than the traditional drill include number sentences, number houses, and number squares similar to those described in Chapter 5.

Developing understanding and mastery of the operation

Correct solutions for what might be called "subtractive situations" can be determined without the knowledge of a distinct procedure known as a subtraction algorithm or mastery of the subtraction facts. Addition of numbers is the inverse of subtraction of numbers, and knowledge of the addition facts and the addition algorithm may be used instead of a separate algorithm for subtraction. For example,

$$567 - 235 = \square \text{ may be approached as } 235 + \square = 567$$

$$
\begin{array}{r}
5\ 6\ 7 \\
-\ 2\ 3\ 5 \\
\hline
\square \triangle \bigcirc
\end{array}
$$

5 ones + $\bigcirc$ ones = 7 ones
3 tens + $\triangle$ tens = 6 tens
2 hundreds + $\square$ hundreds = 5 hundreds

$$
\begin{array}{r}
2\ 3\ 5 \\
+\ \square \triangle \bigcirc \\
\hline
5\ 6\ 7
\end{array}
$$

The need for a distinct procedure becomes apparent when the addition facts to be used involve regrouping. The use of the additive procedure becomes much more complicated when the situation involves an example such as $5,216 - 3,847 = \square$ or $3,847 + \square = 5,216$. The known sum, 5,216 is renamed as regrouping occurs and the nature of the regrouping and renaming must be remembered.

$$
\begin{array}{r}
4\ 11\ 10\ 16 \\
5\ 2\ 1\ 6 \\
-\ 3\ 8\ 4\ 7 \\
\hline
\bigcirc \bigcirc \triangle \square
\end{array}
$$

7 ones + $\square$ ones = 16 ones
4 tens + $\triangle$ tens = 10 tens
8 hundreds + $\bigcirc$ hundreds = 11 hundreds
3 thousands + $\bigcirc$ thousands = 4 thousands

$$
\begin{array}{r}
3\ 8\ 4\ 7 \\
+\ \bigcirc \bigcirc \triangle \square \\
\hline
1\ 6 \\
1\ 0 \\
1\ 1 \\
4 \\
\hline
5\ 2\ 1\ 6
\end{array}
$$

Th.	H.	T.	O.
		1	6
	1	0	
1	1		
4			
5	2	1	6

There are several techniques for performing a subtraction algorithm that will all arrive at the same "correct" difference. One of these is the additive method illustrated in the preceding paragraphs. Another is a procedure involving *equal additions* to the known sum (minuend) and the known addend (subtrahend). The method can be briefly described in the two ways in which the technique can be applied.

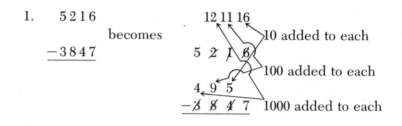

Either the additive ideas or the subtraction facts can now be utilized to find the difference.

2. $5\,2\,1\,6\, + \begin{array}{l}\text{same number as added}\\ \text{to known addend}\end{array}$ $= 5{,}216 + 153 = 5\,3\,6\,9$

     $-3\,8\,4\,7\, + \begin{array}{l}\text{number needed to make}\\ \text{even thousands}\end{array}$ $= 3{,}847 + 153 = 4\,0\,0\,0$

At this point, $5{,}369 - 4{,}000 = \Box$, either the additive ideas or the subtraction facts can be applied.

Note that in the method of equal additions, both the minuend and the subtrahend are renamed and the difference is not changed. The possibility of adding the same number to the subtrahend and the minuend without changing the difference is known as the *Law of Compensation.* Consider these numerical statements in view of zero as the identity element for addition: $n + 0 = n$.

$5{,}216 - 3{,}847$ is a name for a number
$(5{,}216 - 3{,}847) + 0$ is a name for the same number
$153 - 153 = 0$
$(5{,}216 - 3{,}847) + (153 - 153)$ is a name for the same number
$(5{,}216 + 153) - (3{,}847 + 153)$ is a name for the same number
$5{,}369 - 4{,}000$ is a name for the same number

The additive method and the method of equal additions have been taught in other countries and in isolated instances in our country as algorithms by which children can find correct responses to subtraction examples. In current elementary mathematics programs, we want children to know more about the subtraction operation than merely a procedure for arriving at a correct solution. We want pupils to develop an understanding of the operational procedure as well as accuracy in computation. We also want children to see the relationships between subtraction and other mathematical concepts and other operations. For these reasons, the *decomposition method* or subtraction algorithm has been almost universally adopted in contemporary elementary mathematics programs.

The decomposition method or algorithm for subtraction would seem to be more efficient in terms of teacher and pupil time and effort spent on developing pupils' understanding and accuracy because (1) it is easier to illustrate using concrete manipulative instructional aids; (2) it is consistent with the uses of the concepts of base and positional value as they are used in developing ideas about number and in performing other operations; (3) it takes advantage of the use of expanded notation to name number; and (4) because of 1, 2, and 3, it is easier for pupils to understand and to rationalize.

The decomposition algorithm for subtraction involves a renaming of the known sum when necessary and application of the subtraction facts. For this reason it is sometimes called the take-away method of subtraction. As children study the operation of subtraction and work with the algorithm, they should become aware of several generalizations or rules. These generalizations should be evident in the developmental instructional procedures and materials used to teach children the algorithm. Materials to be used include bundles of sticks; hundreds, tens, and ones blocks; play money; and place-value pocket charts.

1. Only like units being used to name number can be subtracted. This principle is known as the *Rule of Likeness*. This generalization will continue to apply as children work with rational numbers written as common fractions or as decimal fractions. The subtraction algorithm, as does the addition algorithm, used with whole numbers and decimal

fractions involves a computational form utilizing positional value in which like units are written directly under each other so that the facts may be more easily applied.

	H.	T.	O.
$548-235=\square$ becomes	5	4	8
	-2	3	5

2. The same facts are used when subtracting tens, hundreds, and higher powers of ten as are used when subtracting ones.

9 (ones)	9 tens	9 hundreds	$\cdots$	9 millions	$\cdots$
-2 (ones)	-2 tens	-2 hundreds	$\cdots$	-2 millions	$\cdots$
7 (ones)	7 tens	7 hundreds	$\cdots$	7 millions	$\cdots$

$999-222=\square$

(9 hundreds + 9 tens + 9 ones) − (2 hundreds + 2 tens + 2 ones)

9 hundreds	9 tens	9 ones
-2 hundreds	-2 tens	-2 ones
7 hundreds	7 tens	7 ones

	H.	T.	O.
	9	9	9
	-2	2	2
	7	7	7

3. The algorithm is most easily performed when the subtraction facts are applied to the smaller units first because the necessary regrouping can then be done as the difference is being developed digit by digit, ones to tens to hundreds.

To illustrate this "decomposition" idea, consider the example used to describe the additive and equal additions method of subtraction. Note the regrouping and renaming of the minuend.

a.

Th.	H.	T.	0.
		0	16
5	2	1	6
-3	8	4	7
		6	9

1 ten   6 ones   16 ones $16-7=9$

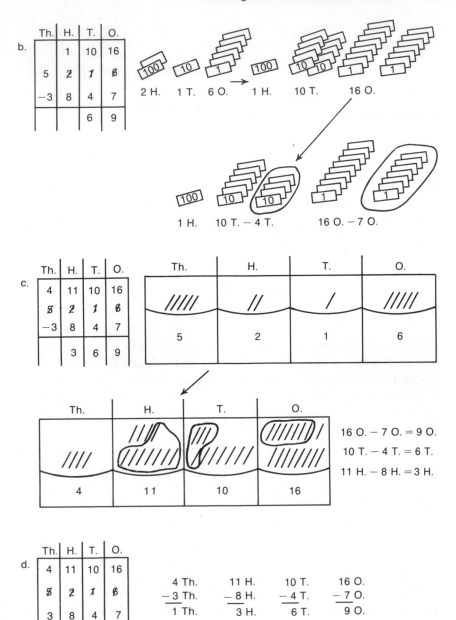

16 O. − 7 O. = 9 O.
10 T. − 4 T. = 6 T.
11 H. − 8 H. = 3 H.

With developmental practice, most children should reach a level of mastery of the algorithm in which they remember the regrouping being done without the use of aids or striking out digits.

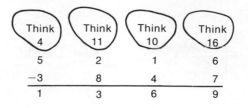

Some textbook programs present the subtraction of tens and hundreds that does not require regrouping soon after the easier facts are established and before the harder facts are introduced. This procedure may give children a false sense of mastery and lead to such pupil mistakes as

$$
\begin{array}{r}
4\,6 \\
-3\,8 \\
\hline
1\,2
\end{array}
\quad \text{or} \quad
\begin{array}{r}
5\,2 \\
-3\,7 \\
\hline
2\,5
\end{array}
$$

when problems requiring regrouping in the operation are introduced. Such mistakes may indicate a lack of understanding of the problem situation and certainly indicate that the pupil does not understand the operational procedure. A pupil may determine through his known processes of verification that he has made a mistake and not understand why. When such mistakes are made, it is incorrect for teachers to tell pupils that the difference is incorrect because "we cannot subtract 8 from 6 or 7 from 2" (we can!). Remedial procedures should emphasize a meaningful redevelopment of the regrouping necessary in establishing the harder facts, the use of facts in the operation, and the regrouping necessary in such examples.

Planning learning experiences for the growth and development of each pupil's understandings and skills in subtraction requires a teacher's knowledge of the sequence in which concepts or ideas are to be introduced and expanded. Provision for pupil differences in adjusting content and instructional procedures to individuals requires diagnostic and prescriptive skills. Attention to individual growth and difficulties is as pertinent in self-contained classrooms as it is in "continuous progress" programs or in schools organized on a "nongraded" plan.

Summary schema for sequence of concepts

Level	Examples	New ideas and generalizations
Separating sets		Subtractive or take-away idea introduced. Subset of elements is taken from set. Can count to find "How many are left?"
Comparing sets		One-to-one correspondence used to find "Which set is greater in number?" Counting to find "How many more?" Knowing one set is equal in number to another set. One-to-one correspondence and counting used to find missing number in subset.
Easier facts of subtraction	$5 - 2 = \square$ 6 9 $8 - 3 = \square$ -4 -3 $7 - 0 = \square$ $6 - 6 = \square$	Number can be named as a subtractive idea. Zero as a known addend and as a missing addend introduced. Relationship to addition facts is stressed. Verification by manipulation of objects and counting and by use of number line.
Harder facts of subtraction	$10 - 4 = \square$ 13 $17 - 8 = \square$ -5 $14 - 7 = \square$ 16 -7	Regrouping introduced. Relationship to addition stressed. Facts arranged in families. Number line, manipulation of objects, and counting used as verification.
Subtracting tens (no regrouping)	4 tens $-$ 2 tens $= \square$ $50 - 20 = \square$ 5 tens 50 -2 tens -20 $27 - 5 = \square$ 2 tens 7 ones 27 $-$ 5 ones -5	Only like units can be subtracted. Tens are subtracted just like ones. Use of facts in subtraction algorithm. Use of expanded notation and positional value chart. Verification by manipulation of objects and counting and number line. Addition introduced as a verification process.

Level	Examples	New ideas and generalizations
	$58 - 23 = \square$	

$$
\begin{array}{r}
5 \text{ tens } 8 \text{ ones} \quad 58 \\
-2 \text{ tens } 3 \text{ ones} \quad -23 \\
\hline
\end{array}
$$

Subtract-
ing tens
with re-
group-
ing)

$23 - 9 = \square$

$$
\begin{array}{r}
2 \text{ tens } 3 \text{ ones} \quad 23 \\
- \quad\quad 9 \text{ ones} \quad -9 \\
\hline
\end{array}
$$

$56 - 28 = \square$

$$
\begin{array}{r}
5 \text{ tens } 6 \text{ ones} \quad 56 \\
-2 \text{ tens } 8 \text{ ones} \quad -28 \\
\hline
\end{array}
$$

Combined application of ideas of two preceding levels. Regrouping necessary. Tens are subtracted like ones. Renaming minuend by expanded notation. Use of counting as way of verification decreased; use of number line decreased because it is cumbersome. Addition emphasized as most efficient means of verification. Equal additions method of subtraction might be introduced as verification.

Subtracting
hundreds
  a. No regrouping

$675 - 43 = \square$

$$
\begin{array}{r}
6 \text{ H. } 7 \text{ T. } 5 \text{ O.} \quad 675 \\
- \quad\quad 4 \text{ T. } 3 \text{ O.} \quad -43 \\
\hline
\end{array}
$$

$869 - 637 = \square$

$$
\begin{array}{r}
8 \text{ H. } 6 \text{ T. } 9 \text{ O.} \quad 869 \\
-6 \text{ H- } 3 \text{ T. } 7 \text{ O.} \quad -637 \\
\hline
\end{array}
$$

Hundreds are subtracted just like tens and ones. Addition stressed as means of verification. Equal additions method of subtraction might be used as a process of verification.

  b. Regrouping
    necessary

$837 - 95 = \square$

$$
\begin{array}{r}
8 \text{ H. } 3 \text{ T. } 7 \text{ O.} \quad 837 \\
- \quad\quad 9 \text{ T. } 5 \text{ O.} \quad -95 \\
\hline
\end{array}
$$

$506 - 185 = \square$

$$
\begin{array}{r}
5 \text{ H. } 0 \text{ T. } 6 \text{ O.} \quad 506 \\
-1 \text{ H. } 8 \text{ T. } 5 \text{ O.} \quad -185 \\
\hline
\end{array}
$$

$643 - 357 = \square$

Regrouping one of the hundreds to tens. Similarity to regrouping of 1 ten to ones.

Combination of regrouping 1 ten to ones and 1 hundred to tens in renam-

Level	Examples	New ideas and generalizations
	6 H. 4 T. 3 O. 643	ing the known sum or minuend. Veri-
	−3 H. 5 T. 7 O. −357	fication primarily by addition.
Extending to subtractions of thousands, ten-thousands, and higher powers of ten		Higher powers of ten are subtracted just as ones, tens, and hundreds. Regrouping procedures are similar. Children who have mastered subtraction with hundreds will have no great difficulty with this extension.
	36095 −18267	

Verification procedures

As children establish the subtraction facts and as they later study and practice with the subtraction algorithm, they should become aware of techniques that they can use to verify their solutions to subtraction problems or examples. Development of their self-reliance and self-reinforcement in regard to responses should be an integral part of learning experiences at all levels of work with the operation. Verifying differences should be a part of most practice experiences or exercises. In most instances appropriate verification techniques will become apparent to children as instructional procedures are used and as relationships to concepts of number and to the inverse operation are stressed.

The first verification procedures that children will have cause to use will involve the techniques by which the facts were established. If they manipulated objects and counted to establish facts, they will be able to use that process any time their knowledge of a fact is in doubt. If the number line was used as an instructional device, they will be able to check their knowledge by counting on a number line. Pupils could use both techniques to reestablish facts they have forgotten. On the other hand, if the teacher was their source of information concerning the facts, that source must be used as the pupils' means of verification.

Emphasis upon the inverse relationship of subtraction to addition and the addend, addend, sum relation will lead to the use of addition as an operation that can be used to verify the result of a subtraction example. Note that the addition facts have not been suggested for use as verification of the subtraction facts. Children might be making the same mistake (for example, $12 - 7 = 6$; $7 + 6 = 12$) in reference to both facts. The idea of using addition facts to verify subtraction facts can be used only if manipulation of objects and counting is employed. The operation of addition is useful as a verification procedure for the operation of subtraction only after the facts of both have been mastered and the verification technique is being applied to the results of performing the subtraction algorithm, that is, subtracting tens, hundreds, and so forth. At some point in their study of the subtraction algorithm, we would expect children to decide that addition is the most efficient verification procedure for checking the result of a subtraction operation in terms of time, effort, and accuracy.

For better pupils, teaches may want to introduce the subtraction method of equal additions as a procedure for verifying the difference obtained when using the decomposition method.

Decomposition	Equal additions	
7 15 12		
8̶ 5̶ 2̶	$862 + 15 = 877$	8 7 7
−3 8 5	$385 + 15 = 400$	−4 0 0
4 7 7		4 7 7

When the procedure used results in nonverification of the original result, children should be encouraged to look in both the original operation and the process of verification for their mistake. There is some credence to the idea that the process of verification should be one in which the pupil has achieved a higher level of mastery than he has in the original operation.

Suggested activities

1. Compose several problems that can be used to introduce the idea that the operation of subtraction can be used to find a missing number propperty when a set is separated into subsets.

2. Compose several problems that can be used to introduce the idea that the operation of subtraction can be used to compare the size of two disjoint sets.

3. Study how the elementary textbooks used in your locale develop understanding of regrouping in subtraction.

4. Develop a lesson plan in which you would use the number line to help children understand that subtraction and addition are inverse operations.

5. Make a collection of the instructional aids you would find most useful or appropriate for helping children understand the operation of subtraction.

Selected references

Bouwsma, W. D., C. G. Corle, and D. F. Clemson, Jr., *Basic Mathematics for Elementary Teachers*. New York: The Ronald Press Company, 1967, Chapter 4, "Subtraction and Negative Integers," pp. 49–83.

Buckingham, B. R., *Elementary Arithmetic — Its Meaning and Practice*. Boston: Ginn & Company, 1953, Chapter 6, "The Subtraction of Whole Numbers," pp. 130–157.

Easterday, K., and H. Easterday, "A Logical Method for Basic Subtraction," *The Arithmetic Teacher*, 13:404–406, May 1966.

Mueller, F. J., *Arithmetic — Its Structure and Concepts*. Englewood Cliffs, N.J.: Prentice-Hall, Inc., 1964, Unit 12, "Operation of Subtraction," and Unit 13, "Subtraction Algorithms," pp. 137–162.

Neureiter, P. R., "The 'Ultimate' Form of the Subtraction Algorithm," *The Arithmetic Teacher*, 12:277–281, April 1965.

Sausjord, G., "What Is the Complementary Method of Subtraction?", *The Arithmetic Teacher*, 10:262–265, May 1963.

Smith, C. W., Jr., "The Witch's Best Game," *The Arithmetic Teacher*, 13:683–684, Dec. 1966.

Teaching 7

multiplication with whole

numbers

The nature of the multiplication operation

The approach to multiplication of whole numbers most common to and most applicable to elementary mathematics programs is through repeated addition. In this approach, multiplication is an operation to be performed upon number that is closely related to the union of disjoint sets. Whereas the operation of addition may be used to find the number property of the union of disjoint sets that are equal or unequal in number, the operation of multiplication is restricted in use to situations in which the disjoint sets that are to be combined are equal in number. The relationship of multiplication to repeated addition may be simply illustrated as

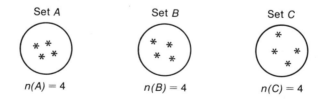

Addition: $4 + 4 + 4 = 12$

Multiplication idea: 3 sets with 4 elements in each
set = 12 elements

Performance of the multiplication operation involves the use of distinct basic facts and rules or principles that are applied in the algorithm. Two number ideas are used as the *factors* involved in making up the *product* or number property of the union of the sets. In the repeated addition approach to multiplication, one of the factors describes the number of sets and the other factor describes the number of elements in each set. Note that in the following illustration the elements in the equivalent sets are not like objects, but the number properties of the sets are the same. This is similar to a problem requiring the number of toys needed to place three toys in each of four gift boxes. The kinds of toys need not be the same.

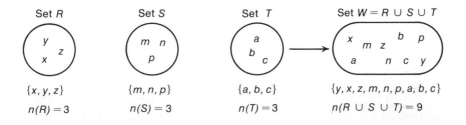

Set R	Set S	Set T	Set W = R U S U T
{x, y, z}	{m, n, p}	{a, b, c}	{y, x, z, m, n, p, a, b, c}
n(R) = 3	n(S) = 3	n(T) = 3	n(R U S U T) = 9

Factor: number of sets = 3
Factor: number of elements in each set = 3
Product: number of elements in the union of the sets = 9

The traditional practice of referring to the factors of multiplication as the multiplicand and the multiplier in regard to their position in the computational form or in regard to the use of number names in problem situations is discouraged in modern elementary mathematics programs.

There are 12 (*multiplicand*) eggs in each carton. How many eggs will there in be 9 (*multiplier*) cartons? $9 \times 12 = \square$

$$5346 \text{ multiplicand}$$
$$\times\ 78 \text{ multiplier}$$

The emphasis is to be upon the *factor, factor, product* relationship in which the product is associated with and determined by the two factors. This emphasis is consistent with the use of the properties of number in multiplication, the use of the multiplication operation in problem solving, the relationship of division to multiplication, and multiplication of rational numbers, which are described later.

The operation of multiplication is a binary operation in that the product of only two factors can be found at one time. When the product of more than two factors is to be found, the product of two of the factors is determined and that product is then used as a factor with one of the remaining factors to determine another product until all the factors have been utilized. For example, suppose the product of the four factors 4, 5, 6, and 7 ($4 \times 5 \times 6 \times 7$) is desired:

$$4 \times 5 = 20 \qquad 20 \times 6 = 120 \qquad 120 \times 7 = 840$$

There are several other ways in which the product might be determined, but all involve using only two factors at one time.

$$4 \times 5 = 20 \qquad 6 \times 7 = 42 \qquad 20 \times 42 = 840$$

The operation of multiplication also may be approached from or used in situations that are unlike the equal additions idea or the union of sets. Consider the problem of finding the number of ordered pairs that can be formed when each element of one set is paired with every element of a second set.

$$\text{set } A = \{1, 2, 3, 4\} \qquad \text{set } B = \{a, b, c\}$$

The set of ordered pairs (listing elements of set A first) may be tabulated as

$$\{(1, a), (1, b), (1, c), (2, a), (2, b), (2, c),$$
$$(3, a), (3, b), (3, c), (4, a), (4, b), (4, c)\}$$

The set of ordered pairs developed as the product of two sets, $A \times B$ (read as "A cross B"), is known as the *Cartesian product* of two sets. At this point we might call attention to the relationship of the number properties of the two sets and the number property of the set of ordered pairs: $n(A) = 4$; $n(B) = 3$; $n(\text{ordered pairs}) = 12$. Note that if the pairs were ordered with the elements of set B listed first, the tabulations would be different, but the number property of the set of ordered pairs would still be 12.

The ordered pairs may be mapped as points on a grid or in a plane as

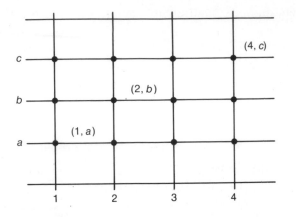

Each pair of elements makes up the coordinates of a point and identifies a point in the plane. The ordered pairs $(1, a)$, $(2, b)$, and so forth, used to identify the points on a grid or in a plane are known as the *Cartesian coordinates* of the ordered pairs.

Removing the grid and leaving the points in an *array* in the plane, we can see the relationship of the number properties of the two sets and the number property of the ordered pairs:

$$n(A) \times n(B) = n(\text{ordered pairs})$$

The number properties of the two sets are used as factors to determine the product or number property of the set of ordered pairs.

The Cartesian product approach to multiplication is not the most appropriate to help children understand the operation of multiplication with whole numbers. The equal additions approach is favored because it is simpler; elementary teachers are more familiar with it; it requires less mathematical background on the part of pupils; and the properties of multiplication may be more easily understood by children. However, this does not mean that the development of the Cartesian coordinate and Cartesian product concepts are not to be a part of the elementary mathematics program. Contemporary mathematics programs include the development of these ideas with problem situations. A simple problem of this type might involve finding the blouse-skirt combinations a girl might wear if she has five blouses and three skirts. More complex problems might call for finding the ordered pairs in a solution set that has been limited by certain conditions.

Establishing and mastering the facts of multiplication

Before children begin the formal or systematic study of the multiplication facts, they should have acquired basic understandings of combining sets and number concepts similar to those described as prerequisites for the study of addition facts. They should also have a sound foundation of experiences dealing with

1. Counting in subsets of 2, 3, and 5 to find how many elements in a collection.

two   four   six   eight   ● ● ●

2. Finding "How many?" in the new set formed by combining three or more sets that are equal in number by counting and by applying addition facts.

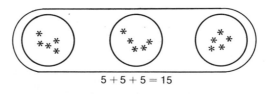

5 + 5 + 5 = 15

3. Finding the point location on a number line of an object (such as a bug) that began at point zero (0) and made several successive jumps of equal size.

"Where will the bug be if he begins at point zero and takes five jumps, each jump three units in length?"

Such experiences will help children to understand the meaning of multiplication facts and how they are established when systematic instruction begins.

The basic facts to be used in performing the operation of multiplication consist of all the possible combinations that can be formed with two one-digit numbers and their associated products. The number of possible combinations can be determined by selecting one element from each of the identical sets A and B to serve as factors to be associated with a product. If we approach the facts

$$\text{set } A = \{0, 1, 2, 3, 4, 5, 6, 7, 8, 9\}$$
$$\text{set } B = \{0, 1, 2, 3, 4, 5, 6, 7, 8, 9\}$$

singularly ($0 \times 0, 0 \times 1, 0 \times 2$, and so forth), there appear to be 100 combinations or basic facts of multiplication. However, if we emphasize the factor, factor, product association and consider the ideas discussed more completely in later paragraphs that

1. If zero is a factor, the product is zero: $0 \times n = 0$ and $n \times 0 = 0$
2. If 1 is a factor, the product is the same as the other factor: $1 \times b = b$ and $b \times 1 = b$
3. That $a \times d$ has the same product as $d \times a$

the number of facts that children must commit to memory is reduced from 100 to 38. These 38 facts are illustrated in the following chart and legend.

The multiplication facts are not as easily divided into categories of "easier" and "harder" facts as are the addition and subtraction facts. Only a few of the products in multiplication facts do not involve regrouping. The sequence of introducing basic facts varies from one program or group of pupils to another, but facts with products of smaller numbers and facts that are easier for pupils to remember are generally established first.

×	0	1	2	3	4	5	6	7	8	9
0										
1										
2			4	*a*	*b*	*c*	*d*	*e*	*f*	*g*
3			*a′*	9	*h*	*i*	*j*	*k*	*l*	*m*
4			*b′*	*h′*	16	*n*	*o*	*p*	*q*	*r*
5			*c′*	*i′*	*n′*	25	*s*	*t*	*u*	*v*
6			*d′*	*j′*	*o′*	*s′*	36	*w*	*x*	*y*
7			*e′*	*k′*	*p′*	*t′*	*w′*	49	*z*	*A*
8			*f′*	*l′*	*q′*	*u′*	*x′*	*z′*	64	*B*
9			*g′*	*m′*	*r′*	*v′*	*y′*	*A′*	*B′*	81

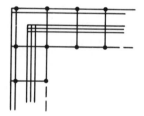

Zero is a factor; product is zero.

1 major idea

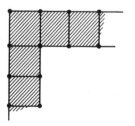

One is a factor; product is same as other factor.

1 major idea

{4, 9, 16, . . ., 81}

two factors are identical.

8 facts or ideas

$\{(a, a'),\ (b, b'),\ (c, c'),\ \ldots,\ (B, B')\}$

Facts in which the fac-   28 related facts
tors are the same but in
different order; product
is the same for fact a
and a'.

Introductory lessons dealing with establishing basic facts of multiplication are concerned with helping pupils to understand how the facts are derived and what they mean. Initial problems to be solved by pupils usually deal with more than two equivalent sets, and solution activities involve the manipulation of loose concrete objects grouped in equivalent sets and then regrouped.

"We have three boxes of crayons with eight crayons in each box. How many crayons altogether?"

Subsequent introduction of problems may involve families of facts based on a common factor or families of facts based on a common product.

Common Factor Family   **Common Product Family**

$3 \times 2 = 6$ $24 = 3 \times 8$
$3 \times 3 = 9$ $24 = 8 \times 3$
$3 \times 4 = 12$ $24 = 4 \times 6$
$\vdots$ $24 = 6 \times 4$

$3 \times 9 = 27$

Materials used by pupils to establish the multiplication facts and to reestablish any forgotten combination of fact will include

Sticks that can be grouped and regrouped

3 sets of sticks with six sticks in each set becomes 1 set of ten sticks and eight sticks

Counters or blocks that can be placed in arrays

o o o o o   5 objects in each row
o o o o o   3 rows
o o o o o   15 objects in the array

Number line that will facilitate counting by multiples

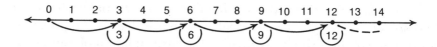

As children are establishing the basic facts of multiplication, a sincere effort on the part of the teacher must be made to develop an understanding of the vocabulary and symbolism used in the operation. The terms times, factor, and product and the symbol "×" are meaningless to children until associated with an idea. Because children cannot discover names or symbols, they will have to be told or shown these terms. The meaningful development of vocabulary requires more than one or two brief lessons with a few facts. One might begin by referring to a problem from which a multiplication fact is to be derived and have children name or describe a total number in a new set in terms of the number of elements in each equivalent set and the number of equivalent sets.

"Mary has three vases. She puts four flowers in each vase. How many flowers did she use?"

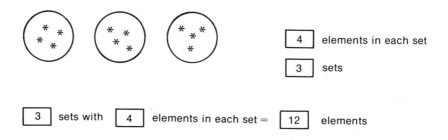

After utilizing several such quantitative situations and descriptions, shorter and more abstract ways of stating the facts can be introduced, eventually leading to the introduction of the multiplication symbol (×) and the use of number sentences.

$$\boxed{3} \text{ sets of } \boxed{4} = \boxed{12}$$
$$\boxed{4}, \boxed{3} \text{ times} = \boxed{12}$$

$$\boxed{3} \text{ times } \boxed{4} = \boxed{12}$$
$$\boxed{3} \times \boxed{4} = \boxed{12}$$

The procedure could then lead to the naming of the ideas. What facts or ideas help us to produce or find the total number? When the operation of multiplication is used, we call these ideas factors. The total number that is produced or made up from the factors is called the product.

Utilizing properties of number

The properties of number in the operation of multiplication are to be introduced to children as they establish the basic facts. Children should become familiar with the *commutative property,* the *identity element,* and the *zero property* of multiplication as concepts or ideas and to use the ideas as they work with the facts. If the *associative property* and the *distributive property* are introduced and applied to some of the easier basic facts, some children will be able to use those ideas to establish other facts. A complete generalization regarding *closure* cannot be formulated by children studying basic facts, but an idea about the nature of the product when the factors are whole numbers can be introduced. Similarly, the foundation for developing children's understanding of division as the *inverse operation* of multiplication can be laid during their early work with multiplication facts.

The major concern at this level of learning should not be with having children memorize names and formal definitions for the properties. Insistence upon the development of formal vocabulary may stifle the use of the "rough idea." Instead, the ideas of the properties are to be used to help children understand and master the basic facts. At later levels the ideas will be used to help them understand and master the operational algorithm.

The commutative property of multiplication. After children understand how the multiplication facts are derived and what they mean, instructional procedures used to help pupils establish facts should incorporate the idea that the order of the two factors does not affect the product. The teacher can structure situations in which the pupils can use sticks, arrays, and the number line to show the factors in two different ways and the resulting same product. These situations can be applied in problems such as

"How many pencils are there in three boxes if each box contains four pencils?"

"How many pencils are there if four boxes each contain three pencils?"

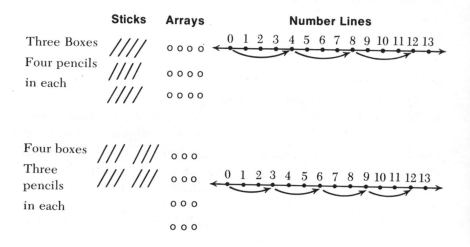

We would want pupils to make the correct illustrations for the problem situations but to generalize that for two factors, regardless of their order, there is one product. The fact to be remembered concerns the numbers in the factor, factor, product association. Thus 3 × 5 and 5 × 3 are names for the same number, 15, and can be considered as one fact. The property of number that allows the order of two factors to be changed without affecting the product is called *the commutative property of multiplication.*

$$4 \times 5 = 5 \times 4 \qquad 3 \times 8 = 8 \times 3 \qquad 18 \times 32 = 32 \times 18$$

To generalize: If *a* and *d* are whole numbers, $a \times d$ has the same product as $d \times a$.

The identity element of multiplication.   The basic fact in which one (1) is a factor used to find a product is generally not established until after children have had experiences with and found other basic facts. The idea that 1 set of *n* elements equals *n* elements and *n* sets of 1 element each equals *n* elements is not difficult for children to grasp and to extend beyond an *n* (number) described by a single-digit numeral.

1 set of 7 elements = 7 elements
$$1 \times 7 = 7$$

7 sets of 1 element each
= 7 elements
$$7 \times 1 = 7$$

To generalize: $1 \times n = n$, $n \times 1 = n$, $1 \times n = n \times 1$

The idea that when 1 is a factor, the product is equal to the other factor should be developed as one basic fact. One (1) as *the identity element* of multiplication will be used by children later in their mathematics programs to rename fractional numbers and to help in operations with rational numbers, both common and decimal fractions.

Property of zero in multiplication. Some elementary mathematics programs prefer to delay dealing with zero in multiplication until multiplication with tens is introduced. It would seem more appropriate to consider zero (0) as a factor when the basic facts are being established. Children may enjoy making up problem situations such as

"There are zero (0) saber-toothed tigers in each of the eight rooms of our school. How many saber-toothed tigers are in the school?"

"There are four wheels on each automobile. We have zero automobiles in our room. How many automobile wheels do we have in our room?"

Through such problem situations, children will be able to generalize with one fact that when zero (0) is a factor, the product is zero: $0 \times n = 0$ or $n \times 0 = 0$. Consider the importance of pupil understanding of this fact when the product of two factors such as 305 and 260 is to be computed.

The associative property of multiplication. The associative property of multiplication is concerned with three or more factors and the fact that multiplication is a binary operation (the product of only two factors can be found at one time). Consider the problem of finding the number of blocks in a stack that is two blocks wide, three blocks high, and four blocks long.

Using multiplication, we might find the total number (product) of blocks by grouping the factors in different ways.

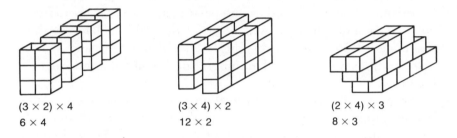

(3 × 2) × 4   (3 × 4) × 2   (2 × 4) × 3
6 × 4   12 × 2   8 × 3

The possibility of changing the grouping of the factors when three or more factors are involved without affecting the product is *the associative property of multiplication*. If a, b, and c are whole numbers, the unique product of $a \times b \times c$ can be found by $(a \times b) \times c$, $(a \times c) \times b$, or $(b \times c) \times a$.

Children could establish all the multiplication facts using sticks, arrays, or the number line without reference to or use of the associative property. Introduction to the associative property with easier factor combinations illustrated with blocks or cubes and described by number sentences will give children the power to establish some of the harder facts in another way.

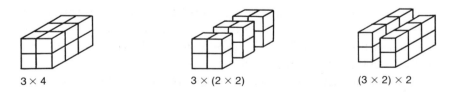

3 × 4   3 × (2 × 2)   (3 × 2) × 2

In an example such as 6 × 7, the procedure will involve

$$6 \times 7 = \square$$

1. Renaming one of the factors as a multiplication
   idea: $6 = 2 \times 3$ $(2 \times 3) \times 7 = \square$
2. Regrouping the factors $2 \times (3 \times 7) = \square$
3. So that children can use facts they already
   know $2 \times 21 = \square$
4. And/or applying addition $21 + 21 = \square$

With proper development, better pupils will be able to use this procedure or process to find products of harder basic combinations without manipulating blocks and to extend use of the idea to "shortcut" mental calculations of products of other factors.

The distributive property. Consider the idea that another name for seven (7) is $6 + 1$. Then 4×7 can also be thought of as $4 \times (6 + 1)$. In an array, $4 \times (6 + 1)$ might be represented as

```
✻ ✻ ✻ ✻ ✻    ✻
✻ ✻ ✻ ✻ ✻    ✻
✻ ✻ ✻ ✻ ✻    ✻
✻ ✻ ✻ ✻ ✻    ✻
```

From the array, we can see that

$$4 \times 7 \text{ or } 4 \times (6 + 1) = (4 \times 6) + (4 \times 1)$$
$$4 \times (6 + 1) = 24 + 4$$
$$4 \times 7 \text{ or } 4 \times (6 + 1) = 28$$

This is the distributive property in its simplest form. The product of a given number and the sum of several numbers can be determined by either adding the several numbers and multiplying that sum by the given number or by multiplying each of the several numbers by the given number and adding the resulting products. The same statement can be made in regard to finding the product of a given number and the difference of two numbers. Multiplication is distributive with respect to addition and subtraction on the set of whole numbers. If r, s, and t are whole numbers,

$$r \times (s + t) = (r \times s) + (r \times t) \qquad \text{and}$$
$$r \times (s - t) = (r \times s) - (r \times t)$$

Introduction of this idea when basic facts are being established will not only help children establish other basic facts but will also build a sound foundation for applying the distributive property in developing understanding of the multiplication algorithm. The modern algorithm of multiplication of whole numbers is fundamentally a utilization of the distributive property. Pupils' understanding of this property will also help them to do shortcut mental calculations (without paper and pencil) such as

$$99 \times 99 = 99 \times (100 - 1) = 9,900 - 99 = 9,801$$

Closure.   As previously stated, a complete generalization concerning the set of whole numbers and closure cannot be formulated when children are working with basic facts. But as children are establishing facts, attention can be called to the nature of the products—all are whole numbers. This attention can be continued as children work with multiplication of whole numbers at higher levels until the idea that the set of whole numbers is closed under the operation of multiplication is generalized. If a and b are whole numbers, then $a \times b = c$, and c is also a whole number. Through later experiences, children will extend the generalization to the set of rational numbers and finally to the set of real numbers.

The inverse of multiplication.   The inverse or opposite of knowing two factors and seeking their product is knowing the product and one of the factors and seeking the other factor. Early in the child's experiences with multiplication facts, but after he is familiar with ways of deriving facts, he should encounter quantitative situations in which the product and one factor are known and the problem is to find the other factor.

1. "We want to plant the same number of seeds in each of 4 containers. We have 24 seeds. How many shall we plant in each container?"
2. "We have 32 crayons. If we place an equal number of crayons in each of 4 boxes, how many crayons will we put in each box?"

Examples of number sentences ensuing from such situations are

$$\square \times 8 = 24 \qquad 4 \times \square = 20 \qquad \square \times 8 = 56$$

Similar number sentences can be used in practice exercises directed toward children's recall or knowledge of previously established facts.

Techniques of finding the unknown factor would include arranging the product or total number into an array utilizing the known factor, illustrations on a number line, and/or application of known multiplication facts.

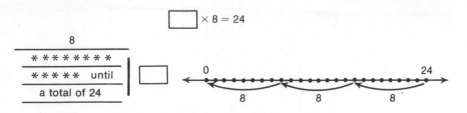

Factors, multiples, square numbers, and prime and composite numbers

As children establish multiplication facts and record them in some organized manner, their understanding of the term factor can be extended, and the term or concept of *multiple* can be meaningfully introduced. Elementary or foundation ideas concerning *common multiples, square numbers,* and *prime* and *composite numbers* can also be introduced through experiences and exercises involving the record of established facts, a number chart, and the use of arrays.

Teachers can use a device such as the following partially completed table of multiplication facts to help children see that factors are "makers" of products. The products associated with any one factor can be referred to as multiples of that factor.

Some guiding questions leading to the development of ideas might include

1. Consider the multiples of ③ (or other factors) in the table. What are some other multiples of ③?
2. Do the factors 3 and 4 (or other pairs of factors) have any multiples in common? What are some of these common multiples?
3. What numbers are factors of 18? 24? 35?
4. Can you show by using number sentences that one (1) is a factor of every whole number?
5. Which of the products in the table can be formed by multiplying two identical factors? Can you illustrate these products and the identical factors by using arrays?

Multiplication facts

×	0	1	2	3	4	5	6	7	8	9
0										
1				3	4	5				
2				6	8	10				
3			3	6	9	12	15	18	21	24	27
4			4	8	12	16	20	24	28	32	36
5				15	20					
6				18	24					
7				21	28					
8				24	32					
9				27	36					

A *prime number* is a whole number that is greater than one and that has only one (1) and itself as integral (whole number) factors. Whole numbers that are greater than one can be classified into two sets: those numbers that are prime and those numbers that are not prime. Whole numbers that are greater than one and that are not prime are called *composite numbers.* In their early work, children will want to include one (1) in the set of prime numbers, but with later experiences in using prime numbers they will find that it is of little use and no longer feel the need of considering it as prime.

By making rectangular arrays to illustrate products, children can concretely determine whether a number is prime or composite. Beginning with a set of sequential numbers such as {2, 3, 4, . . ., 12}, children could be asked to make as many arrays as possible that illustrate each of these numbers as a product. They might also be asked to ascertain which products can be illustrated by arrays shaped like a square.

The expected generalization is that a number is prime if the only possible arrays have just one row or one column. The only factors of such numbers are 1 and the number itself. The set of sequential numbers and the search for "primeness" could be extended as far as necessary or desired, but this procedure of ascertaining whether a whole number is prime or composite should come to be regarded by pupils as too tedious and they should begin to apply their under-standings of factors and multiples to the task. Relating the concept

Product	Possible Arrays				
2	* *	* *			
3	* * *	* * *			
4	****	* * * *	* * * *		
.					
.					
.					
12	************	* * * * * * * * * * * *	****** ******	* * * * * * * * * * * *	**** **** ****	* * * * * * * * * * * *

of factors, primes, and multiples to a number chart, pupils could extend their discoveries of prime numbers through such exercises as

a. Two is a prime number. Draw a circle around all the multiples of 2 in the following number chart.
b. Three is a prime number. Draw a square around all the multiples of 3 in the following number chart.
c. □ is a prime number. Draw a triangle around all the multiples of it in the following number chart.

.

.

.

n. What is the *next* prime number? Draw a line under all multiples of it in the following number chart.

A Number Chart

0	1	2	3	4	5	6	7	8	9
10	11	12	13	14	15	16	17	18	19
20	21	22	23	24	25	26	27	28	29
30	31	32	33	34	35	36	37	38	39
40	41	42	43	44	45	46	47	48	49
50									

All numbers remaining on the chart not enclosed in a geometric figure or underlined are prime because the only factors each has are 1 and the number itself. Familiarity with prime numbers between 1 and 50 should lead to more efficiency in completely factoring composite numbers.

Children in the later grades should be able to factor a number so that the number is renamed as a product of prime factors. In this book the terms *completely factoring a number* and *prime factorization* are used synonymously.

The fundamental theorem of arithmetic — that a composite number can be expressed as a product of prime numbers in one and only one way — can also be illustrated by factor tree diagrams. Many middle- and upper-grade children find the construction of factor tree diagrams to be both interesting and profitable experiences. Factor trees for 12 and 30 are

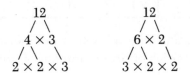

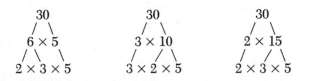

Regardless of the initial pair of factors used for any product, the final set of prime numbers will be the same. There is only *one* set of prime factors for any one product.

When children's understandings of division as the operation that seeks the missing factor are being developed and their abilities to perform the operation are being extended, the problems of determining whether a number is prime and of determining the prime factors of a number will become procedures of division. Beginning with a known prime factor of the product (number), the missing factor is determined. The newly determined factor is then considered as a product and the procedure is repeated until all the factors are prime.

"What are the prime factors of 105?"

5 is a known prime factor of 105: $5 \times \square = 105$

$5 \times 21 = 105$

3 is a known prime factor of 21: $3 \times \square = 21$

$3 \times 7 = 21$

7 is a prime number

$5 \times 3 \times 7 = 105$

$$5 \overline{)105}$$
$$3 \overline{)21}$$
$$7$$

Developing the multiplication algorithm

Current objectives in teaching the multiplication algorithm to children include developing their understanding of each of the several steps in the algorithm and a total understanding and knowledge of how and why the algorithm or procedure works. The formal algorithm of multiplication is a method of determining the product of two factors by applying knowledge of the multiplication facts, concepts of base and place value, and the distributive property. Knowledge of the multiplication facts is all that is required when both of the factors are described by one-digit numerals. The need for an understandable procedure occurs when one or both of the factors is described by a numeral of more than one digit. Two major categories or levels are discernable in helping children develop understanding of the algorithm: (1) One of the factors is described by a two- or more-digit numeral, and (2) both of the factors are described by two- or more-digit numerals.

One factor is a two- or more-digit numeral.   The first two-digit factors to be considered should be multiples of ten (10, 20, 30, . . ., 90). Understanding products of multiples of ten and a single-digit factor is a prerequisite to understanding the algorithm with any two-digit factor. Bundles of 10 sticks can be used to develop the idea of multiplying tens just as single sticks or counters were used to establish the facts. The idea to be developed is the use of the multiplication facts when tens are involved.

From illustrative problems and examples, the vocabulary and symbolism used in the computational procedure can be developed.

"Four sets of 2 tens are 8 tens."   "Four sets of 20 are 80."

4×2 tens $= 8$ tens   2 tens

$$\begin{array}{r} 2 \text{ tens} \\ \times 4 \\ \hline 8 \text{ tens} \end{array}$$

$4 \times 20 = 4 \times (2 \times 10)$ 20

$\quad\quad\quad = (4 \times 2) \times 10$ $\times 4$

$\quad\quad\quad = 8 \times 10 = 80$ 80

Other devices used to increase pupils' understandings and skills include rectangular arrays, play money, a place-value pocket chart using stick markers, and place-value diagrams for computation.

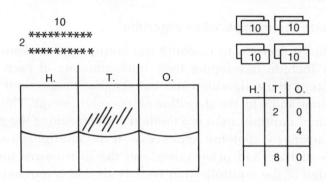

Such devices are also useful in illustrating the regrouping of tens to hundreds and at later levels when the two-digit factor is not a multiple of ten.

When problems are introduced that include a two-digit factor that is not a multiple of ten, application of the distributive property becomes the foundation of the algorithm. The first few such problems should not involve regrouping of ones to tens or tens to hundreds ($3 \times 13 = \bigcirc$, $2 \times 23 = \bigcirc$), but the learning experiences could move quickly to such examples as $6 \times 43 = \bigcirc$. Using the children's knowledge of number—that $43 = 4$ tens and 3 ones or $40 + 3$—the exercises could lead directly to a computational algorithm in which each *partial* product or multiplication step is visible.

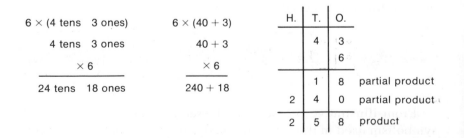

To provide a foundation for the short procedure and the later multiplication of tens × tens, attention should be given to the idea that 6 × 40 is actually 6 × 4 tens or 6 × (4 × 10) or (6 × 4) × 10. After sufficient practice for each child to understand and master this long procedure, teachers should encourage and guide children to a shorter procedure that involves less writing but that requires remembering or using a symbol to help remember the number of tens from the first partial product. Children should not be asked to remember the number of tens or even to use a symbol as an aid to remembering before they understand why the number of regrouped tens is added to the partial product of tens.

H.	T.	O.
	5	6
		7
	4	2
3	5	0
3	9	2

H.	T.	O.
④	5	6
		7
3	9	2

H.	T.	O.
	5	6
	₄	7
3	9	2

Developing the multiplication of larger numbers (three or more digits) by a one-digit number or multiplying a two-digit number by a two-digit number should not be undertaken until children have mastered the procedure of multiplying a two-digit number by a one-digit number. After this mastery is established, children will have little difficulty in expanding their understandings and skills. Initial exercises should involve multiples of hundreds and thousands to develop the idea that the product will also be in terms of hundreds and thousands.

8 × 4 hundreds = 32 hundreds
8 × 400 = 8 × (4 × 100) = (8 × 4) × 100 = 32 × 100

7 × 6 thousands = 42 thousands
7 × 6,000 = 7 × (6 × 1,000) = (7 × 6) × 1,000 = 42 × 1,000

When the example includes a three-digit factor that is not a multiple of 100, the short procedure is developed as with a factor of two digits. It will not be unusual for some children to want to proceed immediately to the "shortcut."

$6 \times 327 = 6 \times (300 + 20 + 7)$

3 H.	2 T.	7 O.
	×6	
18 H.	12 T.	42 O.

$300 + 20 + 7$
×6
$1800 + 120 + 42$

Th.	H.	T.	O.
	3	2	7
			6
		4	2
	1	2	0
1	8	0	0
1	9	6	2

To emphasize the correct use of place value, it may be appropriate to give children some practice in recognizing and recording the partial products as tens and hundreds without using zeros.

Th.	H.	T.	O.
	3	2	7
			6
		4	2
	1	2	
1	8		
1	9	6	2

Th.	H.	T.	O.
①, 3	④ 2	7	
		6	
1	9	6	2

$$327 \times 6 \over 1962$$

Pupil mastery of any level of the multiplication algorithm cannot be most effectively achieved through mere teacher demonstration and pupils' imitation. Learning experiences should be based on active pupil participation and discussion in the development of appropriate moves and generalizations. Even after pupils understand the reasons for the moves, a great deal of practice may be necessary to achieve mastery of the computational skill.

Both factors are two- or more-digit numerals. The development of the algorithm at this level begins with helping pupils develop a generalization about the product of two factors that are both two-digit multiples of ten. From their experiences in working with the number ideas of base, positional value, and counting, they should already understand that 10 sets with ten in each set (commonly called 10 tens) is 1 hundred: $10 \times 10 = 100$. Introductory problems will require finding the product of two factors from the set $\{10, 20, 30, 40, 50, 60, 70, 80, 90\}$.

To help pupils develop the generalization that the product of two factors that are multiples of ten can be named in hundreds, the procedure involves renaming the factors,

$$30 \times 70 = (3 \times 10) \times (7 \times 10)$$

and regrouping the new factors, using the associative property,

$$(3 \times 10) \times (7 \times 10) = (3 \times 7) \times (10 \times 10)$$

so that children can use the facts they know.

$$(3 \times 7) \times (10 \times 10) = 21 \times 100 = 2{,}100$$

Practice in renaming such factors and regrouping the new factors for multiplication with number sentences similar to

$$20 \times 60 = (2 \times \square) \times (6 \times \square)$$
$$20 \times 60 = (2 \times 6) \times (\square \times \square)$$
$$2 \times 6 = \bigcirc$$
$$\square \times \square = \triangle$$
$$20 \times 60 = \bigcirc \times \triangle$$
$$\bigcirc \times \triangle = \bigcirc$$
$$20 \times 60 = \bigcirc$$

should precede the working of practice examples in vertical form.

$$
\begin{array}{cccc}
50 & 60 & 70 & 90 \\
\times 30 & \times 20 & \times 50 & \times 80 \\
\hline
1500 & 1200 & &
\end{array}
$$

Finding the product of a multiple of ten and any two-digit number requires application of previously learned multiplication ideas. Concrete illustrations of the commutative property will help pupils understand that $3 \times 20 = 20 \times 3$ and to generalize that ones $\times$ tens $=$ tens   and   tens $\times$ ones $=$ tens. Complete concrete illustration of an example such as 30×24 may be more confusing to pupils than helpful because of the number of objects required. The suggested procedure is to rename the factor that is not a multiple of ten in terms of addition, to multiply each of the terms by the other factor, and to find the sum of the partial products.

a. $20 \times 32 = 20 \times (30 + 2)$

$$30 + 2$$
$$\underline{\times\, 20}$$
$$600 + 40$$

H.	T.	O.
	3	2
	2	0
	4	0
6	0	0
6	4	0

$$\begin{array}{r} 32 \\ \times\, 20 \\ \hline 640 \end{array}$$

b. $40 \times 57 = 40 \times (50 + 7)$

$$50 + 7$$
$$\underline{\times\, 40}$$
$$2{,}000 + 280$$

Th.	H.	T.	O.
		5	7
		4	0
	2	8	0
2	0	0	0
2	2	8	0

$$\begin{array}{r} ② \\ 57 \\ \times\, 40 \\ \hline 2280 \end{array}$$

An analysis of the preceding examples will indicate that if introductory problems and examples at this level do not involve regrouping, better pupil understanding is likely to be accomplished.

Children's mastery of multiplying any two-digit number by a one-digit number and of multiplying any two-digit number by a multiple of ten should enable them to apply their understandings and abilities to finding the product of any two two-digit numbers. Initial work with examples such as 43×57 should involve the distributive property so that four partial products are determined, recorded, and added in such a way that pupils will understand each step of the procedure.

$$43 \times 57 = (40 + 3) \times (50 + 7) \qquad (50 + 7)$$
$$\times (40 + 3)$$

$$
\begin{array}{cc}
\begin{array}{r} 50 + 7 \\ \times 3 \\ \hline 150 + 21 \end{array} \; + \;
\begin{array}{r} 50 + 7 \\ \times 40 \\ \hline 2{,}000 + 280 \end{array}
\end{array}
\qquad
\begin{array}{rl}
57 & \\
\times 43 & \\
\hline
21 & \leftarrow 3 \times 7 \\
150 & \leftarrow 3 \times 50 \\
280 & \leftarrow 40 \times 7 \\
2000 & \leftarrow 40 \times 50 \\
\hline
2451 &
\end{array}
$$

$$150 + 21 + 2{,}000 + 280 = 2{,}451$$

Better pupils should be eager and able to proceed quickly to the shorter procedure, also using the distributive property but renaming only one of the factors. Less talented pupils should be encouraged in the use of the shorter procedure as their abilities permit.

$$38 \times 47 = (30 + 8) \times 47 \qquad 47$$
$$\times 38$$

$$
\begin{array}{cc}
\begin{array}{r} 47 \\ \times 8 \\ \hline 376 \end{array} \; + \;
\begin{array}{r} 47 \\ \times 30 \\ \hline 1410 \end{array}
\end{array}
\qquad
\begin{array}{rl}
376 & \leftarrow 8 \times 47 \\
1410 & \leftarrow 30 \times 47 \\
\hline
1786 &
\end{array}
$$

$$376 + 1{,}410 = 1{,}786$$

When a pupil's mastery of computing the products of any two-digit factors has been developed, no really new principles will be involved in expanding his abilities to finding products of larger numbers, as in the following examples.

$$
\begin{array}{lllll}
413 & 648 & 509 & 758 & 5280 \\
\times 32 & \times 43 & \times 67 & \times 694 & \times 437
\end{array}
$$

Some discussion relating to base and positional value and utilizing the associative property may center on developing the generalizations about the nature of the product when the factors are multiples of ten (including hundreds and thousands). Practice exercises will include number sentences and computational form.

$$20 \times 400 = (2 \times 10) \times (4 \times 100) = (2 \times 4) \times (10 \times 100) = 8 \times 1{,}000$$
$$300 \times 500 = (3 \times 100) \times (5 \times 100)$$
$$= (3 \times 5) \times (100 \times 100) = 15 \times 10{,}000$$
$$500 \times 7{,}000 = (5 \times 100) \times (7 \times 1{,}000)$$
$$= (5 \times 7) \times (100 \times 1{,}000) = 35 \times 100{,}000$$
$$3{,}000 \times 3{,}000 = (3 \times 1{,}000) \times (3 \times 1{,}000)$$
$$= (3 \times 3) \times (1{,}000 \times 1{,}000) = 9 \times 1{,}000{,}000$$

$$
\begin{array}{r}
400 \\
\times 20 \\
\hline
8000
\end{array}
\qquad
\begin{array}{r}
500 \\
\times 300 \\
\hline
150{,}000
\end{array}
\qquad
\begin{array}{r}
7000 \\
\times 500 \\
\hline
3{,}500{,}000
\end{array}
\qquad
\begin{array}{r}
3000 \\
\times 3000 \\
\hline
9{,}000{,}000
\end{array}
$$

If the distributive property is used in developing the algorithm, zeros in the tens or hundreds place should cause no major pupil difficulties.

Adjusting instruction to pupil differences requires that teachers be well acquainted with the sequential development of levels of performance with the algorithm and the nature of pupil under-standings and abilities necessary for performance at each level.

Processes of verification

Encouraging children to verify the result of their computational operations should be a continuous concern of teachers. Positive encouragement approaches should be used that help children to see the value of verification. Discussions of the various verification procedures used by pupils on specific examples and most effi-cient procedures in terms of time, effort, and required knowledge are appropriate. Verification or checking should not be considered by pupils to be extra work that adds to the total of practice assign-ments, but an integral part of the assignment. Because many of the verification processes for multiplication examples also employ multiplication techniques, the number of products to be computed and verified as a practice assignment could be reduced.

Verification procedures to be used by children as they estab-lish and practice the multiplication facts and in their early work with two-digit factors include the manipulation of objects, count-ing, and addition.

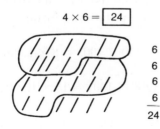

2 tens 4 ones

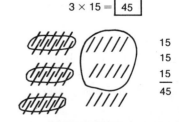

4 tens 5 ones

As more facts are learned and as work with two-digit factors is continued, the associative property can be utilized. Advantages of this procedure are that multiplication ideas are being practiced, that facts other than those in the original example are used, and that often there are several ways of renaming the original factors.

$$3 \times 6 = \boxed{18} \qquad 4 \times 18 = \boxed{72} \qquad 24 \times 43 = \boxed{1032}$$
$$3 \times (3 \times 2) \qquad 4 \times (2 \times 9) \qquad (3 \times 8) \times 43$$
$$(3 \times 3) \times 2 \qquad (4 \times 9) \times 2 \qquad 3 \times (8 \times 43)$$
$$9 \times 2 = \boxed{18} \qquad 36 \times 2 = \boxed{72} \qquad 3 \times 344 = \boxed{1032}$$

Perhaps the most commonly used means of verification and the procedure that will come to be regarded by pupils as the most efficient when both factors have at least two digits is an application of the commutative property.

$$37 \times 52 = 52 \times 37$$

$$
\begin{array}{cc}
52 & 37 \\
\times 37 & \times 52 \\
\hline
14 \longleftrightarrow 14 \\
350 \searrow \nearrow 60 \\
60 \nearrow \searrow 350 \\
1500 \longleftrightarrow 1500 \\
\hline
1924 & 1924
\end{array}
$$

$$
\begin{array}{cc}
52 & 37 \\
\times 37 & \times 52 \\
\hline
364 & 74 \\
1560 & 1850 \\
\hline
1924 & 1924
\end{array}
$$

The examples indicate that when four partial products are recorded, they are identical because the same facts are being applied. When only two partial products are recorded, the partial products are not the same because the regrouping is different.

Some pupils might also be encouraged to use the distributive property as a means of verification. One of the factors is renamed using subtraction, the terms of that expression are multiplied by the other factor, and the partial products are subtracted.

$$3 \times 98 = \boxed{294} \qquad 98 = 100 - 2 \qquad 3 \times 98 = 3 \times (100 - 2)$$

$$
\begin{array}{ll}
98 & 100 - 2 \\
\times 3 & \times 3 \\
\hline
\boxed{294} & 300 - 6 \qquad 300 - 6 = \boxed{294}
\end{array}
$$

Renaming the factor in terms of addition and multiplying might be considered a less effective verification process because it is merely a redoing of the original, using the same facts and recording the partial products.

Other operational procedures for multiplication can be used to expand pupils' understandings of number and the operation and could be included or used as procedures of verification for the general algorithm. Perhaps the most useful of these procedures is *lattice multiplication*. This procedure arranges the factors so that the separate facts are isolated in a lattice and involves the addition of partial products in much the same way as the commonly used algorithm.

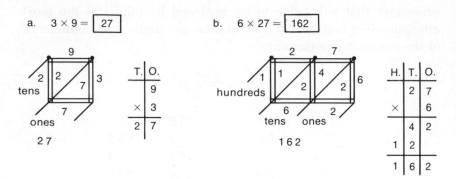

a. $3 \times 9 =$ 27

b. $6 \times 27 =$ 162

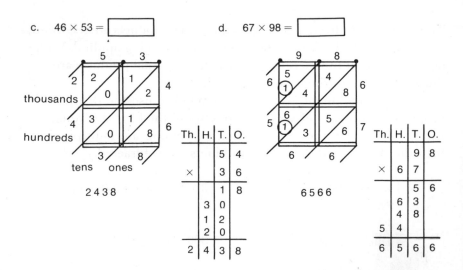

c. $46 \times 53 =$

d. $67 \times 98 =$

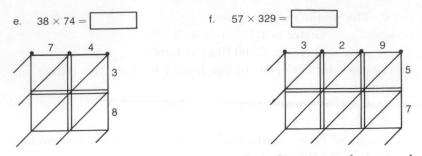

e. 38 × 74 = ☐   f. 57 × 329 = ☐

Because of the difference in approach and yet a similarity in the use of facts and partial products, lattice multiplication may be used to reintroduce multiplication at intermediate levels to children who have some idea of the algorithm but little success in their performance or, for diagnostic purposes at intermediate levels, to ascertain the facts that a child has not mastered.

Use of other procedures for finding the product of two factors, for example, *halving and doubling*, are not recommended for verification processes or supplementary work unless provision is made for developing pupils' understanding of the procedure.

When a pupil has reached the level where an assurance that the computed product is a reasonable result is all that is required, *estimation* becomes a useful means of partial verification. As computation with two-digit factors is developed, estimation of reasonable products should become an integral part of the program. The estimation of a reasonable answer is generally to be done mentally (without paper and pencil) and requires the use of the inequality relations of less than (<) and greater than (>). In most instances, pupils should be encouraged to estimate a reasonable product before computation. The computed product is then compared to the estimate. The estimation of products will depend upon pupils' abilities to think of numbers in multiples of ten (including hundreds and thousands) and to calculate mentally the products of such multiples. Pupils' skills in estimating products may be developed through practice exercises such as

    a. Without computation, answer each of the following items *true* or *false* and give the reason for your answer.
       1. The product of 8 × 27 is
          _____ less than the product of 8 × 20
          _____ greater than the product of 8 × 20
          _____ less than the product of 8 × 30
          _____ greater than the product of 8 × 30

2. The product of 7 × 286 is

_____ nearer to 1,400 than to 2,100

_____ nearer to 2,100 than to 1,400

b. Using estimation, fill in the blanks to make the statements true.

1. 4 × 37 is greater than _____, but less than _____

2. _____ < 6 × 43 < _____

c. Which of these would give the best estimate of the product of 42 × 78? Why?

_____ 40 × 70

_____ 40 × 80

_____ 50 × 70

_____ 50 × 80

d. Without performing the actual computation with the factors, what would be a good estimate of the products of the following examples? Use the symbols for greater than (>) or less than (<) in the circles.

8 × 33 ◯ _____   42 × 53 ◯ _____

6 × 486 ◯ _____   59 × 783 ◯ _____

The inverse of any operation may be used to verify (by "undoing") the results of the operation. The *inverse operation* of multiplication, *division,* may be used as a verification procedure for multiplication examples. The procedure is to use the computed product and one of the factors and the division operation to ascertain a second factor, undoing the original operation. The result of the division operation is then compared to the second factor and the decision is made as to whether the computed product is the true product of the two factors.

$$43 \times 58 = \boxed{2,494}$$

$$43 \times \bigcirc = 2{,}494$$
$$2{,}494 \div 43 = \bigcirc$$

$$\bigcirc \times 58 = 2{,}494$$
$$2{,}494 \div 58 = \bigcirc$$

$$43 \overline{)2494}$$
$$\underline{2150} \quad 50$$
$$344$$
$$\underline{344} \quad \underline{8}$$
$$58$$
$$43 \times \boxed{58} = 2{,}494$$

$$58$$
$$\times 43$$
$$\overline{174}$$
$$2320$$
$$\overline{2494}$$

$$58 \overline{)2494}$$
$$\underline{2320} \quad 40$$
$$174$$
$$\underline{174} \quad \underline{3}$$
$$43$$
$$\boxed{43} \times 58 = 2{,}494$$

In the preceding example, note that there are two possibilities for using division to verify a product. In one of these division examples, the multiplication is the same as that used in the multiplication example. This division possibility allows pupils to repeat a multiplication error and falsely indicate verification. The division operation and the relationship of division to multiplication is more completely described in Chapter 8.

The inclusion of processes of verification as an integral part of the program provides opportunities for children to review known facts and procedures and to help them see relationships between operations. Teachers should expect some of the efforts of children to result in nonverification and should encourage the search for mistakes in the original computation and the verification process.

Suggested activities

1. Construct arrays that will illustrate (a) the commutative property of multiplication, $4 \times 6 = 6 \times 4$; and (b) the distributive property of multiplication, $3 \times 18 = 3(10 + 8)$.

2. Develop a lesson plan to introduce the concept of prime factor.

3. Collect a set of word problems that involve finding the product of three factors.

4. Compare two contemporary textbook series as to methods of introducing multiplication with factors of two digits.

5. Construct a set of physical models to illustrate that $10^1 = 10$, $10^2 = 100$, and $10^3 = 1000$.

6. Estimate the product of 423×697. Compute the product and verify by using (a) the commutative property, (b) the distributive property, and (c) lattice multiplication.

Selected references

Bouwsma, W. D., C. G. Corle, and D. F. Clemson, Jr., *Basic Mathematics for Elementary Teachers.* New York: The Ronald Press Company, 1967, Chapter 5, "Multiplication," pp. 84–106.

Buckingham, B. R., *Elementary Arithmetic—Its Meaning and Practice.* Boston: Ginn & Company, 1953, Chapter 7, "The Multiplication of Whole Numbers," pp. 158–187.

Hervey, M. A., "Children's Responses to Two Types of Multiplication Problems," *The Arithmetic Teacher,* 13:288–292, April 1966.

Knigge, W., "Effortless Multiplication," *The Arithmetic Teacher,* 14:307, April 1967.

Mueller, F. J., *Arithmetic—Its Structure and Concepts.* Englewood Cliffs, N.J.: Prentice-Hall, Inc., 1964, Unit 8, "Operation of Multiplication," and Unit 9, "Multiplication Algorithms," pp. 82–112.

Rappaport, D., "Multiplication—Logical or Pedagogical?" *The Arithmetic Teacher*, 15:158–160, Feb. 1968.

Yates, W. E., "The Trachtenberg System as a Motivational Device," *The Arithmetic Teacher*, 13:677–678, Dec. 1966.

Teaching 8

division with whole

numbers

Historically the operation of division has posed greater teacher-learner problems than the other operations on number. Teachers seem to have had great difficulties in helping pupils develop mastery in performing the operation and in applying it to appropriate problem situations. The causes for these difficulties with division in the traditional arithmetic program have been many and varied, and some of the more obvious may be mentioned. In many instances, pupils were asked to begin formal work with the operation before they had acquired the necessary prerequisite learnings. Performance of the division algorithm requires application of multiplication and subtraction, and many children were forced into work with division before they were sufficiently competent with those operations. For some unexplainable reason, physical representation or manipulation of objects was rarely used to give meaning to the operation. The operation itself was taught in a rote fashion of dull routine involving the steps of dividing, multiplying, subtracting, comparing, bringing down the next digit, and going on and on until the example was completed.

In contemporary mathematics programs there is no substantial reason for the development of children's understandings and skills with the operation of division to be more difficult than with the other operations. Concepts are introduced with premathematical experiences at early primary levels by manipulating objects to separate or to compare sets. When the operation is formally introduced, mathematical meaning and application of the operation are

171

developed through the manipulation of objects, drawings and illustrations, and emphasis upon the relationship of division to multiplication and subtraction. The formal algorithm is developed sequentially with the multiplication algorithm stressing the inverse relationship. At every level of teaching division with whole numbers, emphasis is upon developing pupils' understanding of the operation rather than upon the rote memorization of rules and steps.

The nature of the division operation

The operation of division is mathematically defined through its inverse relationship to multiplication. Multiplication is used to find the unknown product of two factors: $a \times b = \boxed{c}$. Division as the inverse operation seeks an unknown factor when the product and one factor are known: $\boxed{a} \times b = c$ or $a \times \boxed{b} = c$. Using the symbol $\div$ to indicate that the division operation is to be performed to find the missing factor, the relationship may be illustrated as $a \times b = c$, $c \div b = \boxed{a}$, and $c \div a = \boxed{b}$. This definition is general in that it applies to all real numbers—whole numbers, integers, rationals, and irrationals. Note that if the known factor is zero, the known product is also zero; therefore, division by zero is meaningless because the unknown factor can be any number: $\boxed{n} \times 0 = 0$, $0 \times \boxed{n} = 0$, *and* $0 \div 0 = \boxed{n}$. If the known product is zero and the known factor is not zero, the unknown factor is zero: $\boxed{o} \times n = 0$, $n \times \boxed{o} = 0$, and $0 \div n = \boxed{o}$.

Some elementary mathematics programs introduce and develop division with whole numbers through its relationship to subtraction. The ideas being developed are that division situations involving whole numbers can be solved by subtraction and that division is a shortcut operation for those situations. For example, the number sentence $24 \div 6 = \square$ may be derived from a problem situation that asks, "How many groups of 6 are contained in a group of 24?" The solution could be obtained by manipulating objects and counting, but it could also be obtained by subtracting and counting the number of subtractions.

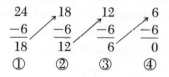

This procedure may be appropriate for early work with division of whole numbers, but it becomes tedious when many subtractions are required. It is not applicable at later levels when the missing factor is less than 1. The procedure also will be very difficult to use when the known factor is less than 1.

To be precise in our communications about division, the "parts" of the division operation are named and distinct symbolism is used to indicate that the operation is to be or has been performed. As previously implied, when efforts are being made to emphasize the relationship to multiplication, the terms *known factor, unknown factor,* and *product* are utilized.

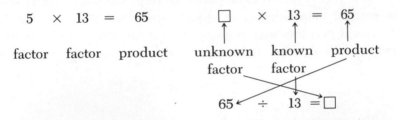

In direct reference to a division example or the division algorithm, specific terms name the parts. The number to be divided (product) is called the *dividend,* the divider number (known factor) is called the *divisor,* and the result of the operation (unknown factor) is called the *quotient.* In cases of uneven division, the term *remainder* is used to designate the number left. As pupils study the operation of division, they should learn to name number with symbolic expressions of division in several ways: (a) $\square \times 23 = 161$, (b) $161 \div 23 = \square$, (c) $23\overline{)161}$, and (d) $\frac{161}{23} = \square$. Developing abilities to read and to write such expressions with understanding, and to use the correct terms in reference to parts, is an important aspect of the total program.

In preceding chapters the operations of addition and multiplication were related to quantitative problem situations that required finding the total number when sets were to be combined. Subtraction was described as an operation used to find a missing number property when a set is to be separated into two disjoint sets or when the numbers of two disjoint sets are to be compared. Division may also be thought of as an operation on number that may be applied to certain situations involving sets or used to answer questions about those situations. The operation of division is applicable to situations which require the *separation* of a set into subsets that are equal in number and to situations that seek a *comparison* of the numbers of two disjoint sets.

Separation of a set in measurement and partition type problems. There are two types of quantitative situations that require the separation of a set into several subsets that are equal in number. In both these situations the number property of the set to be separated is known. In one situation the number property of the equivalent subsets is known, and the number of subsets is sought. Historically, this has been called *measurement* division. Most elementary programs introduce division with this type of situation because it is believed to be easier for pupils to understand because of ease of manipulation of objects and illustration by drawings. A typical problem may require finding the number of groups if a group of 28 objects is to be separated into groups of 7 objects each.

$$\square \times 7 = 28 \rightarrow 28 \div 7 = \square$$

The missing factor may be found by counting or measuring out groups of seven and then counting the number of groups.

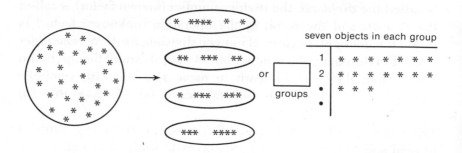

When subtraction is used for solution, the number being subtracted is the number of elements or objects in each small group.

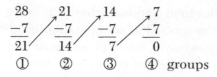

The situation that requires separating a set into a given number of equivalent subsets is known as *partition* division. The number of smaller subsets to be formed from a large set is known and the size or number in each small subset is to be determined. A problem may seek the number of objects in each subset if a set of 15 is to be distributed into three subsets of equal size or number. Finding the number of elements to be in each small subset by manipulating objects and counting involves placing one object in each of the required subsets in turn until the objects have been equally distributed or partitioned.

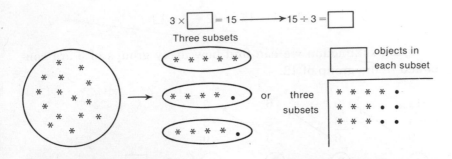

This type of separation situation can also be solved by subtraction, but it must be made clear that the number being subtracted is the number of elements required to place one element in each of the small groups.

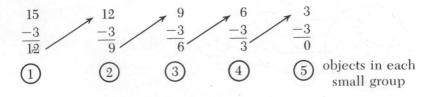

The terms measurement division and partition division are used only to refer to types of problem situations. The division algorithm that is described in a later section of this chapter is used identically in both situations to find the missing factor. It is not really necessary for children studying the division operation to use the terms in naming types of problems as measurement or partition division. To learn to identify those quantitative situations that require the separation of a set into equivalent subsets as a division operation and to understand the nature of the problems is most important.

Comparison of the numbers of two disjoint sets. Problems often arise that require a comparison of the size or number of a set to the size or number of a disjoint set. If the situation merely asks the number of the difference in number between the two sets, it involves the operation of subtraction. If the situation seeks the relationship between two magnitudes in respect to the number of times one is contained in the other, the operation to be used might be subtraction or division. For example, we may be asked to compare the size of a group of 12 with the size of a group of 3. "Paul has 12 marbles and John has 3 marbles. How many *times* as many marbles does Paul have as John has?"

$$\square \times 3 = 12 \rightarrow 12 \div 3 = \square$$

Using subtraction we can find how many groups of 3 are contained in the group of 12.

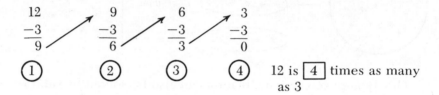

12 is $\boxed{4}$ times as many as 3

Using the idea of one-to-one correspondence, we can match subsets in the set of 12 to the set of 3.

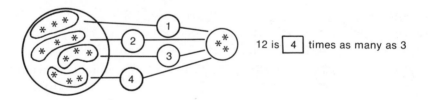

12 is $\boxed{4}$ times as many as 3

In a problem related to measurement we might be asked to find the relationship between a distance of 4 miles and a distance of 12 miles. "Jane lives 4 miles from the zoo and Jack lives 12 miles from the zoo. How many *times* as far does Jack have to travel to the zoo as Jane has to travel?"

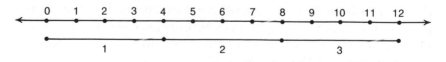

12 miles is $\boxed{3}$ times as long as 4 miles

Properties to be considered in teaching division

Closure.   In the preceding illustrations the separations and comparisons were *exact* or *even divisions*—there were no remainders. Many of the problems in everyday situations do not result in exact division. Often the separation of a set into equivalent subsets leaves a remainder subset. Consider a problem that requires finding the number of groups of 7 each that are contained in a group of 25.

$$\square \times 7 = 25 \rightarrow 25 \div 7 = \square$$

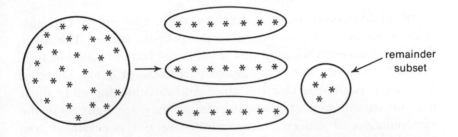

remainder subset

There is no whole number to satisfy the number sentences because 25 is not a multiple of 7: $2 \times 7 = 14$, $3 \times 7 = 21$, $4 \times 7 = 28$. The procedure when *division with a remainder* is involved is to (1) find the missing factor that obtains a product nearest to and less than the number of the group to be divided (product) and (2) ascertain the number of the remainder subset. The solution can be checked by determining if the sum of the remainder and the product of the two factors is equal to the dividend.

$$25 = (\square \times 7) + \bigcirc$$
$$25 = (\boxed{3} \times 7) + \bigcirc$$
$$25 = (\boxed{3} \times 7) + \textcircled{4}$$

Or, to generalize for all whole numbers, $p = (\square \times f) + r$. Note that this generalization is also true for exact division situations. If the number of the remainder subset is equal to zero ($r = 0$), then $p = (\square \times f) + 0$ or $p = \square \times f$. Because the division of any whole number by any other whole number does not always result in a whole number, *the set of whole numbers is not closed under the operation of division.*

Identity element. The identity element of multiplication (1) was discussed and illustrated in Chapter 7: $1 \times n = n$ and $n \times 1 = n$. Since the operation of division is defined as the inverse of multiplication and seeks a missing factor, two ideas are evident when one (1) is either the known factor or the missing factor in a division situation. When 1 is the known factor, $1 \times \square = n$, it becomes apparent that any number divided by 1 is that same number, $n \div 1 = n$. One is the unknown factor, $n \times \boxed{1} = n$, only when a number is divided by itself, $n \div n = \boxed{1}$.

Early activities with division

In contemporary mathematics programs, elementary concepts of division are introduced early in the primary grades. The introduction of division ideas at this level is not left to chance or incidental happenings but is a planned part of the program. Directed learning experiences that introduce and develop the early ideas may be called premathematical because they are built upon the manipulation of objects, observations are not generalized into facts, the symbolism of division is not introduced, and there is little or no formal reference to the operation of division.

Children's first experiences with a division idea will involve separating a set into equivalent subsets of a known number. The only prerequisite for such experiences is the children's ability to count objects. Within the classroom environment, the teacher can structure many problem situations in which equivalent small groups are to be formed from a large group. Children should be actively participating in moving and grouping the objects and in discussing the groupings and the numbers involved in such situations as

> "Paul has 10 crayons. Paul, give 2 crayons to each person."
> "We have 12 chairs. Let's put 4 chairs in each row."
> "Six people can sit at each table. How many tables do we
>   need for our class of 30 pupils?"

Discussion should center on how the groups were made and on answering the number questions: "How many objects all together?", "How many objects in each group?", and "How many groups?" Each of the number questions can be answered by counting. A general oral statement of the grouping result may take the form of (a) from ◯ we can make ▢ groups of △ or (b) ▢ groups of △ are ◯. It is not necessary for all the problem situations to result in exact division. The concept of remainder can be introduced by referring to the number "left over" after the possible groupings are made.

Other early experiences will involve separating a set into a certain number of equivalent subsets. Some type of container can be utilized to designate the subsets or small groups with problems such as

"We have 8 pencils. Let's put the same number of pencils in each of the 4 boxes."

The "sharing" situations so typical of young children are also examples of this type of separation of a group.

"John, you have 15 marbles. Will you share them equally with Mike and Joe?"

Children will probably use the procedure of placing one object in each group in turn until all the objects are distributed. In instances where exact division is not possible, attention must be paid to the equivalence or equality of number in each group and the number left over. The discussion about each of these situations will be much the same as that described previously: "How many objects did we have?", "How many groups did we make?", "How many objects in each group?", and "How many objects left over?"

After children have developed a number line with whole numbers and have used the line with subtraction situations, problems requiring repeated subtraction may be used to further develop elementary concepts of division. The problems will be very similar to those used in earlier experiences with separating sets. In the teaching procedure, children should actually use objects and the physical regrouping of the objects. The extension will be to the use of the number line and the subtraction operation for describing the situation and finding the result and to the development of children's abilities to solve such problems without actually manipulating objects. The number line illustration and the repeated subtraction become symbolic representations of the concrete experience. Consider the following illustrations of a problem that required separating a group of 18 into groups of 6.

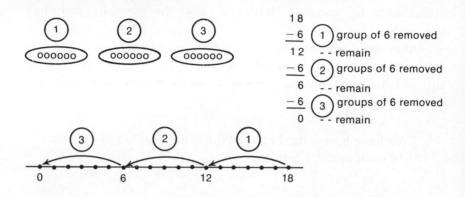

Note that in the number line illustration we begin at the number of the group to be separated (18) and count backward in terms of the size or number of each small group until zero is reached. There are two purposes for moving in this direction: (1) It is directly related to the repeated subtraction; and (2) when problems involve a remainder, the number of the remainder is apparent. Suppose that the problem asked how many groups of 6 are contained in a group of 20.

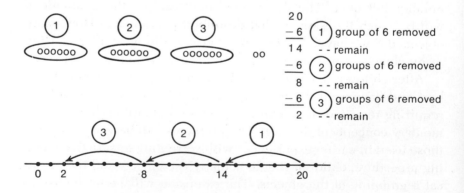

At a later level when the division algorithm is being formally introduced, the repeated subtraction can be directly related to the operational procedure.

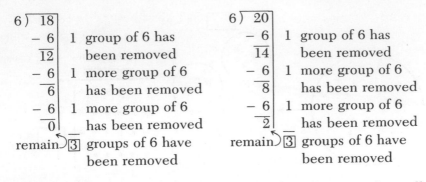

In modern elementary mathematics programs some, if not all, of the multiplication facts are introduced or established before any formal consideration of the division algorithm. One way of having children practice for mastery of the multiplication facts is to present two known factors and to have them derive or recall the associated product. Derivation of the product will usually involve manipulation of objects and counting, number line illustrations, or addition. Recall exercises are generally presented in the form of number sentences or computational arrangements.

$$3 \times 4 = \square$$
$$5 \times 3 = \square \qquad 5 \qquad 7 \qquad 9$$
$$7 \times 8 = \square \qquad \underline{\times 4} \quad \underline{\times 2} \quad \underline{\times 6}$$

When emphasizing the factor, factor, product association in recall exercises, examples can be presented in which the product is known and one of the factors is missing.

$$\square \times 3 = 6 \qquad 4 \times \square = 16 \qquad \square \qquad \square \qquad 5 \qquad 9$$
$$\square \times 5 = 25 \qquad 6 \times \square = 30 \qquad \underline{\times 3} \quad \underline{\times 8} \quad \underline{\times \square} \quad \underline{\times \square}$$
$$\square \times 7 = 42 \qquad 8 \times \square = 56 \qquad 18 \quad 48 \quad 20 \quad 54$$

If children are unable to recall a fact but understand how the multiplication facts are derived, they should be able to reestablish the fact or find the missing factor by grouping objects or by using number line illustrations, arrays, or addition.

The emphasis in such exercises is upon finding the missing factor. Although *dividing* or *division* is not a part of the terminology being used, it should be clear to teachers that such exercises are a part of the foundation program for division and that the inverse relationship of multiplication to division is being introduced.

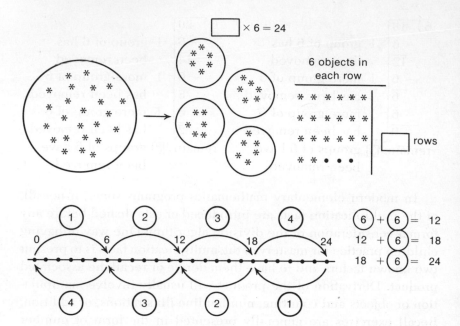

The division facts

In preceding chapters reference was made to the use of the addition, subtraction, and multiplication facts in the operational algorithms. In computation with the algorithms of addition, subtraction, and multiplication, the facts are used and mastery of the facts is a requirement for successful performance. When the operation of division is approached as the inverse of multiplication that seeks a missing factor, the division algorithm may be performed without using the traditional division facts. As described in a following section, children in modern programs can find the missing factor

$$
\begin{array}{r}
210 \\
\hline
10 \\
100 \\
100 \\
18\overline{)3784} \\
\end{array}
$$

$100 \times 18 = 1,800$

$100 \times 18 = 1,800$

$10 \times 18 = 180$

$$
18\overline{)3784} \\
\begin{array}{r}
-1800 \\
\hline
1984 \\
-1800 \\
\hline
184 \\
-180 \\
\hline
4 \\
\end{array}
\begin{array}{r}
100 \\
\\
100 \\
\\
10 \\
\hline
210 \\
\end{array}
$$

$$
18\overline{)3784} \\
\begin{array}{r}
-1800 \\
\hline
1984 \\
-1800 \\
\hline
184 \\
-180 \\
\hline
4 \\
\end{array}
$$

or compute the quotient and not apply facts that are strictly division facts.

For example, one can compute the quotient of 3,784 ÷ 18 without thinking in terms of division facts by utilizing facts and procedures of multiplication, subtraction, and addition.

In the traditional arithmetic programs of the past, as much emphasis was placed upon pupils' memorization of the division facts as upon memorization of the facts of the other operations. The algorithm was taught by a rote rule approach that involved "rounding off" the divisor and trying to apply division facts in relation to a trial divisor.

Pupils' knowledge of the division facts may continue to be one of our goals in modern programs. The purpose of this objective is not so pupils can apply the facts in the division algorithm, but to help them respond quickly to simple division situations and to understand the nature of division and its relationship to multiplication. Because of these purposes and the fact that the set of whole numbers is not closed under the operation of division, the modern approach to division facts is somewhat different from the approach to facts of the other operations.

After children have established some of the multiplication facts by combining sets, learning experiences should be structured in which they look at the same situations in regard to separating the new set that was formed. Children should be helped to understand that from each combining situation two statements can be made about the separation of the newly formed set. To write number sentences describing the separation, the symbol ÷ will need to be introduced and explained. The terms *division* and *divided by* can also be given meaning in these activities.

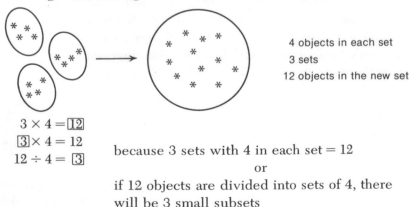

4 objects in each set
3 sets
12 objects in the new set

$3 \times 4 = \boxed{12}$
$\boxed{3} \times 4 = 12$
$12 \div 4 = \boxed{3}$

because 3 sets with 4 in each set = 12

or

if 12 objects are divided into sets of 4, there will be 3 small subsets

$3 \times \boxed{4} = 12$

$12 \div 3 = \boxed{4}$ because 3 sets with 4 in each set = 12

or

if 12 objects are divided into 3 sets, there will
be 4 objects in each small subset

Having children build a distinct table of exact division facts will
do little to help children learn the facts or understand the operation
because of the complexity of the table and the many uneven division situations that occur even with one-digit factors. If reference
to a table of facts is required, children can be taught to read the
multiplication fact table in regard to division. Knowing one factor
(divisor), they can read into the multiples of that factor until they
reach the known product (dividend) and read "out" to the unknown
factor (quotient).

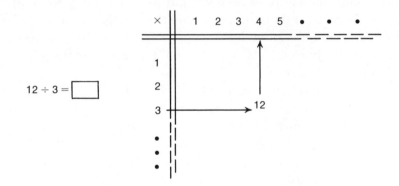

The computational symbol for division and the names of the
parts of the operation, $\text{divisor} \overline{)\, \text{dividend}}^{\text{quotient}}$, can be introduced early
in the experiences that relate division facts to multiplication facts.
Naming the parts should be regarded as a means of developing
children's vocabulary so that they can communicate more precisely
about the division operation.

known	known	missing
product	factor	factor
48 $\div$	6 =	$\boxed{8}$
dividend	divisor	quotient

Children will have already learned that there are many names
for the same number and should be helped to recognize that $6\,\overline{)\,48}$

is another way of describing the number named by $48 \div 6$ and is read the same way. The usefulness of the computational form should be stressed from the viewpoint that we can include in it a record of our thinking. Reasons for using this form will become more apparent to children as problems with uneven division and larger numbers arise.

$$
\begin{array}{r}
8 \\
6 \overline{)\ 48} \\
-48 \leftarrow 8 \times 6 = 48 \\
\hline
0
\end{array}
$$

Relating exact division facts to the multiplication facts should be closely followed by division with remainders. In early work with problems that involve uneven division, the remainder should be exactly that—a number that remains or that is left over. A quick analysis of possible division situations or reference to a number chart on which the multiples of a number, n, have been marked will reveal that there are many more uneven division situations than there are exact divisions. For every number that is evenly divisible by 2, there is a number that is not evenly divisible by 2 (⓪, 1, ②, 3, ④, 5, ⑥, 7, . . .); for every number that is evenly divisible by 3, there are 2 that are not (⓪, 1, 2, ③, 4, 5, ⑥, 7, 8, ⑨, 10, 11, ⑫, . . .); for every number that is evenly divisible by 4, there are 3 that are not; and so forth, until, for every number that is evenly divisible by 9, there are 8 numbers that are not.

When teachers are certain that pupils understand certain multiplication facts and the related exact division facts, they should introduce problems that have the same factors but that involve division with remainders. Practice exercises may take the form of computational examples or number sentences.

a. $15 \div 3 = \square$
$$
\begin{array}{r}
5 \\
3 \overline{)\ 15} \\
-15 \\
\hline
0
\end{array}
$$
$15 \div 3 = (3 \times \square) + \bigcirc$

b. $16 \div 3 = \square$
$$
\begin{array}{r}
5 \\
3 \overline{)\ 16} \\
-15 \\
\hline
1
\end{array}
$$
$16 \div 3 = (3 \times \square) + \bigcirc$

$$5$$

c. $17 \div 3 = \square$ $3\overline{\smash{)}17}$ $17 \div 3 = (3 \times \square) + \bigcirc$
                            $\underline{-15}$
                            2

d. $18 \div 3 = \square$ $3\overline{\smash{)}18}$ $18 \div 3 = (3 \times \square) + \bigcirc$

The generalization to be reached for all situations is that the

$$\text{dividend} = (\text{divisor} \times \text{quotient}) + \text{remainder}$$

The division facts, including those with remainders, and their relationship to the multiplication facts thus become the vehicle for the formal introduction of the division operation and the algorithm.

Remainders in problem situations

It will be extremely difficult for children to understand the nature of remainders and the use of remainders without direct reference to problem situations. They cannot be expected to apply the concept of remainder to problem situations if practice with computational examples constitutes their total experience. It becomes the teacher's responsibility to select suitable problems for developing a specific remainder idea. There are at least three types of problem situations in which the consideration and disposition of a remainder is relevant to the response required for the problem question.

1. The remainder is simply a remainder—a number left over. Some practical decision might be made as to the disposition of the *objects* remaining.
    "John has 10 marbles. He shares them equally with Joe and Jim. How many marbles does each boy get?"

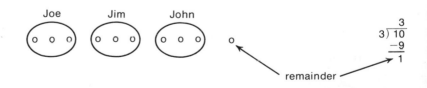

In this case the boys may decide to disregard the remaining marble, or if a game is being played, they may decide to make the marble a part of the game.

2. The remainder cannot be used and is discarded. The part or number that remains is of no use insofar as the problem is concerned. To include the number of the remainder in the response to the problem question would be ridiculous.

"Mary is making doll ribbons each 2 inches long. How many doll ribbons can she make from a piece of ribbon that is 9 inches long?"

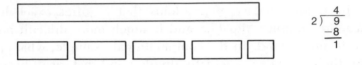

$$\begin{array}{r} 4 \\ 2\overline{)\ 9} \\ -8 \\ \hline 1 \end{array}$$

The first impression may be that this type of problem is identical to the first situation. However, the marble in the first problem remained a usable marble that could be applied to the major purpose of the problem. The remaining piece of ribbon cannot be used in that way.

3. The existence of a remainder requires an adjustment of the quotient for an appropriate solution to the problem.

"Four children can sit at each table. How many tables are needed for 15 children?"

$$\begin{array}{r} 3 \\ 4\overline{)\ 15} \\ -12 \\ \hline 3 \end{array}$$

Another table is needed for the 3 remaining children that cannot be seated at the three full tables.

When one of the ideas related to remainders is being developed with children, teachers need to select carefully those problems that apply the idea. A great deal of pupils' confusion about remainders can result from a lack of careful planning.

Problems involving exact division

There are two major categories of problems in which remainders do not exist—the division is exact. In one of these categories an even division results from the computational procedure. The problem situation may be of any type, but the computed remainder is zero.

$$
\begin{array}{r}
4 \\
8\overline{)32} \\
32 \\
\hline
0
\end{array}
\qquad
\begin{array}{r}
11 \\
12\overline{)132} \\
12 \\
\hline
12 \\
12 \\
\hline
0
\end{array}
$$

The other category of problems that requires exact division is a more complex situation and is much more difficult for children to understand. In the computational example, what appears to be the remainder is actually divided and that result becomes a part of the total quotient. Introductory problems seeking such exact division are usually partition division situations, and it is possible to partition the objects in the group to be divided into equal parts.

"If Joe and Jim share 5 cookies, how many cookies will each boy get?"

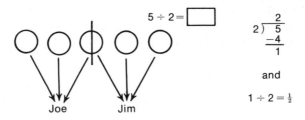

$$5 \div 2 = \boxed{}$$

$$
\begin{array}{r}
2 \\
2\overline{)5} \\
-4 \\
\hline
1
\end{array}
$$

and

$$1 \div 2 = \tfrac{1}{2}$$

The total quotient is $2 + \tfrac{1}{2}$ or $2\tfrac{1}{2}$. Joe and Jim each get $2\tfrac{1}{2}$ cookies.

Obviously, children will not be able to understand this procedure until they have had concrete learning experiences with partition division situations in which the number to be divided is less than the number of groups to be formed. The nature of the result also indicates that pupils need an understanding of naming equal parts of a unit. As described in Chapter 9, the development of the concept of equal parts of a unit and naming one or more of those equal parts are foundation experiences in early work with fractional numbers.

Before children are required to find quotients of exact division with problem examples such as $5 \div 2$, $8 \div 3$, $11 \div 4$, and so forth, they should have many concrete opportunities to find results in situations such as

What will the size of each part be if

1. *One unit or object is divided into two equal parts?*

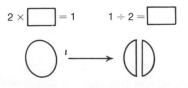

Each of the equal parts is ½ unit.

2. *Two units or objects are divided into three equal parts?*

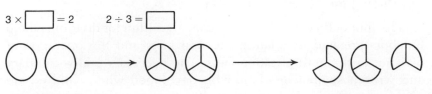

Each of the equal parts is ⅔ unit.

3. *Three units or objects are divided into four equal parts?*

Each of the equal parts is ¾ unit.

Number line illustrations may also be used to find the size of each equal part, but such diagrams are more abstract than those using circular or rectangular regions. For example, $3 \div 4 = \Box$ may be illustrated as a line 3 units long which has been partitioned into four equal parts.

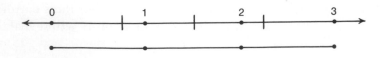

The line that is 3 units long is first divided into two equal parts, then each of these two parts is divided into two equal parts. Each of the resulting four equal parts is $\frac{3}{4}$ unit long.

Children should be helped to understand that the quotient written as a fractional numeral ($\frac{3}{4}$) names the same number as the division expression $3 \div 4$. This idea can be extended to include problems of even division such as $4 \div 2 = \frac{4}{2}$ and $9 \div 3 = \frac{9}{3}$, where the quotient can be named either as a fraction or as a whole number, and to more complex examples that require exact division and the total quotient may be either a fraction or a mixed number (whole number plus a fraction): $5 \div 2 = \frac{5}{2}$ or $2\frac{1}{2}$. By giving some attention to the manner in which fractional quotients are renamed, children will obtain some understanding of the idea that fractional numerals can be used to indicate that a division is to be performed.

Developing the division algorithm

The foundations for developing an algorithm for dividing whole numbers are laid in relating division facts and the operation of division to the multiplication facts. The necessary oral vocabulary and written symbolism should be developed when children are working at the level of one-digit divisors and one-digit quotients. When including the possibilities of uneven division, these early experiences include examples in which the divisor is from the set $\{2, 3, 4, 5, 6, 7, 8, 9\}$, and the possible dividends for each divisor may be tabulated as

Divisor	Possible dividends
2	$\{2, 3, 4, \ldots, 19\}$
3	$\{3, 4, 5, \ldots, 29\}$
.	.
.	.
.	.
8	$\{8, 9, 10, \ldots, 79\}$
9	$\{9, 10, 11, \ldots, 89\}$

A survey of contemporary textual materials for children may lead one to believe that there are several division algorithms currently employed in elementary programs. Closer scrutiny will reveal that the procedures are quite similar but that the notation differs in regard to placement of the partial quotients and the total quotient.

$$
\begin{array}{c}
\dfrac{234}{}\\
\left.\begin{array}{c}1\\1\\1\\1\end{array}\right\}\ 4\\
\left.\begin{array}{c}10\\10\\10\end{array}\right\}\ 30\\
\left.\begin{array}{c}100\\100\end{array}\right\}200\\
\end{array}
$$

$$
\begin{array}{r}
63\,)\,14{,}750\\
-6\ 300\\ \hline
8\ 450\\
-6\ 300\\ \hline
2\ 150\\
-\ \ 630\\ \hline
1\ 520\\
-\ \ 630\\ \hline
890\\
-630\\ \hline
260\\
-\ 63\\ \hline
197\\
-\ 63\\ \hline
134\\
-\ 63\\ \hline
71\\
-\ 63\\ \hline
8
\end{array}
\qquad
\begin{array}{r}
63\,)\,14{,}750\\
-6\ 300\quad\left.\begin{array}{c}100\end{array}\right.\\ \hline
8\ 450\quad\ \ \ \ \Big\}200\\
-6\ 300\quad\left.100\right.\\ \hline
2\ 150\\
-\ \ 630\quad\left.10\right.\\ \hline
1\ 520\\
-\ \ 630\quad 10\Big\}30\\ \hline
890\\
-630\quad\left.10\right.\\ \hline
260\\
-\ 63\quad\left.1\right.\\ \hline
197\\
-\ 63\quad 1\\ \hline
134\quad\ \ \Big\}4\\
-\ 63\quad 1\\ \hline
71\\
-\ 63\quad\left.1\right.\\ \hline
8\ |\ 234
\end{array}
$$

The operational procedure for finding the total quotient in a modern approach to the division algorithm is based upon *estimation*. Pupils are to be taught to estimate partial quotients in terms of multiples of the positional values of our decimal number system. Or, we could say that the estimates are to be in powers of ten (. . ., 1,000, 100, 10, 1) and decades of powers of ten. In the above example(s) it should be obvious that the first estimate is a multiple of 100 because 63 cannot be contained in 14,750 at least 1,000 times; $1,000 \times 63 = 63,000$ and that number is greater than the dividend. The example illustrates that the correct total quotient can be arrived at by underestimating, and there are many other estimates that could have been used and that would have resulted in the correct quotient.

Current elementary mathematics textbook programs may differ on the extent to which they encourage pupils to make more efficient estimates of the partial quotients. Some programs and some teachers are content to allow children to make many small estimates, finally arriving at a correct total quotient if the multiplication and subtraction computations are correct. The hope is that children will discover the possibilities of making larger or better estimates and begin to do so. In many instances, pupils do not begin to make better estimates of their own volition, and the tedium of trying to arrive at total quotients using small estimates creates frustration and undesirable attitudes.

Other programs and other teachers seek to guide or help children to make better or more efficient estimates that will eliminate some of the multiplication and subtraction computations. They may suggest using a procedure in which several estimates are made, the multiplications are performed, and a decision is made as to the best estimate. Some of the calculations will be mentally performed by pupils. For $63\overline{)14,750}$ the thinking might involve part or all the following:

Estimate × Divisor = Product					Decision
1,000	×	63	=	63,000	No good. $63,000 > 14,750$
100	×	63	=	6,300	Could use. $6,300 < 14,750$
200	×	63	=	12,600	Better. $12,600 < 14,750$
300	×	63	=	18,900	Cannot use. $18,900 > 14,750$

The best first estimate of a partial quotient appears to be 200.

The authors of this text favor helping children learn techniques and procedures of estimating quotients in relation to their learning to perform the multiplication algorithm with multiples of 10, 100, 1,000 and so forth. If the division operation is sufficiently related to the operation of multiplication, and if children understand multiplication with multiples of 10 and 100, they will be able to make more efficient estimates of the partial quotients.

Techniques for meaningfully developing the division algorithm include using a problem approach in which the use of problems involving the separation of a set into equivalent sets provides reasons for performing the operation. The problems may be either of the measurement (seeking the number of groups) or partition (seeking the size of each group) type. With either type of problem, the computation in the algorithm should be related to the problem situation so that the completed procedure is actually a written record of the separation. Consider the problem (measurement):

"A farmer gathers 409 eggs. He puts 12 eggs in each carton. How many cartons can he fill?"

$$
\begin{array}{r}
12\overline{)\ 409} \\
-240 \\
\hline 169 \\
-120 \\
\hline 49 \\
-48 \\
\hline 1
\end{array}
$$

12) 409
   −240 20 cartons of 12 eggs = 240 eggs
   ─────
    169
   −120 10 cartons of 12 eggs = 120 eggs
   ────
     49
    −48   4 cartons of 12 eggs = 48 eggs
   ────
      1 34 cartons of 12 eggs = 408 eggs *and* 1 egg remains

If the problem were of a partition type, the descriptions could be in the form, "□ eggs in each of 15 cartons = ○ eggs."

Understanding the mastery of the operational procedure is also furthered by continued reference to the relationship of division to multiplication. The natural sequence is for each level of development with the multiplication algorithm to be closely followed by the development of the division operation using similar numbers. For example, soon after children have learned to multiply a two-digit factor by a one-digit factor ($4 \times 26 = \square$), they should be introduced to problems of division with a one-digit divisor and a two-digit quotient ($104 \div 4 = \square$).

```
    26      4 ) 104
   ×4        −80 │ 20
   ──         ──
    24         24
    80        −24 │  6
   ───        ─── 
   104          0 │ 26
```

At each level of development, children should be helped to learn to make the best estimate of the partial quotient by using what they know about multiplying multiples of 10, 100, and other powers of ten. A pupil may arrive at a correct total quotient by using gross underestimations of partial quotients. Such computational procedures are to be accepted as solutions; examples completed by a pupil in a manner somewhat similar to the following should indicate to the teacher that (1) it may be appropriate to review the pupil's skills in multiplying and (2) the pupil needs help in making more efficient estimates. Using small partial quotient estimates

```
  8 ) 5280          34 ) 1786
    - 40 | 5           - 34 | 1
    ─────              ─────
    5240               1752
    - 40 | 5           - 34 | 1
    ─────              ─────
    5200               1718
    - 40 | 5          '- 34 | 1
       .                  .
       .    .             .    .
       .                  .
```

may lessen the possibility of making an error in multiplication, but it increases the possibility of making errors in subtraction. Sufficient practice must be provided at each level for pupils to become quick and accurate with the computation before they are forced to more difficult levels. Introduction of the so-called "short form" or traditional algorithm should be delayed at least until children have mastered division with two-digit divisors in which they write partial products as multiples of 100, 10, and 1 and find the total quotient by finding the sum of the partial quotients.

One digit divisors.   The division algorithm is introduced with examples that have a one-digit divisor and a resulting total quotient of two digits. If the divisor and the total quotient are one-digit numerals, the example merely involves a single multiplication or division fact. Because the necessary symbolism and the nature of remainders were developed while working with the facts, the new learning at this level involves utilizing several multiplication ideas in a procedure that results in a total quotient of more than one digit. The order for developing pupils' understandings and skills with the division algorithm is basically that of developing skills with the inverse operation, multiplication.

Multiplication examples	Division examples		Ideas and generalizations
$7 \times 9 = \square$	$\square \times 9 = 63$		Derivation of facts. Finding the missing factor.
	$7 \times \square = 63$		
$6 \times 8 = \square$	$48 \div 6 = \square$		Division is the inverse of multiplication. Symbolism of number sentences describing division and the computational form. Relationship of division to subtraction.
	$48 \div 8 = \square$		
	8	6	
	6) 48	8) 48	
	−48	−48	
	0	0	
	7	0	Concepts of remainders introduced.
	5) 37	6) 3	
	−35	−0	
	2	3	
$4 \times 20 = \square$	20		Dividend of two digits. Quotient is a multiple of ten. Knowledge of multiplying ones × tens used in estimate.
	4) 83		
20	−80		
×4	3		
80			
37	37		Dividend of three digits. Quotient of tens and ones. First partial quotient is a multiple of tens; the second is ones. Total quotient is sum of partial quotients.
×5	7		
35	30		
150	5) 187		
185	−150		
	37		
	−35		
	2		
400	400		Dividend of three or four digits. Quotient is a multiple of 100. Knowledge of multiplying ones × hundreds used in estimate of quotient.
×6	6) 2405		
2400	−2400		
	5		
432	2 ⌉		Estimating partial quotients in multiples of 100, 10, and 1 as necessary. Zero could appear as the digit in the tens place in the total quotient. Children who succeed at this level of difficulty should have no real trouble dividing any number by a single-digit divisor.
×3	30 ⊦432		
6	400 ⌋		
90	3) 1298		
1200	−1200		
1296	98		
	−90		
	8		
	−6		
	2		

Two digit divisors. Children should have reached a relatively high degree of proficiency using one-digit divisors before they approach problems with two-digit divisors. Initial two-digit divisors of even multiples of ten $(30\overline{)}\ , 40\overline{)}\ )$ should not cause pupils great difficulties. Their estimates of partial quotients in such examples will probably be as accurate or efficient as their estimates with one-digit divisors. In the sequential development of pupils' abilities with two-digit divisors, problems with one-digit quotients should precede those with multi-digit quotients.

When the divisors are not even multiples of ten $(24\overline{)}\ , 37\overline{)}\ )$, less efficient partial quotient estimates by pupils are to be expected. Estimates that are too high will not be uncommon, and some pupils may tend to regress to making estimates that are quite small. Of course they will be able to arrive at the correct total quotient with continued small estimates. Helping children to think of the divisor as an even multiple of ten will assist them in estimations of the quotient.

Some programs that emphasize using *trial divisors* arrived at by *rounding off* to the nearest multiple of ten sequence the problems and procedures so that

1. The divisors used first are rounded *down* to the existing multiple of ten $(32 \rightarrow 30)$. The number of units in the ones place indicate that the number is closer to 30 than it is to 40.
2. Succeeding examples involve rounding *up* to the next multiple of ten $(38 \rightarrow 40)$, because the number of the divisor is closer to that multiple than it is to the lower multiple.
3. Finally, there are situations in which the decision to round down or up to arrive at a trial divisor is not apparent and the pupil resorts to using his own judgment.

The sequential schema for developing pupils' understanding and skills with dividing by two-digit divisors is much the same as the procedure for developing abilities with one-digit divisors. It is obvious that the pupils' capabilities with the division algorithm are dependent upon their skills in multiplication.

When working with one- or two-digit divisors, the pupil's first decision should involve the number of places in the total quotient. In the procedure we have described, the pupil should be doing this by using his knowledge of multiplying multiples of tens and hundreds to make the best first estimate of a partial quotient. Refer-

Multiplication examples	Division examples	Ideas and generalizations
$\square \times 30 = \bigcirc$	$30\overline{)126}$	Two-digit divisor is a multiple of 10. Problem involves one-digit quotient. Knowledge of ones $\times$ tens is used in estimate of the quotient.
	$20\overline{)846}$ $40\overline{)2346}$	Two-digit divisor is multiple of 10. Problem involves two-digit quotient. Dividend of three or four digits. Knowledge of tens $\times$ tens is used in making the first estimate of the quotient.
$\square \times 43 = \bigcirc$	$43\overline{)96}$ $43\overline{)136}$	Two-digit divisor has tens and ones units. Problems involve one-digit quotients. Dividend of two or three digits. Concept of trial divisor introduced and used. Knowledge of ones $\times$ tens used in estimate of quotient.
	$28\overline{)632}$ $53\overline{)1784}$	Problems involve two-digit quotients; dividends of three or four digits. Use of trial divisors continued. Knowledge of tens $\times$ tens used in first estimate.
	$37\overline{)6456}$ $76\overline{)16432}$	Problems involve three digits in quotients. Use of trial divisors. Knowledge of hundreds $\times$ tens used in first estimate and tens $\times$ tens used in second estimate.
	$52\overline{)78394}$	Extension to examples with four-digit quotients in same manner. Knowledge of tens $\times$ thousands used in first estimate of partial quotient, and so forth.
$\square \times 400 = \bigcirc$	$400\overline{)}$ $430\overline{)}$	Extension to use of three-digit divisors in a similar sequential order: one-digit quotients, two-digit quotients, and so forth. Continued use of trial divisors but trial divisors are in multiples of 100. No really new concepts, but greater skills in multiplication are required.
$\square \times 483 = \bigcirc$	$483\overline{)}$	

ence to positional value in the dividend and the unit characteristics of each position should help pupils decide on the number of places in the total quotient.

48$\overline{)5286}$ thought of as 48$\overline{)5\text{ thousands 2 hundreds 8 tens 6 ones}}$
But, 5 units of one-thousand cannot be separated into
groups of 48, or into 48 groups of equal size. The thousands units can be thought of or renamed as units of one-
hundred.

48$\overline{)\underline{5}286}$ thought of as 48$\overline{)52\text{ hundreds 8 tens 6 ones}}$
52 units of one-hundred can be separated, so there will be
at least 100 in each group (or 100 groups). The total quotient will have three places: hundreds, tens, and ones.

Pupil understanding of this process can be greatly enhanced by
the use of practical problem situations and concrete or semiconcrete aids (such as play money) in which the actual separation can
be visualized. Practice exercises directed toward helping pupils
make a good or correct decision can be provided by using examples
in which the only required response is an indication of the power
of ten (number of places) in the total quotient.

$$
\overset{\times 00}{5\overline{)\underline{638}}} \quad \text{or} \quad 8\overline{)5421} \quad \text{or} \quad \overset{\bigcirc}{27\overline{)7368}} \quad \text{or} \quad 43\overline{)14\overset{\uparrow}{0}6}
$$

One advantage of writing the partial quotients above the division symbol as the algorithm is being sequentially developed with
children is that continued emphasis can more easily be given to the
use of positional value. The extension of pupils' skills to the short
or adult algorithm requires an understanding of the positional value
relationship between the dividend and the quotient. Even at this
level, reference to and discussion of problem situations should
continue. A place-value chart or diagram similar to that described
in preceding chapters may be used to help children understand
that zeros in the partial quotients need not be written if the quotient
digits are written in the proper position.

Developing pupils' understandings and abilities with the longer procedure is of much more importance than hurrying them to a shorter process. Success with the longer procedure should be a prerequisite to practicing the shorter form. There should be no hurry to get pupils to incorporate the elimination of zeros in the computation and the bringing down of digits from the dividend as needed into their operational process. They may adopt these techniques when they know *why* and see the advantage of doing so.

Verifying operations of division

As with the other operations, manipulation of objects and counting should be pupils' first experiences with verifying ideas about solutions to division situations. Their first abstract verification procedures for division situations should utilize the operations of subtraction and/or addition.

$$\boxed{4} \times 8 = 32 \qquad 32 \div 8 = \boxed{4}$$

Subtraction:

32	24	16	8
-8	-8	-8	-8
24	16	8	0
①	②	③	④

Addition:

$$8 \enspace \text{①} \enspace 16 \qquad\qquad 24$$
$$\underline{+8} \enspace \text{②} \enspace \underline{+8} \enspace \text{③} \enspace \underline{+8} \enspace \text{④}$$
$$16 \qquad\quad 24 \qquad\quad 32$$

The use of multiplication as an early verification process is risky because the application of misinformation may be repeated. What appears to be verification of a solution may actually result when the solution is incorrect. Suppose that a pupil believes that $7 \times 8 = 54$, and he attempts verification for $8 \overline{)60}$ in the following manner:

$$
\begin{array}{c}
7 \\
8\overline{)\ 60} \\
\underline{-54} \\
6
\end{array}
\qquad
\begin{array}{c}
8 \\
\underline{\times 7} \\
54
\end{array}
\qquad
\begin{array}{c}
54 \\
\underline{+6} \\
60
\end{array}
\qquad
\begin{array}{l}
60 = \boxed{7} \times 8 + \text{⑥} \\[4pt]
60 = 54 + 6 \\[4pt]
60 = 60
\end{array}
$$

The same possibility of error verification procedure exists when the examples involve larger numbers and the algorithm is more complex. What mistake exists in the following attempted verification?

```
              387
      36 ) 13932          387          36        13912
          -10800          ×36        ×387        +20
            3132         2302         252        13932
           -2860        11610        2860
             272        13912       10800
            -252                    13912
              20
```

Children's use of multiplication as a verification process of the operation of division is appropriate only when they have reached a level or degree of accuracy with multiplication that makes mistakes in the multiplication procedure highly unlikely.

One verification procedure for division examples that is often overlooked or used infrequently in elementary programs is the process of redividing the dividend, using the observed quotient as the divisor to ascertain whether the original divisor will be the newly observed quotient. This procedure may help to more firmly establish the relationship of division to multiplication: If $a \times b = c$, then $c \div a = b$ *and* $c \div b = a$.

```
              38                                        43
      43 )  1640                              38 )  1640
          -1290                                   -1520
            350          note                       120
          -344          same                      -114
             6  ←—— remainder ——————→ 6
```

Asking pupils to verify solutions to problems in this manner is realistic because it reverses the nature of the question from "If a group of n objects is separated into groups of □ objects each, there will be ○ groups with △ objects remaining" to "If a group of n objects is separated into ○ equal size groups, there will be □ objects in each group with △ objects remaining." An incidental teaching or learning advantage to this verification procedure is that pupils will be practicing the division algorithm in the process.

As with verification procedures for other operations, children should be encouraged and taught to verify their work with division with procedures that (1) are related to physical problem situations, (2) further understandings of the relationship of the operation to other operations, and (3) develop understandings of and abilities with the operation itself.

Suggested activities

1. Write several problems that illustrate measurement division and several that illustrate partition division.
2. Develop a set of problems that illustrate situations that require the comparison of two sets and in which division can be used as the means of solution.
3. Compare the approaches of two contemporary elementary textbook series for developing understanding and mastery of the division algorithm.
4. Prepare a lesson plan in which division with a two-digit divisor is to be introduced.
5. Estimate the quotient of $8,634 \div 257 = \square$. Compute the quotient and verify by (a) subtraction, (b) multiplication, and (c) division.

Selected references

Bouwsma, W. D., C. G. Corle, and D. F. Clemson, Jr., *Basic Mathematics for Elementary Teachers*. New York: The Ronald Press Company, 1967, Chapter 9, "Division," pp. 149–162.

Buckingham, B. R., *Elementary Arithmetic—Its Meaning and Practice*. Boston: Ginn & Company, 1953, Chapter 8, "The Division of Whole Numbers," pp. 188–241.

Collier, C. C., "When You Teach Division . . . Focus on the Underlying Why," *Professional Growth For Teachers,* Second Quarter Issue, 1966–1967. New London, Conn.: Croft Educational Services, 1966.

Mueller, F. J., *Arithmetic—Its Structure and Concepts*. Englewood Cliffs, N.J.: Prentice-Hall, Inc., 1964, Unit 14, "Operation of Division," and Unit 15, "Division Algorithms," pp. 163–188.

Peck, L. C., and D. Niswonger, "Measurement and Partition—Commutativity of Multiplication," *The Arithmetic Teacher,* 11:258–259, April 1964.

Reeve, F., "The Missing Factor in Division," *The Arithmetic Teacher,* 15:275–277, March 1968.

Spitzer, H. F., "Measurement of Partition Division for Introducing Study of the Division Operation," *The Arithmetic Teacher,* 14:369–372, May 1967.

Teaching 9
rational numbers:
common fractions

As a rule, people possess a fragmentary understanding and operational knowledge of fractions[1] and tend to "shy away from" them when possible. This tendency to avoid fractions seems to have been the history of their use. Although adequate notations for fractions were available to the Egyptians, Babylonians, and Greeks, they avoided their use with the exception of such unit fractions as 1/2, 1/3, and 1/4.

Confusion in the use of fractions in the past may have stemmed from an inadequate background on the part of the learner. When adults express doubts about their ability to use fractions and when student scores on achievement tests are examined, apparently schools have not been very successful in recent years in helping students become confident and competent in their use of fractions. This continuing lack of fractional number understanding and skill is indefensible when the child before entering school, usually has heard and has actually been learning to use fraction expressions in numerous situations. For instance, the following are familiar expressions of young children. "Come on and be fair, divide it up evenly"; "You gave me the smallest part"; "If we cut it into four pieces, everybody will get one"; "I'll meet you half way"; and "I'll give you this part."

Listening to the conversations of children in and out of the classroom demonstrates that youngsters use a wide range of fractional

---

[1] The authors of this book use the terms rational number, fractional number, and fraction interchangeably.

number expressions spontaneously. Frequently, elementary school children are able to use fraction terms in their speaking vocabularies more effectively than their actual understanding of fraction concepts warrants. Even though the child may hear and use expressions like those listed, his concepts are often vague and incomplete. Although a child uses the fraction term half-day in speaking, he does not necessarily think of the half-day in its relation to the whole day. When bringing a half-pint of cream from the store, though he may bring at the same time a pint of milk, he does not think of the half-pint as a division of the pint. The half-pint is a whole bottle just as the pint is a whole bottle. The only apparent relation between the two is that the half-pint bottle is smaller than the pint bottle.

The child's early everyday experiences aid him in developing a convenient means of expression, but they do not, in themselves, provide him with an adequate understanding of the meanings of a fraction. However, these early experiences enable the child to approach the systematic study of fractions in the early elementary grades with some degree of familiarity. The teacher's job is continually to help the child as he progresses through the elementary school to develop further these beginning concepts of fractions until they become precise and usable in present as well as in future situations. The ideas presented in this chapter are designed to help the elementary teacher provide students with a variety of experiences to develop the understanding and skills needed to use the symbolic representation of the fraction concept freely and easily.

Why fractional numbers?

Historians tell us that many of our mathematical advances have been the result of intellectual curiosity. The invention of fractional numbers, however, resulted from the recognition of a practical need, together with the mathematicians desire for completeness. The need for fractions arose from problems requiring division. In working with division, man soon discovered that many natural situations arise in which it is not feasible to divide one whole number by another and get a whole number result. For example, with only the set of whole numbers available, there is no whole number such that $n = 1 \div 2$ or such that $2 \times n = 1$.

The whole numbers are inadequate for solving various measurement situations calling for subdivision of the unit of measure. Man's search for an extension of number that would make division and measurement or the relative comparison between any two sets always possible produced numbers of a new kind—rational numbers (commonly called fractional numbers or fractions) represented by fraction symbols or fraction numerals.

A fraction number is expressed by an ordered pair of whole numbers (a, b), or, written in simplest form, one whole number over the other with a line or bar between them, $\frac{a}{b}$, a/b with $b \neq 0$.

The term *fraction* is derived from the Latin *fractio* or *frangere* "to break." It is little wonder, then, that for many years people considered fractions as "broken numbers." In a fraction number named by the form a/b, the b is called the denominator and the a is called the numerator. The term *denominator* is derived from the Latin *denominatus* "to nominate" or "to name" and names the fractional part under consideration. The term *numerator* is derived from the Latin *numeratus* "to count" and counts or tells the number of named parts under consideration. For example, if we substitute for a/b the ordered pair of whole numbers 2/3, the denominator (3) names the part under consideration—thirds. The numerator (2) shows how many thirds are under consideration—two. The number name, therefore, for the form 2/3 is two thirds.

Fractional number meanings

Fractions can be interpreted in several ways to communicate or to interpret quantitative ideas derived from the physical world. Teachers have a responsibility to help the pupil interpret the meaning of fractions in terms of the situation in which the fraction is used.

Most mathematicians and educators agree that by the time a student finishes the elementary school he should be able to interpret and use fractions in terms of the following concepts.

1. A fraction may represent an equal part or equal parts into which a whole object or figure has been divided. This is

probably the most familiar interpretation of fractions. For example, if a candy bar has been cut into three parts each the same size and the parts are distributed to three boys, each boy would have one third (1/3) of the original object.

2. A fraction may be used to refer to one or more of the equal parts of a collection or to a particular subset of a given set of objects. In this respect a boy might say, "I sold 1/3 of my stamp collection." A girl might be using a recipe that calls for 1/2 dozen eggs.

3. A fraction can be used to represent a division of any whole number (0, 1, 2, 3, 4, . . .) by any counting number (1, 2, 3, 4, . . .). The example $1 \div 3$ means one divided by three or 1/3. A solution to $5 \div 3$ is 5/3 or 1 2/3. Sometimes a fraction may represent the actual quotient of two numbers, $5/1 = 5$ or $15/3 = 5$. In other words, the numerals 5/1, 15/3, and 5 name the same number. The fraction form indicates a division of two integers, the number above the bar being the dividend and the number below the bar representing the divisor. Thus $a \div b = c$ if and only if $b \times c = a$. There will always be a c if b, the denominator or divisor, is not zero.

4. A fraction may express a comparison or ratio. This idea of fractions is a part of children's everyday conversation. No doubt you have heard children say, "I am one half as tall as my dad" or "I can run twice as fast as David." If Johnny is 3 feet tall and his dad is 6 feet tall, by comparing the two heights we get the ratio 3 to 6 or the fraction $3/6 = 1/2$. If it takes Johnny 10 seconds to run 100 yards and it takes David 20 seconds to run the same distance, by comparing the two speeds, we get the ratio 10 to 20 or the fraction 1/2. It takes Johnny one half as long as David to run 100 yards; therefore he runs twice as fast as David.

Developing fraction meanings

In the primary grades we strive with great care and diligence to ensure that children develop an understanding of whole numbers so that they are able to associate a name (four) with the word (four), with a symbol (4), with a quantitative meaning—a set of four objects (x x x x). Care is taken to be certain that children learn the relationship of particular whole number symbols, names, and quantitative meanings. The meaning and relationship of fractions need to be developed with the same precision and regard for detail.

In helping youngsters develop meaningful concepts of fractions and effective skills in operation with them, we need to utilize a three-step interrelated process. The three steps are readiness, understanding, and practice. The steps are not new, but teachers are taking a new look at the way in which they perceive children handling these steps to success with fractions. We know that some pupils have already taken the first step, readiness, before we see them. Others are ready to take one or another of the steps and would do so with a little encouragement. Still others either try to take the steps too rapidly or they are encouraged to take them too rapidly, thereby losing their balance. These pupils need to feel free to drop back to the step where they can stand on their own. At this point teachers need to help them build competence and confidence to move successfully forward again.

Teacher experience and research study indicate that the emphasis in the early school years should be on helping the child develop fraction concepts related to fraction terminology rather than on exercises concerned with fraction symbols and operations. Let us explore a variety of classroom approaches in developing the understandings needed to use the fraction concept meaningfully and effectively in terms of the four interpretations of fractions discussed earlier.

Equal parts of an object or of a collection of objects.   Children need many concrete experiences of seeing and dealing with fractional parts of real things before the abstract symbols for fractions are introduced. Teachers need to take advantage of the many situations that arise daily in relating meanings of fractions to the experiences of youngsters. Since most children enter school with some understanding of "half," probably the first fraction concept to develop is the relationship of parts to the whole. Some early school experiences that lend themselves to helping children develop a correct and meaningful concept of one half are as follows. We shall each have a half-pint of milk this morning. Half of the buses will leave at noon. You may give half of your cookie to Bill. We shall have music for half an hour. Here are six pieces of drawing paper, Sue; come and take one half of them. We shall divide the class equally into two groups for this game.

Rarely has a kindergarten teacher been in a classroom very long before she hears a child complain "Johnny's half is bigger than mine." When a child makes this complaint he is ready for and needs help in understanding there are no bigger or smaller halves. When we speak of one half, we are talking about one of the *two equal parts* into which an object or a collection of objects has been divided. Fractions are not easy for children to understand. In most schools, involvement of children with concrete materials and visual aids is not continued long enough. Although effective learning materials and teaching techniques are known, many children are taught that $1/2 + 1/2 = 1$ whole before they have a good understanding of what halves mean. Two halves must refer to the same *unit* or like units of measure and be *equal* to each other before we can combine them into any meaningful whole. For example, a sheet of notebook paper may be cut into two equal parts and each labeled 1/2 to show their relationship to the whole sheet of paper. Likewise a chalkboard may be separated into two equal parts by drawing a chalk line through the center of the board. Each of these parts may rightly be labeled 1/2. However, combining 1/2 sheet of notebook paper with 1/2 of the chalk board would not result in a whole unit of any comprehensible nature.

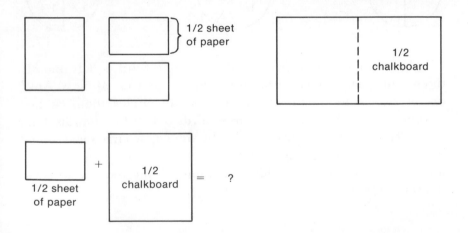

Teachers need to assist pupils to discover many ways to determine if two fractional parts are equal. For example, two halves may be equal with regard to size, shape, weight, value, area, volume, and so forth. Children need many experiences with fractional number concepts and terminology before beginning to work with symbols that represent a fraction.

Geometric regions — squares, rectangles, circles — are often used in the early elementary grades to develop the meanings of 1/2, 1/4, and 1/3. For example, if the unit region [   ] is separated into two congruent parts 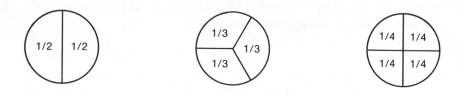 the shaded part is one half of the unit. Children should be encouraged to compare the shaded part with the unshaded part to determine if they are the same size and shape. If the two parts are congruent, either part represents 1/2 of the unit. The concept of 1/2 can be meaningfully developed by presenting situations requiring children to separate various unit regions and concrete objects into two parts and checking to determine if the two parts are equal in terms of size, shape, or area. A similar approach should be used to help children develop meaning for one fourth and one third.

Experiences with naming whole units in terms of equal parts provide an excellent opportunity to develop the concept "many names for one."

One half equals one of two equal parts; one third equals one of three equal parts; one fourth equals one of four equal parts. Any *one* of the whole units represented above by circles, then, can be renamed as two halves 2/2, or three thirds 3/3, or four fourths 4/4.

These fraction concepts can also be shown on a fractional number line. The making of a fraction number line can be an effective learning experience for children. A number line like the following should be familiar.

Pupils should know that the whole numbers show three equal units of length. Let us take the whole number unit on the line from 0 to 1 and subdivide it into two equal parts, three equal parts, and four equal parts, naming each division.

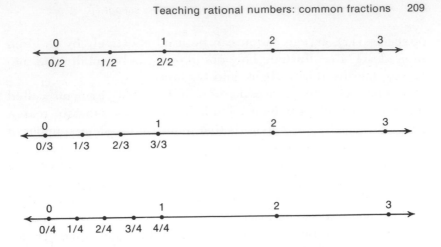

To determine if fractions are equal with reference to volume or weight, pint, quart, and gallon plastic containers can be used effectively in the classroom. Using sand or water, pupils discover that it requires the contents of two pint containers to fill one quart container, or eight pints to make one gallon, or four quarts to equal one gallon. Thus children observe that a pint is 1/2 quart or 1/8 gallon; a quart is 1/4 gallon.

Young children often hear adults use the terms quarter and half in talking about money and time. These fraction terms can be clarified by providing school experiences that relate half-dollar and quarter to the basic unit—one dollar, with a *value* of 100 cents. A quarter (25 cents) is *equal* to one fourth the *value* of a dollar and a half-dollar (50 cents) is *equal in value* to one-half dollar (100 cents).

Similarly, children need to relate the lengths of time—quarter hour (15 minutes) and half hour (30 minutes) to one hour (60 minutes). We can call a 15-minute period of time 1/4 hour because it would take four 15-minute lengths of time to equal one hour. Two lengths of time each 30 minutes long equal one hour; therefore 30 minutes equal one-half (1/2) hour.

Teachers can take advantage of children's daily experiences of living to help them learn how to deal with fractional parts of a collection of objects. Most stores stock a variety of items that are commonly packaged as a unit collection. For instance, eggs are usually purchased in a carton with a label "one dozen." Inspection of the carton reveals individual spaces for 12 eggs. By considering the relationship of one or more of these spaces to the total number of spaces (12), an egg carton can be used effectively by children in grades 1–4 to illustrate how one dozen can be subdivided into halves, fourths, thirds, sixths, and twelfths.

A one-foot ruler is a collection of 12 equal segments called inches. A foot ruler can be used to help children see that the reason we call six inches "1/2 foot" is that there are the same number of equal segments (inches) to the left of six as to the right of six.

A package of popular chewing gum might be opened to reveal six equal pieces of gum. The teacher can ask children to show her the number of pieces of gum that represents 1/2 the package, 1/3 the package, and 1/6 the package.

A more appropriate illustration for middle and upper grades could be to picture 16 objects, arranged in four columns with 4 objects in each column on a piece of cardboard approximately 24 inches square. Provide pieces of string and ask the students to illustrate 1/4 of the objects, 1/2 of the objects, 1/8 of the objects, and 1/16 of the objects. Ask children to explain the meaning of each fraction as it is illustrated.

Students who have had many experiences with separating a single object or a collection of objects into congruent parts have a basis for understanding, when they deal with fraction symbols, that the number below the bar names the equal parts into which a unit (or like units) has been divided. Such experiences also make it easier for children to sense that "the more the parts, the smaller each part." Therefore, when dealing with unit fractions, a person is not likely to think 1/4 larger than 1/3 or 1/3 larger than 1/2.

An unperformed division or a quotient of two numbers. In middle and upper grades there are many instances where fractions are utilized to show totals equal to or greater than one whole unit or one whole collection. Textbooks usually refer to fractions having numerators equal to or larger than the denominators, such as 2/2, 12/4, 6/3, and 5/2, as representing an unperformed division or the quotient of two numbers. Such fractions may be further refined by the student. For instance, if we divide the numerator of each of these fractions by the denominator, each fraction may be renamed: $2/2 = 1$, $12/4 = 3$, $6/3 = 2$, and $5/2 = 2\frac{1}{2}$.

Money situations involving, for example, four or more quarters can be used to illustrate how fractions expressed as unperformed division may be encountered and handled.

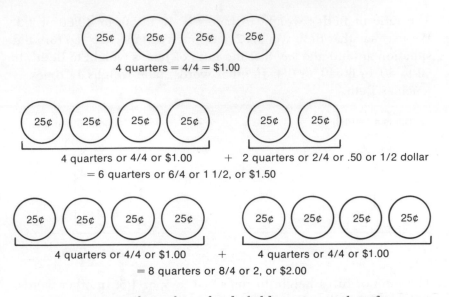

4 quarters = 4/4 = $1.00

4 quarters or 4/4 or $1.00   +   2 quarters or 2/4 or .50 or 1/2 dollar

= 6 quarters or 6/4 or 1 1/2, or $1.50

4 quarters or 4/4 or $1.00   +   4 quarters or 4/4 or $1.00

= 8 quarters or 8/4 or 2, or $2.00

Experiences such as these lead children to see that if we consider the numerator as the dividend and the denominator as the divisor, the division process may be performed so that 4/4 = 1, 6/4 = 1½, and 8/4 = 2.

A comparison or ratio. Numerous situations arise during the everyday activities of a school year that can be utilized to illustrate the use of fractions in expressing a comparison or a ratio. Teachers can take advantage of the verbal expressions relating to comparisons often used during "weighing and measuring" time to help pupils utilize the concepts in symbolic representation. For instance,

Beth weighs 40 pounds

40 pounds

Jane weighs 60 pounds

60 pounds

The ratio of Beth's weight to Jane's is 40 to 60, or 40/60 or 2/3. We may say that Beth weighs 2/3 as much as Jane. We can turn the situation around and say that the ratio of Jane's weight to Beth's is 60 to 40, or 60/40, or 6/4. In other words, Jane weighs 1½ times as much as Beth.

Bill is 4 feet tall   Jon is 5 feet tall

The ratio of Bill's height to Jon's is 4 to 5, or 4/5. In other words, Bill is 4/5 as tall as Jon.

The physical education teacher may be checking to see how many push-ups the boys in your class can do. Tom did 10 push-ups and Joe did 5 push-ups. By utilizing fractions in comparing the number of push-ups, the pupils should be able to express the result either as "Joe did 1/2 as many as Tom" or "Tom did twice as many as Joe."

Children like to compare their age with someone else's age. If Mary is 9 years old and Sue is 12 years old, the ratio of Mary's age to Sue's is 9 to 12 or 9/12. In other words, Mary is 3/4 as old as Sue. John may say he is 1/3 as old as his father meaning he is 10 years old and his father is 30 years old. John might like to determine the fraction that would express the ratio of his age to his father's age 10 years later when he is 20 and his father is 40.

The everyday usage of fractions is often vague, indeterminate, and even erroneous. Instead of allowing such usage to serve as a deterrent to children's understandings, teachers can turn the situation into a creative learning experience. Upper-grade children find it both enjoyable and instructive to discuss and interpret the meanings of fractions as they are used in various situations, expressions, and phrases. For instance, what does the statement "I've half a mind to turn you over my knee and spank you" mean? Does it mean the person's mind is divided into two parts and one part says spank, or does it mean the ratio of my chances of getting spanked is about one in two? When you see the newspaper head-line "Hilltop's Tigers Rip Newschool's Bobcats in Half," what does it mean to you? What does the radio announcer mean when he says "Roger just missed getting a home run by a fraction."

If fractions are going to be useful in solving many everyday problems, we must help children to understand the true meanings of fractions and how to apply these meanings realistically to vary-ing situations.

Comparing fractions

When studying the set of whole numbers, children developed the idea of betweenness, greater than, less than, and equivalence or many names for the same number. These are also useful concepts to develop with fractional numbers. In the early stages of develop-ing these concepts, pupils should work with concrete materials.

Regions divided into fractional parts assist pupils to discover that 1/4 is smaller than 1/3 and that 1/3 is smaller than 1/2. Select different colored material to use on flannel board and cut square pieces all the same size. Ask children to leave the white square intact, cut the red into halves, the yellow into thirds, and the blue into fourths. Then have a pupil place one of the red fractional parts to cover 1/2 of the white square; next place a yellow 1/3 over the red and a blue 1/4 over the yellow.

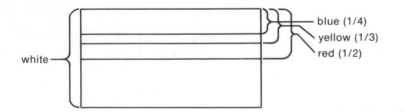

The experience should lead to the conclusion that of the three frac-tions named, 1/2 is the largest, 1/4 is the smallest, and 1/3 is be-tween 1/4 and 1/2.

Using like circular regions with a different fractional part shaded on each, a good learning experience is to arrange the fractions to illustrate the order of size from the smallest to the largest as 1/6, 1/5, 1/4, 1/3, and 1/2.

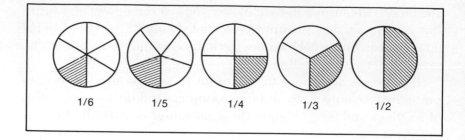

Unit fractions so arranged show that the more parts the whole is divided into, the smaller will be the parts. This understanding is important in recognizing that if two fractions have the same numerator, the fraction that has the largest denominator is the smallest.

A fraction chart is helpful in developing the ability to compare and order fractions in terms of size. For example, 1/8 < 1/6 < 1/5 < 1/4 < 1/3 < 1/2.

Fraction Chart

1 whole							
1/2				1/2			
1/3		1/3			1/3		
1/4		1/4		1/4		1/4	
1/5		1/5	1/5		1/5		1/5
1/6		1/6	1/6		1/6	1/6	1/6
1/8	1/8	1/8	1/8	1/8	1/8	1/8	1/8

This type of chart can also be used effectively by children to discover equivalent fractions. By placing a pencil (or some type of straightedge) along the left margin of the chart and then moving the pencil across the chart, a child can determine corresponding lines that partition like regions into fractional parts. For instance, when the pencil is aligned on two or more partitioning lines, the child can check to see which fractional parts are equivalent. As he moves from left to right, the pupil should discover that 1/4 = 2/8, 1/3 = 2/6, 1/2 = 2/4 = 3/6 = 4/8, 2/3 = 4/6, and 3/4 = 6/8.

Studying the fractional parts on the commonly used foot ruler that has inch segments divided into sixteenths should help children see that other names for 1/2 are 2/4, 4/8, and 8/16. This experience can later be extended to the yardstick — that 1 yard equals 3 feet, or 36 inches; 1 foot = 1/3 or 12/36 yard; and 2 feet = 2/3 or 24/36 yard.

Knowing that a multiple fraction is composed of a number of unit fractions is useful in comparing fractions with like denominators. Study the following number line, which has been divided into fourths.

If we count the fourths, 1/4, 2/4, 3/4, 4/4, 5/4, and so forth, it is easy to see that, for example, 5/4 is really 1/4 + 1/4 + 1/4 + 1/4 + 1/4. If two fractions have the same denominator, the fraction that has the greater numerator has the greater value.

By observing that the number to the right on the above number line is greater than the number to its left, it is easy to see that 3/4 > 2/4 > 1/4 or 1/4 < 2/4 < 3/4. Because 2/4 is greater than 1/4 and less than 3/4, we say 2/4 is between 1/4 and 3/4.

Following experiences such as these, a good idea is to present several sets of fractions and ask which are sets of equivalent fractions and which are not.

$$A = \{1/2,\ 2/4,\ 4/8,\ 8/16\} \qquad D = \{1/5,\ 2/10,\ 4/20,\ 8/40\}$$
$$B = \{1/3,\ 2/6,\ 4/12,\ 8/24\} \qquad E = \{1/2,\ 2/4,\ 4/12,\ 8/32\}$$
$$C = \{1/4,\ 2/8,\ 3/16,\ 8/24\} \qquad F = \{2/3,\ 6/9,\ 18/27,\ 54/81\}$$

Each fraction in set A names the same fractional number; therefore A can be called a set of equivalent fractions. For the same reason, B, D, and F are sets of equivalent fractions.

A close observation of the fractions from left to right and from right to left in sets A, B, D, and F should assist pupils to *discover* two important ideas in working with fractions:

If the numerator and denominator of a given fraction are both multiplied by the same counting number, the resulting fraction and the given fraction represent the same fractional number.

If the numerator and the denominator of a given fraction are both divided by the same counting number, the resulting fraction and the given fraction represent the same fractional number.

In the upper grades, teachers may wish to encourage pupils to use the cross-products test to determine if two fractions name the same number. Do 8/12 and 18/27 name the same number?

$$8 \times 27 = 12 \times 18$$
$$\frac{8}{12} = \frac{18}{27}$$
$$216 = 216$$

The products are equal; therefore 8/12 and 18/27 are equivalent fractions. For any two given fractions x/y and a/d, if $x \times d = y \times a$, then $x/y = a/d$.

Place the correct sign $<$ or $>$ between the fractions in the following sets.

$$\frac{1}{3} \square \frac{1}{5} \qquad \frac{1}{6} \square \frac{1}{4}$$

$$\frac{1}{2} \square \frac{1}{4} \qquad \frac{3}{4} \square \frac{2}{3}$$

$$\frac{2}{3} \square \frac{1}{2} \qquad \frac{2}{3} \square \frac{3}{6}$$

Supply the missing equivalent fraction in the following sets.

{1/2, 2/4, 4/8, , 16/32}
{1/4, 2/8, , 8/32, 16/64}
{1/3, , 9/27, 27/81, 81/243}
{2/3, 4/6, 8/12, , 32/48}
{1/3, 4/12, , 64/192, 256/768}

Factors, primes, and common denominators

Many addition and subtraction situations involving fractions require finding the common denominator. Prior to instruction in determining the common denominator, teachers find it profitable to *review* and *extend* children's understanding of *factors* and *primes*. Children should have many opportunities and experiences to develop ideas of prime numbers, common multiples, and common divisors of whole numbers before they are asked to apply the ideas in working with common fractions. Problems and exercises involving these concepts can be an integral part of their mathematics program soon after they have established the basic multiplication facts. For a detailed description of how to determine prime numbers and ways of expressing composite numbers as products of prime numbers, see Chapter 6.

Greatest common factor. In dealing with fractions, the GCF (greatest common factor) or the GCD (greatest common divisor) is often used. Two frequently used means of determining the GCF or GCD are (1) formulating the set of *all factors* for each number and selecting the greatest factor in the intersection set and (2) formulating the set of *prime factors* for each number and selecting the factors common to each set.

What is the greatest GCF or GCD of 18 and 24?

The factors of 18 are $A = \{1, 2, 3, 6, 9, 18\}$. The factors of 24 are $B = \{1, 3, 4, 6, 8, 24\}$. $A \cap B = C\{1, 3, 6\}$. The GCF or GCD of 18 and 24 is 6.

Complete factorization may also be used to find the GCF or GCD of 18 and 24:

$$18 = \{3 \times 2 \times 3\} \qquad 24 = \{2 \times 2 \times 2 \times 3\}$$

By inspection we find that 2 and 3 are common to both sets of prime factors. In the prime factorization of 18 the factor 2 appears only once, and in the prime factorization of 24 the factor 3 appears only once. The GCF or GCD is found by taking the prime factors the minimum number of times they appear and computing their product. Thus (2×3) or 6 is the GCF or GCD of 18 and 24.

Sometimes we wish to express a fraction in its simplest form. Let us consider the fraction 18/24. We have just learned that the greatest number by which both 18 and 24 can be divided is 6, $\frac{18 \div 6}{24 \div 6} = \frac{3}{4}$. Both 18/24 and 3/4 name the same number. If we desire to change the fractions 4/8, 3/9, 12/15, and 10/25 into simplest form, we divide both the numerator and denominator by the GCF. The GCF of 4 and 8 is 4, $\frac{4 \div 4}{8 \div 4} = \frac{1}{2}$. The GCF of 3 and 9 is 3, $\frac{3 \div 3}{9 \div 3} = \frac{1}{3}$. The GCF of 12 and 15 is 3, $\frac{12 \div 3}{15 \div 3} = \frac{4}{5}$. The GCF of 10 and 25 is 5,

$\frac{10 \div 5}{25 \div 5} = \frac{2}{5}$. The numbers $\frac{4}{4}$, $\frac{3}{3}$, and $\frac{5}{5}$ have been used as divisors. Each of these numbers can be renamed as 1, the identity number of multiplication. After working several examples similar to these, children should arrive at the generalization that both the numerator and denominator of a fraction can be divided by a common factor without changing the value of the original fraction.

Least common multiple.   Common multiples and least common multiples are useful concepts in finding common denominators and least common denominators in adding and subtracting fractions. Multiples of a number are products resulting from multiplying the number by other numbers. Multiples of 3 would be {6, 9, 12, 15, . . .}. Children should be helped to see that all multiples in the above set would be evenly divisible by 3.

After children have listed sets of multiples for several numbers, ask if anyone can find a multiple that is common to two or more of the sets. Consider the following sets of the first six multiples of

2: {2, 4, 6, 8, 10, 12}
4: {4, 8, 12, 16, 20, 24}
3: {3, 6, 9, 12, 15, 18}
6: {6, 12, 18, 24, 30, 36}
5: {5, 10, 15, 20, 25, 30}
10: {10, 20, 30, 40, 50, 60}

Note that 4, 8, and 12 are common multiples of 2 and 4. Are there other numbers that have a common multiple? Yes, 6, 12, and 18 are common multiples of 3 and 6. We also find that 10, 20, and 30 are common multiples of 5 and 10. Because a multiple of a number can be divided evenly by that number, a common multiple is evenly divisible by all numbers of which it is a multiple.

After we have found a set of common multiples, the least common multiple is relatively easy to determine. If {4, 8, 12} is a set of common multiples for 2 and 4, the least common multiple is 4. If {6, 12, 18} is a set of common multiples for 3 and 6, the least common multiple is 6. What is the least common multiple for 5 and 10; 3 and 4; 2, 3, and 8?

The least common multiple and the least common denominator are analogous because in both cases we are concerned with the smallest counting number in the set of common multiples. Since we have made this association, other ways of finding the LCM or LCD will be discussed at this point, although we recognize that the most opportune time in an elementary school program to teach the finding of a common denominator or the least common denominator is when children are faced with solving a problem involving the addition of fractions.

Another way to find the LCM or LCD is prime factorization. For example, to find the LCM or LCD of 10, 6, and 16, first completely factor each number:

$10 = 2 \times 5$
$6 = 2 \times 3$ or use factor trees
$16 = 2 \times 2 \times 2 \times 2$

Second, use each prime factor the maximum number of times it appears in any one of the factorizations — 2 appears four times as a factor of 16, 3 appears once as a factor of 6, and 5 appears once as a factor of 10. The factorization of the LCM or LCD would be $2 \times 2 \times 2 \times 2 \times 3 \times 5$.

Third, find the product of these prime factors. $2 \times 2 \times 2 \times 2 \times 3 \times 5 = 240$, the LCM or LCD of 10, 6, and 16.

The LCM of several numbers may be found through a series of divisions, using 2 as a divisor until it is no longer a factor of one of the numbers. When 2 no longer works, use successive primes as a divisor until the product of the numbers in the quotient is a prime number. The product of the quotient and the divisors is the LCM. For example, the LCM of 6, 21, 3, 8 can be found by

	6	21	3	8
2	3	21	3	4
2	3	21	3	2
2	3	21	3	1
3	1	7	1	1

$2 \times 2 \times 2 \times 3 \times 7 = 168$, the LCM of 6, 21, 3, and 8.

Using one of the methods described, find the LCM of each pair of numbers.

8, 18	5, 25	3, 8, 14
15, 27	6, 21	24, 36, 9

Knowledge of prime numbers and prime factors is essential in understanding Greatest Common Divisor and Least Common Multiple; concepts needed to develop competency in operations on fractions.

Operations on fractions

Before pupils begin an organized program of adding, subtracting, multiplying, and dividing fractions, a good background of experiences in developing meaningful concepts of fractions should be provided. This has not been characteristic of past programs of instruction in elementary school. Although historically "practice" in use of fractions has probably been the least neglected step in teaching fractions, concentration on the development of readiness and understanding in current programs should not be stressed to the neglect of practice. Children need to be given time and situations in which to apply their knowledge and understanding. The suggested approach offered for helping children understand and build competence in the fundamental operations of fractions is built upon previous learning experiences discussed in this book. We believe the following prerequisite learnings are important for the study of operations on fractions.

1. Readiness for and understanding of the concept of fractional parts.
2. Knowledge of what abstract symbols for fractions mean.
3. Understanding of the basic fraction ideas such as numerator, denominator, unit fraction, like and unlike fraction, and equivalent fractions.
4. Knowledge of what is meant by primes, factors, and multiples.
5. Possession of competence in operations on whole numbers and the basic facts associated with these operations.

The need for developing more unifying principles or continuity of meaning in elementary school mathematics has been emphasized repeatedly. Let us explore how to help the child recognize that principles involved in operations on fractions are closely related to principles of operation on whole numbers.

Addition of fractions.   Pupils know from past experience that addition is a binary operation. We also add two fractions at a time. When we add 2 and 3 to get a sum of 5, we are adding 2 ones and 3 ones to get 5 ones, $2 + 3 = 5$. We add 4 tens and 3 tens to get 7 tens, $40 + 30 = 70$. In both cases we are observing the *principle of likeness*. We are adding whole numbers of like place value.

The same principle applies to the addition of fractions. Instead of adding whole numbers of "like" decimal value, we add "like parts" of units such as thirds, fourths, and ninths. Like fractions are those that have like denominators. The position of the digit (place value) tells what kind of whole numbers are being added. The denominator tells what kind of fractions are added.

Instruction should start with experiences that are familiar to children and move forward as rapidly as learning can occur effectively. The addition algorithms such as $1/4 + 1/4 = 2/4$ or $1/2$; $1/3 + 1/3 = 2/3$; and $1/4 + 2/4 = 3/4$ become meaningful if they are associated with children's past experiences with fourths and thirds using concrete models. Then move to illustrations such as the following:

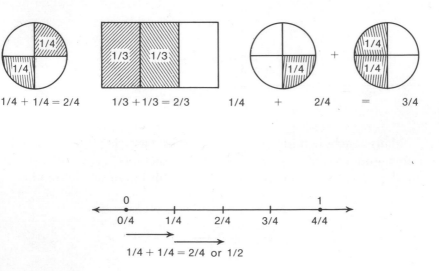

$1/4 + 1/4 = 2/4$ $1/3 + 1/3 = 2/3$ $1/4$ + $2/4$ = $3/4$

$1/4 + 1/4 = 2/4$ or $1/2$

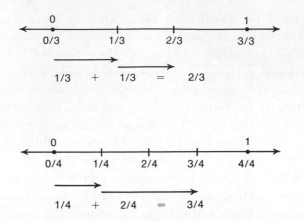

In the addition operation on fractions, the pupil should perceive each fraction in the algorithm as an addend in the same way he saw whole numbers as addends when adding whole numbers. The use of concrete models along with the algorithm in beginning addition should help the pupil to understand that the denominators name the equal size parts to be added and the numerators tell how many of those parts are represented in each fraction. This should lead to the following generalization: When adding two or more fractions, the denominator in the sum will be the common denominator of the fractions and the numerator will be the sum of all the numerators to be added.
Thus

$$\frac{1}{5} + \frac{3}{5} = \frac{1+3}{5} = \frac{4}{5}$$

$$\frac{1}{6} + \frac{4}{6} = \frac{1+4}{6} = \frac{5}{6}$$

$$\frac{5}{8} + \frac{7}{8} = \frac{5+7}{8} = \frac{12}{8}$$

Many teachers find that the number line assists pupils in developing understanding of addition with fractions, especially since children have used the number line in addition of whole numbers.

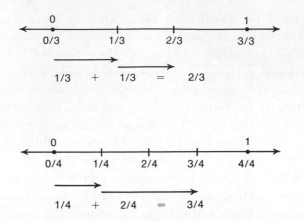

$\dfrac{2}{3} + \dfrac{1}{3} = \dfrac{3}{3}$ or 1 $\dfrac{1}{3} + \dfrac{2}{3} = \dfrac{3}{3}$ or 1

By locating the point labeled 2/3 and taking a jump of 1/3 to the right, we reach the point 3/3 or 1. If the commutative property is utilized, we can start at 1/3, take a jump of 2/3, and reach the point 3/3 or 1. Because the same point on the number line was reached in both operations, what might one conclude? The order in which fractions are added does not affect the sum: $1/3 + 2/3 = 2/3 + 1/3 = 3/3 = 1$.

Sometimes we need to find the sum of three or more fractions. Children learned that the associative property applied to addition of whole numbers; now let us determine if the property applies to addition of fractions. For example, to find the sum of $1/5 + 2/5 + 3/5$, the child may think $(1/5 + 2/5) + 3/5 = 3/5 + 3/5 = 6/5$. Or he may think $1/5 + (2/5 + 3/5) = 1/5 + 5/5 = 6/5$. After solving several examples using the two ways of grouping the addends, children should recognize that the associative property applies to addition of fractions in the same way it applies to addition of whole numbers.

Will the generalization about addition of fractions apply if you need to add fractions that do not have the same denominator? Yes, but before unlike fractions can be added a common or like denominator must be determined to express the fractions in like units. Suppose the need is to add $1/2 + 1/4$. From former work with equivalent fractions using charts or number lines, it is likely that most pupils will remember that another fraction name or form for 1/2 is 2/4. Then $1/2 + 1/4$ can be expressed as $2/4 + 1/4 = 3/4$.

Because much of the everyday computation involving fractions relates to 1/2, 1/4, and 1/3, children's knowledge of equivalent forms for these unit fractions can justifiably be reviewed and extended.

$$A = \{1/2 = 2/4 = 8/16 = 12/24 = 60/120\}$$
$$B = \{1/4 = 2/8 = 6/24 = 12/48 = 26/144\}$$
$$C = \{1/3 = 2/6 = 4/12 = 8/24 = 24/72 = 48/144\}$$

Because any fraction in set A is an equivalent form for 1/2 and any fraction in set B is an equivalent form for 1/4 and any fraction in set C is an equivalent form for 1/3, the addition example

$$1/2 + 1/3 + 1/4 = 12/24 + 6/24 + 8/24 = \frac{12 + 6 + 8}{24} = \frac{26}{24}$$

The common denominator for adding $1/2 + 1/3 + 1/4$ may also be determined by finding the set of common multiples for the denominators 2, 3, and 4. Any common multiple of the denominators of two or more fractions may be used as a common denominator in adding the fractions, but use of the least common denominator may make computation easier. See pages 218–220 for ways of finding the least common denominator.

When faced with the need to add mixed-form numbers, for instance, $2\frac{1}{3} + 3\frac{5}{6}$, there are two choices. The mixed-form numbers may be renamed as like fractions before beginning the addition.

$$2\frac{1}{3} + 3\frac{5}{6} = \frac{7}{3} + \frac{23}{6} = \frac{14}{6} + \frac{23}{6} = \frac{37}{6} = 6\frac{1}{6}$$

The addition also may be accomplished without changing the form of the addends.

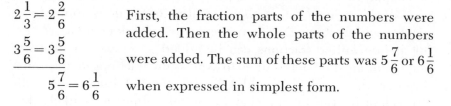

First, the fraction parts of the numbers were added. Then the whole parts of the numbers were added. The sum of these parts was $5\frac{7}{6}$ or $6\frac{1}{6}$ when expressed in simplest form.

Subtraction of fractions. Most elementary school programs introduce the subtraction of fractions at the same time they introduce addition of fractions, or shortly thereafter. Subtraction of fractions is taught in a sequence and through methods very similar to addition of fractions. As discussed and illustrated earlier in this chapter, we can add only like fractions. Also, we can subtract only like fractions. The method of operation in the subtraction algorithm differs only in that numerators are subtracted rather than added.

Teaching the addition and subtraction of like fractions together should assist children in understanding that "subtraction is the inverse of addition" applies to fractions. A fraction chart or number line can be used to illustrate that $1/4 + 1/4 = 2/4$ or $1/2$ and $1/2 - 1/4 = 2/4 - 1/4$ or $1/4$.

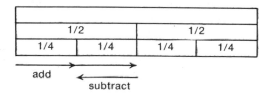

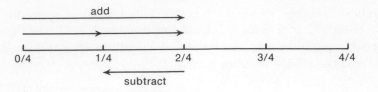

Depending upon the age level, have children use the number line or make drawings to illustrate the relation between addition and subtraction of fractions similar to the following:

$$2/3 + 1/3 = 3/3 \qquad 3/3 - 1/3 = 2/3$$
$$3/7 + 5/7 = 8/7 \qquad 8/7 - 5/7 = 3/7$$
$$3/4 + 2/3 = 17/12 \qquad 17/12 - 2/3 = 3/4$$

The methods for changing or renaming unlike fractions to like fractions (common denominator) before beginning either the addition or subtraction operation are exactly the same. This is another reason for teaching the operations concurrently.

When subtracting mixed-form numbers where the subtrahend has a larger fractional part than the minuend, a new problem is encountered. Assume we need to complete the following subtraction:

$$5\frac{1}{4}$$
$$-2\frac{1}{2}$$

Remembering what has been learned about subtraction of fractions, the first step is to change the fractional parts to a common denominator. Then we have

$$5\frac{1}{4} = 5\frac{1}{4}$$
$$-2\frac{1}{2} = 2\frac{2}{4}$$

Before being able to subtract, $5\frac{1}{4}$ needs to be renamed or expressed in another form. Applying to mixed-form numbers what we know about decomposition method in subtraction of whole numbers, another name for 5 is $4 + 1$ and another name for 1 is 4/4. Then $5\frac{1}{4}$, or $4 + 4/4 + 1/4$, can be renamed as $4\frac{5}{4}$ and the subtraction operation can be completed by subtracting the fractional part and the whole number part.

$$5\frac{1}{4} = 5\frac{1}{4} = 4\frac{5}{4}$$
$$-2\frac{1}{2} = 2\frac{2}{4} = 2\frac{2}{4}$$
$$\overline{\qquad\qquad\qquad 2\frac{3}{4}}$$

The preceding method for subtracting mixed-form numbers is preferred because it relates closely to the method generally used for subtracting whole numbers. However, this problem can be solved by changing both mixed-form numbers to fractional numbers with common denominators.

$$5\frac{1}{4} - 2\frac{1}{2} =$$
$$\frac{21}{4} - \frac{5}{2} =$$
$$\frac{21}{4} - \frac{10}{4} = \frac{11}{4} = 2\frac{3}{4}$$

Multiplication of fractions. Although all the properties that apply to multiplication of whole numbers also apply to multiplication of fractions, pupils experience much difficulty in recognizing continuity of meaning. Part of the difficulty stems from the fact that children, when dealing with multiplication of whole numbers, are accustomed to getting a product that is equal to or greater than either factor. When dealing with multiplication of fractional numbers, children soon discover the product may be less than either or both factors.

Multiplication of whole numbers such as $4 \times 2 = 8$ and $6 \times 3 = 18$ illustrates a "putting together" idea—2 was taken 4 times and 3 was taken 6 times. But the expressions $1/2 \times 6 = 3$ and $1/2 \times 1/2 = 1/4$ presents a contradiction, because they describe a "taking apart" idea. In fact, the above examples illustrate finding a part of a number rather than taking a number a given number of times.

For example, $1/2 \times 6 = 3$ indicates a division. The number 6 has been partitioned into two equal parts and the answer 3 represents one of the two equal parts or 1/2 of 6.

Multiplication of fractions involves three different kinds of problem situations—a fraction multiplied by a whole number, a whole number multiplied by a fraction and a fraction multiplied by a fraction—and each needs to be individually interpreted to give meaning to the multiplication algorithm commonly used with fractional numbers. The authors recognize that some of the newer mathematics for the elementary school develop the multiplication algorithm for fractions by starting with a fraction multiplied by a fraction and some good arguments can be made for this approach. Believing however, that it is important to help pupils view multiplication of fractions as a logical extension of multiplication of whole numbers, we recommend that multiplication of fractions begin with multiplying a fraction by a whole number, as $5 \times 1/2 = N$. Children have learned that a problem involving multiplication of whole numbers can be solved by repeated addition. Multiplication of a fraction by a whole number, for example, $5 \times 1/2$, also can be solved by repeated addition. $1/2 + 1/2 + 1/2 + 1/2 + 1/2 = 5/2 = 2\ 1/2$.

Several approaches may be used in developing meaning for $5 \times 1/2 = N$. For instance, the answer may be found from a number line or from unit regions partitioned into halves.

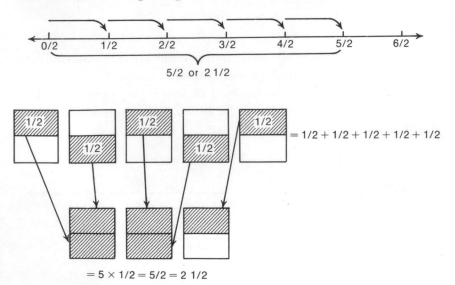

Children should explore ways of verifying answers to problem situations such as

1. A path 1/4 mile long is marked on the playground, how far will Jerry run if he makes six trips around the path?
2. Sue practiced playing the piano 1/2 hour today. How long will she practice if she practices the same length of time each day for 5 days?

From solving situations similar to those described, children should form the following generalization: To multiply a fraction by a whole number, multiply the whole number by the numerator and write the product over the denominator. If the numerator of the resulting fraction is greater than the denominator, the fraction may be renamed as a whole number or mixed-form number by dividing the numerator by the denominator.

A child may remember the commutative property from multiplication of whole numbers and may want to know if $6 \times \frac{1}{2} = N$ and $\frac{1}{2} \times 6 = N$ will result in the same product. If the pupil performs the computations correctly, he should get the same result:

$$6 \times \frac{1}{2} = \frac{6 \times 1}{2} = \frac{6}{2} = 3 \qquad \frac{1}{2} \times 6 = \frac{1 \times 6}{2} = \frac{6}{2} = 3$$

But the two equations describe two completely different problem situations as represented in the physical world. $6 \times \frac{1}{2}$ means $\frac{1}{2}$ taken 6 times. $\frac{1}{2} \times 6$ means taking $\frac{1}{2}$ of 6 or 6 partitioned into two equal parts. $\frac{1}{2} \times 6$ or $\frac{1}{2}$ of 6 may be illustrated on a number line as taking $\frac{1}{2}$ of a segment 6 units long.

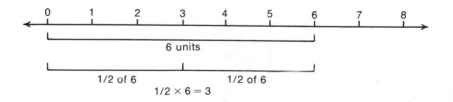

I have six candy bars and wish to give 1/2 of them to my friend; how many will I give my friend? $1/2 \times 6 = N$. The problem may be solved by separating a collection of six objects into two equal parts.

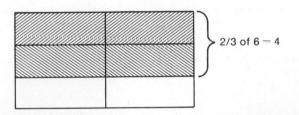

A unit square region may be partitioned into six equal parts and $2/3 \times 6 = 4$ shown by shading 4 of the subdivisions.

$$\left.\begin{array}{c}\end{array}\right\} \text{2/3 of 6 = 4}$$

After meaning for a whole number multiplied by a fraction has been established, the algorithm commonly used in computing the answer to this type of multiplication should be introduced and discussed.

$$\frac{1}{2} \times 6 = \frac{1 \times 6}{2} = \frac{6}{2} = 3$$

$$\frac{2}{3} \times 6 = \frac{2 \times 6}{3} = \frac{12}{3} = 4$$

Children should be helped to recognize that the algorithm applied to multiplying a fraction by a whole number also applies to multiplying a whole number by a fraction.

The third type of multiplication problem, a fraction times a fraction, is generally more difficult to understand than the two types already discussed. Early instruction in multiplying a fraction by a fraction should utilize drawings to develop meaning for the operation.

One way to illustrate $\frac{1}{4}$ of $\frac{1}{2}$ is

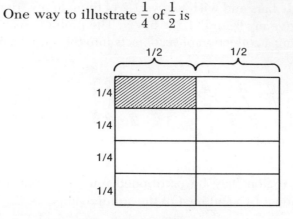

The shaded part represents $\frac{1}{4}$ of $\frac{1}{2}$ or $\frac{1}{8}$ of the unit square. $\frac{1}{4} \times \frac{1}{2} = \frac{1}{8}$.

Another problem, $\frac{3}{4}$ of $\frac{1}{2}$ can be shown as

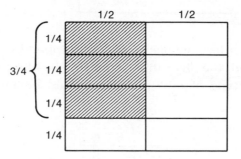

$\frac{3}{4}$ of $\frac{1}{2}$ is shaded or $\frac{3}{8}$ of the unit square is shaded: $\frac{3}{4} \times \frac{1}{2} = \frac{3}{8}$. Observation of the two algorithms should lead to the following discovery: When multiplying a fraction by a fraction, multiply the numerators and express the result over the product of the denominators. Thus

$$\frac{1}{4} \times \frac{1}{2} = \frac{1 \times 1}{4 \times 2} = \frac{1}{8} \qquad \frac{3}{4} \times \frac{1}{2} = \frac{3 \times 1}{4 \times 2} = \frac{3}{8}$$

The denominator shows the size of the new part and the numerator shows the number of these parts.

Division of fractions. Division of fractions as $6 \div \frac{1}{2} = 12$ appears to be a contradiction to the learner's past experiences with division of whole numbers. When a whole number was divided by another whole number other than 1, the quotient was always smaller than the dividend. In $6 \div \frac{1}{2} = 12$, the quotient is larger than the dividend; or, if using the product, known factor, unknown factor relation for division as being the inverse of multiplication, the unknown factor is larger than the product.

How can children be helped to determine that the answer to $6 \div \frac{1}{2}$ is sensible? Division of fractions should be related to division of whole numbers by solving and discussing several examples such as the following. Bobby had 12 marbles. He wished to give four friends an equal number of marbles. $12 \div 4 = 3$. The 3 answers the question "How many 4's are in 12?" In the previous example $6 \div \frac{1}{2} = 12$, the number 12 answers the question "How many $\frac{1}{2}$'s are there in 6?" When division of a whole number by a fraction is thought of in this way, an answer larger than the number to be divided makes sense.

In division of fractions, there are three kinds of situations: (1) a whole number divided by a fraction, (2) a fraction divided by a whole number, and (3) a fraction divided by a fraction. Beginning instruction with a whole number divided by a fraction helps children use what they already know about fractions and the operations on whole numbers. A problem situation such as "How many persons can be served with three grapefruits if each person is to be served $\frac{1}{2}$ of a grapefruit?" will provide a good introduction. Solutions to the problem can be shown with drawings.

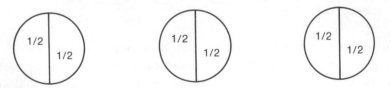

Each of the grapefruits is divided into halves, making a total of six halves. The above problem could be solved by completing a series of subtractions.

3

$-\dfrac{1}{2}$

$2\dfrac{1}{2}$

$-\dfrac{1}{2}$

2

$-\dfrac{1}{2}$

$1\dfrac{1}{2}$ By counting how many times we subtracted,

$-\dfrac{1}{2}$ we can determine how many $\dfrac{1}{2}$'s are in 3.

1 $3 \div \dfrac{1}{2} = 6.$

$-\dfrac{1}{2}$

$\dfrac{1}{2}$

$-\dfrac{1}{2}$

0

Mary uses $\dfrac{1}{2}$ sheet of paper in making a valentine; how many valentines of the same size can she make from three sheets of paper? Again the problem may be defined as $3 \div \dfrac{1}{2} = N$. The solution may be pictured on a number line. $3 \div \dfrac{1}{2} = 6.$

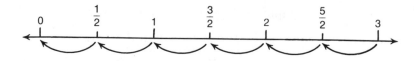

Starting at the point marked 3, it took 6 one-halves to return to the point of origin. Division of fractions as the inverse of multiplication of fractions can also be illustrated by starting at 0 and determining that it requires 6 one-halves to reach 3 on the number lines. A child can use this procedure to check his division of fractions.

Division of a fraction by a whole number means finding a part and can be meaningfully introduced through a problem situation involving the partition idea of division. Consider the problem, "If three boys wish to share equally $\frac{1}{2}$ of a pie, what part of the pie would each get?" Drawings should help pupils think "one half divided into three equal parts" or "what is one third of one half?"

A fraction chart is also an effective means of helping children visualize the size part that results from dividing $\frac{1}{2}$ by 3.

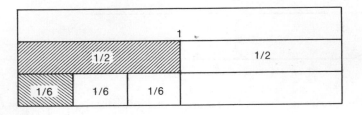

The solution to the problem, as shown by the drawings, is that each boy would get $\frac{1}{6}$ of the pie.

A number line may also be used to illustrate $\frac{1}{2} \div 3 = \frac{1}{6}$.

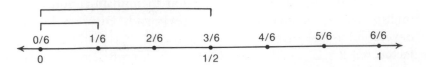

A fraction divided by a fraction can be made meaningful by using the measurement idea of division on a number line, a ruler, or through drawings. The example $\frac{3}{4} \div \frac{1}{2} = \square$ asks how many one-halves are in three fourths. A drawing may be used to show the problem and the solution.

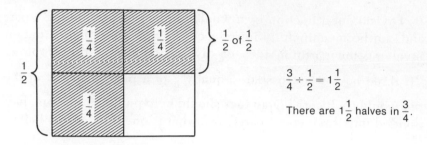

$$\frac{1}{2} \text{ of } \frac{1}{2}$$

$$\frac{3}{4} \div \frac{1}{2} = 1\frac{1}{2}$$

There are $1\frac{1}{2}$ halves in $\frac{3}{4}$.

How many pieces of ribbon $\frac{1}{8}$ yard long can be cut from a piece of ribbon $\frac{3}{4}$ yard long?

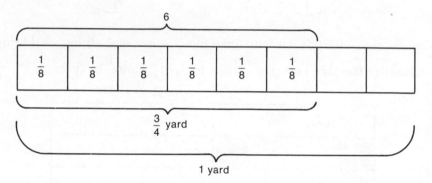

The drawing shows there are 6 one-eighths in $\frac{3}{4}$: $\frac{3}{4} \div \frac{1}{8} = 6$.

Algorithms for division operation

After meaning for division of fractions has been developed through problem situations using concrete materials and drawings, an algorithm for dividing should be introduced and discussed. At this point the relationship of division to multiplication and the multiplicative identity should be reviewed. Division has been developed as the inverse of multiplication or as finding a missing factor. $6 \div 2 = \square$ can be rewritten as $2 \times \square = 6$. $2 \times 3 = 6$; therefore $6 \div 2 = 3$. The example $6 \div \frac{1}{2} = \square$ can be rewritten as $\frac{1}{2} \times \square = 6$. $\frac{1}{2} \times 12 = 6$; therefore $6 \div \frac{1}{2} = 12$. We also remember that the multiplicative identity or the identity element for multiplication is 1. Any given nonzero whole number multiplied by 1 is the given whole number. We also remember that any given nonzero whole number divided by 1 results in the given whole number. One (1) has many names for example, $\frac{2}{2}, \frac{3}{3}, \frac{4}{4}, \frac{5}{5}, \frac{6}{6}$ and so forth. The above ideas were used when changing a fraction to an equivalent form. For instance $\frac{1}{2} \times \frac{4}{4} = \frac{1 \times 4}{2 \times 4} = \frac{4}{8}$ $\frac{4}{8} \div \frac{4}{4} = \frac{4 \div 4}{8 \div 4} = \frac{1}{2}$. The value of a fraction is unchanged if both terms of the fraction are multiplied or divided by the same number.

Now let us consider the example $6 \div \frac{1}{2} = \square$. Another way to express this example is as a fraction, $\dfrac{6}{\frac{1}{2}}$. Ask pupils if the denominator (divisor or factor) can be multiplied by a number to produce 1. $\frac{1}{2} \times \frac{2}{1} = \frac{2}{2} = 1$. When a number multiplied by another number produces 1, the two numbers are reciprocals or multiplicative inverses of each other. $\frac{2}{1}$ is the reciprocal of $\frac{1}{2}$ and $\frac{1}{2}$ is the reciprocal of $\frac{2}{1}$. In multiplying the denominator by $\frac{2}{1}$, does the numerator have to be multiplied by the same number to get an equivalent fraction? Past experience should lead children to say yes. Then $6 \div \frac{1}{2}$ can be rewritten and solved as follows:

$$6 \div \frac{1}{2} = \frac{6}{\frac{1}{2}}$$

$$= \frac{6}{\frac{1}{2}} \times 1$$

$$= \frac{6}{\frac{1}{2}} \times \frac{\frac{2}{1}}{\frac{2}{1}}$$

$$= \frac{6 \times \frac{2}{1}}{\frac{1}{2} \times \frac{2}{1}}$$

$$= \frac{12}{1}$$

$$= 12$$

Let us try another similar example to see if there is not a shorter method of doing the computation. For example, the problem $\frac{2}{3} \div \frac{1}{6} = \Box$, can be rewritten as $\dfrac{\frac{2}{3}}{\frac{1}{6}}$ and both terms of the fraction multiplied by the reciprocal of $\frac{1}{6}$ to change the denominator to 1.

$$\frac{2}{3} \div \frac{1}{6} = \Box$$

$$= \frac{\frac{2}{3} \times 6}{\frac{1}{6} \times 6}$$

$$= \frac{\frac{12}{3}}{1} = \frac{12}{3}$$

$$= 4$$

Notice there are not as many steps in this solution as were in the solution of the first example. As pupils continue to work examples that require division of fractions, they should be encouraged to use only the steps necessary to obtain the answer. Soon pupils will discover that it is only necessary to multiply the product or dividend by the reciprocal of the factor or divisor to divide one fraction by another. For example,

$$\frac{1}{4} \div \frac{2}{3} =$$

$$\frac{1}{4} \times \frac{3}{2} = \frac{3}{8}$$

Some of the better-thinking pupils no doubt will soon discover that it is not necessary to rewrite the example to obtain the answer in the above example,

$$\frac{1}{4} \div \frac{2}{3} = \frac{1 \times 3}{4 \times 2} = \frac{3}{8} \qquad \text{or} \qquad \frac{1}{4} \times \frac{2}{3} = \frac{3}{8}$$

Another commonly used means of dividing fractions is the common denominator method. The example $40 \div 10 = \Box$ asks how many 1 tens are in 4 tens: $40 \div 10 = 4$. Consider the example $3 \div \frac{1}{2} = \Box$. Since another name for 3 is $\frac{6}{2}$, the problem can be rewritten as $\frac{6}{2} \div \frac{1}{2} = \Box$. The fractions to be divided are now expressed as like fractions and we think how many 1 halves in 6 halves. Because we are now dividing like things, we need only divide the numerators to answer the division question, $\frac{6}{2} \div \frac{1}{2} = 6$. How is this method of division related to multiplication? When multiplying two fractions, the numerators are multiplied to get the numerator of the product and the denominators are multiplied to get the denominator of the product. If the fractions to be divided are expressed as like fractions, we can divide the numerators to get the numerator in the answer and divide the denominators to get the denominator in the answer. For example,

$$4 \div \frac{1}{3} = \frac{12}{3} \div \frac{1}{3} = \frac{12 \div 1}{3 \div 3} = \frac{12}{1} = 12$$

$$6 \div \frac{3}{4} = \frac{24}{4} \div \frac{3}{4} = \frac{24 \div 3}{4 \div 4} = \frac{8}{1} = 8$$

$$\frac{3}{4} \div \frac{1}{2} = \frac{3}{4} \div \frac{2}{4} = \frac{3 \div 2}{4 \div 4} = \frac{1\frac{1}{2}}{1} = 1\frac{1}{2}$$

$$\frac{1}{2} \div 3 = \frac{1}{2} \div \frac{6}{2} = \frac{1 \div 6}{2 \div 2} = \frac{\frac{1}{6}}{1} = \frac{1}{6}$$

After dividing several fractions with common denominators, children should recognize that the division of the denominators will always result in 1. Therefore pupils should be helped to form the following generalization: *To divide fractions that have like or common denominators, divide the numerators.*

Children's preschool understanding of fractions need to be clarified and extended during the early years of school in imaginative ways, with little initial emphasis on computation. The need for relating the meanings of fractions to everyday experiences of children has been emphasized. Also, some specific ideas of proved effectiveness have been presented for helping pupils understand the operations with fractions and to develop confidence in computation with fractions.

Suggested activities

1. Why do you think people in general tend to shy away from fraction numbers? What do you plan to do to counteract this tendency?

2. Outline three approaches you could use with children in developing the concepts of "fourths."

3. What teaching techniques and materials would you employ in helping pupils develop the ability to compare and order fractions?

4. Make a list of materials you believe would be most helpful in developing the idea of equivalence with fractional numbers.

5. Do you believe children should have many experiences with prime numbers, common multiples, and common divisors of whole numbers before attempting to apply these ideas to common fractions? Support your answer.

6. Several prerequisite learnings to the operations on fractions were listed in this chapter. Do you agree with these? Why or why not?

7. How can you help a child realize that the answer to $3 \div \frac{1}{4}$ is sensible?

8. Develop a plan, using concrete materials and drawings, to develop meaning for division of fractions.

Selected references

Adachi, Mitsuo, "Addition of Unlike Fractions," *The Arithmetic Teacher*, 15:221–223, March 1968.

Banks, J. A., "Understanding Common Fractions," *Instructor*, 76:98, Jan. 1967.

Baucom, T. V., "Division of Fractions for Understanding," *School Science and Mathematics*, 65:432–435, May 1965.

Botts, Truman, "Fractions in the New Elementary Curriculum," *The Arithmetic Teacher*, 15:216–220, March 1968.

Braunfeld, P., and M. Wolf, "Fractions for Low Achievers," *The Arithmetic Teacher*, 13:647–655, Dec. 1966.

Collier, C. C., "Helping Children Gain Competence and Confidence with Fractions," *Updating Mathematics*, vol. 4, no. 7. New London, Conn.: Croft Educational Services, 1962.

Cornelia, N. H., "Understanding Division of Fractions," *Journal of Business Education*, 41:157–158, Jan. 1966.

Cunningham, George, and David Raskin, "The Pegboard as a Fraction Maker," *The Arithmetic Teacher*, 15:224–227, March 1968.

Fehr, H. F., "Fractions as Operators," *The Arithmetic Teacher*, 15:228–232, March 1968.

Olberg, R., "Visual Aids for Multiplication and Division of Fractions," *The Arithmetic Teacher*, 14:44–46, Jan. 1967.

Pigge, F. L., "Frequencies of Unwritten Algorisms," *The Arithmetic Teacher*, 14:588–593, Nov. 1967.

Teaching 10
decimals

A great deal of argument has recently taken place and could be continued here as to whether or not the term *fraction* should be used in modern programs in regard to rational numbers that are written in the notation of our base ten (decimal) system of numeration. One argument is that the term fraction connotes a numerator and a denominator and that a number described by decimal notation has neither. Confusion persists when we read rational numbers expressed in decimal notation as if a numerator and denominator existed. Some authorities suggest that we refer to such numerals as *decimals* and refrain from using the term *decimal fraction* to avoid confusing children. Others use the term decimal fraction with little or no apprehension about confusing children and even imply that children might better understand and use rational numbers in this form if such terminology is used. Selection and use of a name seem to be of lesser importance than helping children understand the use of such numerals in naming number and in quantitative problems that require computation.

Decimal notation

In this chapter, unless specifically stated otherwise, the term *decimal fraction* will be used only to refer to a fractional number described with decimal notation. The base ten and positional value characteristics of our system of numeration are used in describing the fractional number in units of one tenth, one hundredth, one thousandth, and so forth. A positive decimal fraction refers to a fractional number between zero and one (0 < decimal fraction < 1), a number greater than zero but less than one. Our way of writing numerals for whole numbers is extended to describing fractions or rational numbers less than one in such a way that the relationship between adjacent places in a numeral is retained. Each place in the decimal fraction represents a unit value that is 10 times the unit value of the place to its right, and one tenth the unit value of the place to its left. The relationship between places may be illustrated by a positional value chart extended to include decimal fractions.

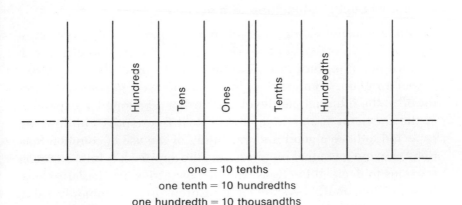

one = 10 tenths
one tenth = 10 hundredths
one hundredth = 10 thousandths

A rational number greater than one cannot be described with decimal notation merely as a decimal fraction. Depending upon the size of the number, the notation requires at least units of ones and perhaps tens, hundreds, or larger units. To facilitate communication in the mathematics classroom, a single term is generally used to refer to all rational numbers (less than one or greater than one) that are described in decimal notation. Each of the following numerals may be called a *decimal numeral* because the number is named in units of our base ten (decimal) system of numeration.

17   0.8   0.56   3.4   15.081

Note that a decimal numeral may be a whole number, a decimal fraction, or a whole number plus a decimal fraction. Just as the term fraction is commonly used to refer to a number expressed as a common fraction, the term decimal is becoming common for reference to a decimal numeral that describes either a fractional number or a whole number plus a fractional number. Although a fraction and a decimal may name the same number and may sound exactly the same when read orally, use of these distinct terms in reference to writing numerals or notations should clearly communicate different ideas.

1. Write thirty-five hundredths as a *fraction*: $\dfrac{35}{100}$

2. Write thirty-five hundredths as a *decimal*: .35

Causes of pupils' difficulties with decimals

Modern mathematics programs in this country continue to introduce and develop concepts of representing rational numbers with decimal notation during the intermediate years of the elementary school program. Computation or operations with *decimals* is introduced at the intermediate level and further developed or expanded at the upper or junior high level. Most frequently, children are expected to have a good understanding of the use of common fractions to name fractional numbers, and the approach is from common fractions to decimal fractions. In other countries, particularly those in which the metric system of measurement is commonly used, decimal notation of fractional numbers is introduced earlier in the school program, the introduction is not dependent upon common fractions, and less emphasis is placed upon the conversion of common fractions to decimal fractions.

Numeration with decimals and computation with decimals have traditionally been areas of great teaching-learning difficulty. One hypothesis is that pupil difficulties in the general area are attributable to incorrect assumptions on the part of teachers that affect their instructional procedures and, in turn, adversely affect the development of pupils' understandings and abilities. Intermediate level teachers often mistakenly assume that because children have encountered or had experiences with describing sums of money in the form $3.45 in the primary grades, they have a foundation of understandings concerning decimal representation of fractional numbers. Even though children may have had experiences with solving problems involving computation with sums of money expressed in this manner, their interpretation of the situation may be void of any understanding that part of the numeral represents a fractional quantity. The teaching approach may have been such that instead of pupils understanding the amount described by $3.45 as 3 units (dollars) and 45 hundredths (cents) of one unit, they perceive the numeral as 3 hundreds (dollars), 4 tens (dimes), and 5 ones (pennies). The decimal point or period may have been referred to only as a means of separating the dollars and cents.

Another false assumption often made by teachers is that if pupils understand the base and positional-value characteristics of our system of numeration in regard to whole numbers, they will be able to extend abstractly these understandings to decimal notation of fractional numbers.

A third false assumption of teachers is that if pupils know about common fractions and can perform the operations with common fractions, they will be able to relate and apply this knowledge easily to work with decimals.

Reliance or dependence upon these assumptions may lead to instructional procedures or learning activities that are devoid of concrete illustrative aids and emphasis upon the relationships of decimals to common fractions and to whole numbers. Difficult or complex concepts and generalizations may be introduced before children have the prerequisite knowledge and skills, and as a result rote memorization or manipulation of symbols replaces meaningful learning. Several examples of inappropriate procedures or activities may be cited. Children may be asked or required to

1. Read and write decimals before they understand how such numerals represent numbers
2. Memorize equivalent common and decimal fractions before they have seen that the numerals name the same number
3. Perform computations with decimals in which correct solutions depend upon the rote memorization and application of a rule for placing the decimal point in the result

If children are to understand the use of decimals to represent rational numbers and computation with decimals, instructional procedures similar to those used in helping younger children understand and use whole numbers and to understand operations with whole numbers should be used. Concrete illustrative aids should be used to help children learn to name number and in physical representations of the computational algorithms. Emphasis upon the concepts of base and positional value through the use of appropriate teaching aids will help children to learn to read and to write decimals. New ideas will be more meaningful to children if they are introduced with practical applications and quantitative problem situations. A variety of learning situations should be structured and guided so that pupils can discover or establish for themselves facts, relationships, generalizations, and rules. The development of children's understanding of relationships and operational skills requires utilization of the pertinent properties of number. Developmental work with the computational algorithms should include keeping a written record of the manipulation of concrete objects; practice on computational skills comes only after the operation is understood.

Content dealing with decimals and instructional procedures related to this content should follow a spiral plan of curriculum development. In the spiral development of content, major concepts are introduced concretely at an early level and reintroduced at later levels, expanding children's knowledge and understandings to more difficult and complex ideas. As the topics arise with increasing complexity at later levels, provision is made for each child to expand his understandings, knowledge and applications of the concepts. Emphasis is upon the search for patterns and understanding relationships between concepts.

Early experiences with numeration

Children's first experiences in the systematic study of concepts of decimals should be directed toward the development of understandings and skills with numeration. A demonstration of the ability to name fractional numbers in units of tenths, hundredths, and so forth, and to read and write decimals that name fractional numbers is prerequisite to the introduction and development of the computational algorithms. The importance of these abilities is such that their development should be complete and unhurried.

Initial learning activities will be concerned with orally naming fractional parts of a unit that has been divided into 10 equal parts and later into 100 equal parts. In these activities the meanings of one tenth, one hundredth, and multiparts (three tenths, thirty hundredths) are to be thoroughly developed. A teacher should not assume that children have these understandings because of their previous work with common fractions.

Appropriate instructional aids

Useful concrete materials for helping children to name fractional parts of a unit orally are square regions that have previously been partitioned into 10 and 100 equal parts. A single square region represents unity or one (1).

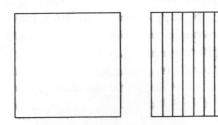

Exercises or activities can involve naming previously shaded parts or shading parts to represent a given numeral on prepared pages. An overhead projector with a variety of prepared transparencies and overlays utilizing this idea might be used to great advantage in small group or class discussions. When using these materials, children should be helped to establish the idea that the number being illustrated can be named in several ways. Many illustrative examples from which conclusions such as the following are drawn should be used.

1. Three tenths names the same number as thirty hundredths.
2. Seventy hundredths names the same number as seven tenths.
3. Three tenths plus four hundredths names the same number as thirty-four hundredths.
4. Fifty-three hundredths names the same number as five tenths plus three hundredths.

The same materials can be used when later learning experiences are directed toward reading and writing decimals and toward developing the idea that several names can be used for the same number.

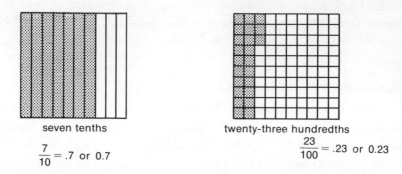

seven tenths

$\frac{7}{10}$ = .7 or 0.7

twenty-three hundredths

$\frac{23}{100}$ = .23 or 0.23

After the concept of one tenth is understood, children can use an agreed upon unit of length to represent one tenth in constructing a number line. Initially, only the points or distances representing whole numbers need to be named and exercises will deal with finding points that represent number names or associating names with predetermined points.

●—● represents one tenth

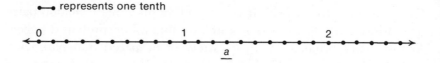

1. Which point represents a distance of seven tenths?
2. What name would you give the point at *a*?
3. Where would the point representing a distance of thirty-five hundredths be?

Later, children can write fractions and decimals to name the points to help develop the idea of alternate names, fractions and decimals, for the same number.

0.0	0.1	0.2	0.3	0.4	0.5	0.6	0.7	0.8	0.9	1.0	1.1
$\frac{0}{10}$	$\frac{1}{10}$	$\frac{2}{10}$	$\frac{3}{10}$	$\frac{4}{10}$	$\frac{5}{10}$	$\frac{6}{10}$	$\frac{7}{10}$	$\frac{8}{10}$	$\frac{9}{10}$	$\frac{10}{10}$	$\frac{11}{10}$

When children can orally name numbers represented by regions, they should have experiences with a positional value pocket chart using counters and a positional value chart using written symbols to develop the communication skills of reading and writing decimal numerals.

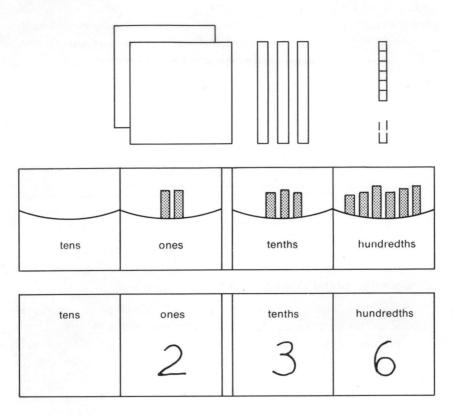

A modified abacus may also be used to help children understand the base and positional value characteristics of decimals. Pupils can be asked to represent an illustrated number by arranging beads on the abacus and/or to illustrate the number represented by the visible beads on the abacus.

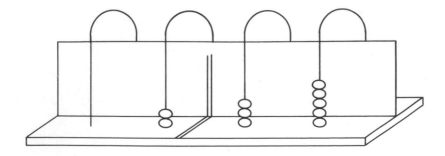

Use of these instructional aids will help children learn to read decimals in terms of the two component parts: the integral or whole number and the less-than-integral parts or fractional units. The integral part is read first, the term *and* is used to separate or identify the two component parts, and the less-than-integral part is read in terms of the smallest fractional unit used.

"two and thirty-six hundredths"

Use of these aids will also help children to understand the symmetry of the positional-value characteristic and the symmetry of the positional-value unit names. The ones place can be identified as the central unit in decimal notation.

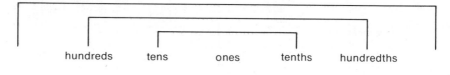

hundreds   tens   ones   tenths   hundredths

Introduction of the decimal point

Only when children can read the numerals or numbers represented on these devices should the decimal point be introduced as a simple notational device that identifies the *ones* position and separates the numeral into two component parts. Practice in writing and reading decimals can be structured around the use of the previously described illustrative materials. The ones position, *not* the decimal point, should be emphasized as the center of the positional system. Special attention is to be given to the use of the term *and* in saying or reading decimals, and some children will need to be discouraged from its incorrect usage in reading whole numbers.

Incorrect: "three hundred and twenty-seven and eight tenths"

327.8

Correct: "three hundred twenty-seven and eight tenths"

Incorrect: "one hundred and eighty-seven thousandths"

.187

Correct: "one hundred eighty-seven thousandths"

Although often used by adults, the reading of decimals as a set of single symbols should be avoided if meaning and understanding of the numerals are to be developed.

327.8   Avoid: "three, two, seven, point, eight"

As a matter of interest and information, it may be pointed out to children that other devices or symbols have been used in the past to serve the same function as the decimal point and that some countries now use other symbols instead of the "period." In Great Britain and Canada the decimal point is placed at midheight of the digits — 3·4 is the same as our 3.4. In some other countries the comma is used.

Decimals and common fractions as alternate names

As children are learning to write decimal fractions to name numbers, they should also be learning to describe the same numbers with common fractions. The idea that different names, decimal and fraction, can be used for the same number should be stressed. Practical problem or quantitative situations should be used to illustrate that at times it is more convenient to use one form than it is the other. At other times it is necessary to convert from one to the other form to perform the necessary computations.

If children can write and read decimals meaningfully, they will have little difficulty in converting decimal fractions to equivalent common fractions. The written numerator is the number of equal parts described in the decimal fraction, and the written denominator is the positional value of the smallest fractional unit used. It will soon be apparent to children that decimals and fractions are read in exactly the same language.

Alternate names

Decimal	Fraction	Read as:
0.8	$\dfrac{8}{10}$	eight tenths
0.27	$\dfrac{27}{100}$	twenty-seven hundredths
0.75	$\dfrac{75}{100}$	seventy-five hundredths
3.07	$3\dfrac{7}{100}$	three and seven hundredths
42.812	$42\dfrac{812}{1000}$	forty-two and eight hundred twelve thousandths

Conversion of decimals to fractions with denominators that are powers of ten should be well understood by pupils before they are asked to rename decimal fractions as common fractions with denominators other than powers of ten. If children have been using common factors to rename common fractions, they should be able to discover that only certain decimal fractions can be renamed in lower terms. Because the initial denominator is always a power of 10, its only prime factors will be 2 and 5. If the numerator does not also have one of these factors (2 or 5), the fraction cannot be renamed in lower terms.

$$.8 = \frac{8}{10} = \frac{2 \times 2 \times 2}{2 \times 5} = \frac{4}{5}$$ 8 and 10 have the common factor 2, so the decimal fraction .8 can be renamed to the common fraction $\frac{4}{5}$.

$$.9 = \frac{9}{10} = \frac{3 \times 3}{2 \times 5} = \frac{9}{10}$$ 9 and 10 have no common factor, so the decimal fraction .9 cannot be renamed to a common fraction with lower terms.

The conversion of common fractions which have denominators that are powers of ten to decimal fractions is as simple as converting decimal fractions to common fractions. The numerator of the fraction is written and the decimal point is placed so that the decimal fraction is read exactly as the common fraction.

$$\frac{6}{100} = .06 \qquad \frac{127}{1000} = .127 \qquad \frac{35}{1000} = .035$$

Fractions which have denominators that are factors of ten or factors of a power of ten are also relatively easy to convert to decimals. The process is the reverse of converting a decimal to a fraction and renaming the fraction in lower terms.

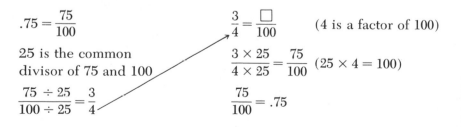

$.75 = \dfrac{75}{100}$

25 is the common divisor of 75 and 100

$\dfrac{75 \div 25}{100 \div 25} = \dfrac{3}{4}$

$\dfrac{3}{4} = \dfrac{\square}{100}$ (4 is a factor of 100)

$\dfrac{3 \times 25}{4 \times 25} = \dfrac{75}{100}$ (25 × 4 = 100)

$\dfrac{75}{100} = .75$

The technique for converting all other common fractions to decimal fractions is simple, but involves division with decimals and is described in that section of this chapter.

Algorithms with decimals

Children's understandings and abilities in performing the operational algorithms with decimals will be dependent upon their knowledge and mastery of the algorithms with whole numbers, their understandings of the properties of number and the relationships between operations, and their abilities to read and write decimals to name numbers. Understanding of and ability to perform the algorithms with common fractions might be helpful but are not prerequisite. No new facts will be needed and no new procedures will be introduced in the algorithms. The computations will be the same as those with whole numbers. The major potential difficulty for children will be in correctly locating the decimal point in the result of the computation. Rote manipulation or rote memorization and application of rules should be avoided. Instructional procedures should develop generalizations about the placement of the decimal point in the result meaningfully through the use of instructional aids and the spiral development of concepts and ideas.

Addition and subtraction.   The algorithms for adding and subtracting with decimals are very much the same as those for adding and subtracting whole numbers. As with whole numbers and common fractions, emphasis should be placed upon the idea that only like units can be added or subtracted. In both algorithms the computational forms make addition and subtraction of like units easier by aligning terms (addends) according to positional value. *Keeping the decimal points directly under each other* is merely a technique for aligning like units. We might better develop the generalization of *adding the ones to the ones and the tenths to the tenths.*

In both addition and subtraction the results (sum or difference) are developed bit by bit from the smallest positional value unit to the largest. The regrouping procedures with decimals involve the same concepts of base and positional value as regrouping with whole numbers. Instructional aids such as the square regions and fractional parts should be used for concrete illustrations. Use of positional value charts to record the physical manipulations will help children better understand the algorithm.

a. $1.7 + 0.6 = \square$

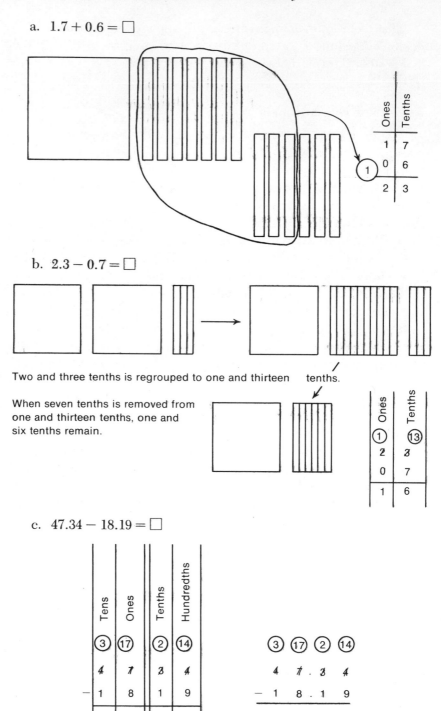

b. $2.3 - 0.7 = \square$

Two and three tenths is regrouped to one and thirteen tenths.

When seven tenths is removed from one and thirteen tenths, one and six tenths remain.

c. $47.34 - 18.19 = \square$

d. $26.47 + 13.83 + 25.98 = \square$

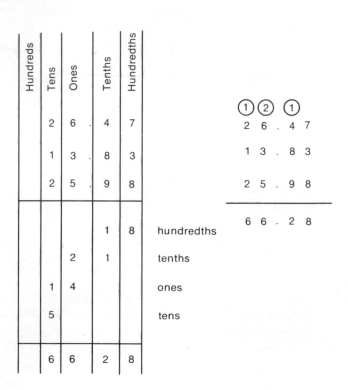

Situations may occur in which the decimals to be added or sub-tracted differ in regard to the number of places to the right of the decimal point. Such situations as the following are said to involve "ragged decimals."

$$4.6 + 3.621 + 3.87 = \square$$
$$5.6 - 3.176 = \square$$
$$4.862 - 2.64 = \square$$

Computations to find sums and differences of "ragged decimals" are made easier by annexing zeros so that all terms will have the same number of places to the right of the decimal and so that addition and subtraction of like units is facilitated.

a.   4.6   4.600   b.   5.6   5.600
      3.621   3.621   −3.176   −3.176
     +3.87   +3.870

When annexing zeros in this manner is necessary, the approach should be one of developing another name for a number. Annexing zeros to the right in a decimal fraction does not change the number value being described. It merely renames the number in terms of smaller units, without changing its value, so that all of the decimal fractions being added or subtracted will have the same denominators.

$$.4 = \{.4, .40, .400, . . .\}$$

If the computational example is derived from a problem that involves measurement, the meaning attached to the result may be questioned in terms of preciseness. The sum or difference will be no less or no more precise than the least precise of the measurements involved. If one of the terms is precise only to tenths, the result will be precise only to tenths regardless of how precise the other measurements were.

Multiplication. The actual computational algorithm for multiplication with decimals is identical to that of multiplying whole numbers with one exception—locating the decimal point in the product. Instructional procedures in the systematic study of multiplication with decimals should be directed toward meaningfully developing the following generalization: There are as many digits to the right of the decimal point in the product as the *total* number of digits to the right of the decimal point in the two factors. Too often, this generalization is memorized and utilized as a rote rule, and children mechanically place the decimal point in the product without understanding the *why* or rationale of the procedure.

A planned meaningful establishment of the generalization will involve the use of concrete and illustrative materials, emphasis upon relationships between operations and within the operation of multiplication, and a logical, sequential, spiral introduction and development of the ideas.

The easiest problem situation to illustrate and for children to understand is multiplication of a decimal by a whole number. Using numbers that are easy to illustrate, solutions can be determined by counting, by addition, and by application of multiplication facts. Multiplication with fractions can be used to reinforce ideas. Simpler problems should lead to more complex situations in which the ideas are utilized in the multiplication algorithm.

a. $3 \times .4 = \boxed{}$

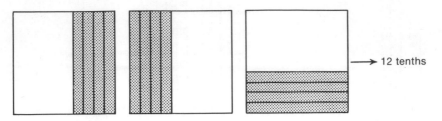

→ 12 tenths

4 tenths + 4 tenths + 4 tenths = 12 tenths

$$\frac{4}{10} \quad + \quad \frac{4}{10} \quad + \quad \frac{4}{10} \quad = \frac{12}{10} = 1\frac{2}{10} = 1.2$$

$$.4 \quad + \quad .4 \quad + \quad .4 \quad = 1.2$$

$$3 \times \frac{4}{10} = \frac{12}{10}$$

4 tenths	.4
×3	×3
12 tenths	1.2

b. $3 \times 5.4 = \square$

5.4
×3
12 tenths ($3 \times .4$)
15 ones (3×5)
16.2

c. $23 \times 5.4 = \square$

5.4
×23
12 tenths ($3 \times .4$)
15 ones (3×5)
80 tenths ($20 \times .4$)
100 ones (20×5)
124.2

Although the problem situations will be quite different, similar procedures can be utilized when a whole number is to be multiplied by a decimal. However, addition cannot be used as a means of solution.

.4 of 6 = $\square$
$.4 \times 6 = 6 \times .4$ commutative property

Beginning with six units and taking four tenths of each of the units, we can count twenty-four tenths. The twenty-four tenths can then be rearranged to make two units and four tenths of a unit. The completed drawing or diagram will look just like the drawing for $6 \times .4$, but the procedure is different.

a.

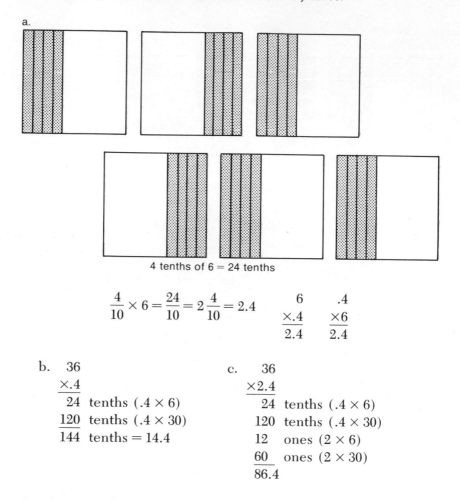

4 tenths of 6 = 24 tenths

$$\frac{4}{10} \times 6 = \frac{24}{10} = 2\frac{4}{10} = 2.4$$

$$
\begin{array}{r}
6 \\
\times.4 \\
\hline
2.4
\end{array}
\qquad
\begin{array}{r}
.4 \\
\times 6 \\
\hline
2.4
\end{array}
$$

b.
$$
\begin{array}{r}
36 \\
\times.4 \\
\hline
24 \\
120 \\
\hline
144
\end{array}
\begin{array}{l}
\\
\\
\text{tenths } (.4 \times 6) \\
\text{tenths } (.4 \times 30) \\
\text{tenths } = 14.4
\end{array}
$$

c.
$$
\begin{array}{r}
36 \\
\times 2.4 \\
\hline
24 \\
120 \\
12 \\
60 \\
\hline
86.4
\end{array}
\begin{array}{l}
\\
\\
\text{tenths } (.4 \times 6) \\
\text{tenths } (.4 \times 30) \\
\text{ones } (2 \times 6) \\
\text{ones } (2 \times 30) \\
\end{array}
$$

When both factors are decimal fractions, illustrations will involve the intersection of regions. Thus the product of tenths × tenths can be illustrated to be hundredths, tenths × hundredths = thousandths, and so forth.

.3 of .4 = ☐ ⟶ .3 × .4 = ☐

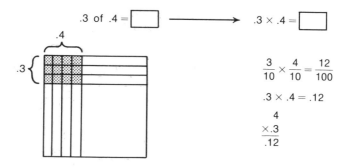

$$\frac{3}{10} \times \frac{4}{10} = \frac{12}{100}$$

$$.3 \times .4 = .12$$

$$
\begin{array}{r}
4 \\
\times.3 \\
\hline
.12
\end{array}
$$

The illustrations are more complex when one or both of the factors has an integral part.

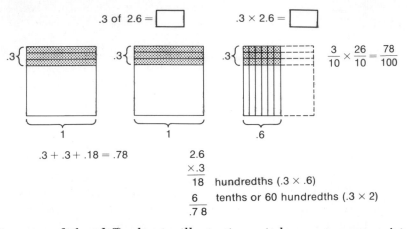

$.3 + .3 + .18 = .78$

$$\begin{array}{r} 2.6 \\ \times .3 \\ \hline 18 \\ 6 \\ \hline .78 \end{array}$$ hundredths $(.3 \times .6)$
tenths or 60 hundredths $(.3 \times 2)$

Because of the difficulty in illustrations, it becomes appropriate to use a procedure that is mathematically meaningful to develop understanding of the placement of the decimal point in the product. Children will be asked to apply their understandings and knowledge of the commutative and associative properties and their abilities to multiply fractions and decimals.

a. $3.7 \times 8.6 = \square$

$$\frac{37}{10} \times \frac{86}{10} = \frac{3,182}{100} = 31\frac{82}{100} = 31.82$$

b. $\qquad 4.3 \times 18.7 = \square$

$\left(43 \times \dfrac{1}{10}\right) \times \left(187 \times \dfrac{1}{10}\right) = \square \qquad$ renaming the factors

$43 \times \dfrac{1}{10} \times 187 \times \dfrac{1}{10} = \square$

$43 \times 187 \times \dfrac{1}{10} \times \dfrac{1}{10} = \square \qquad$ commutative property (changing the order of the factors)

$(43 \times 187) \times \left(\dfrac{1}{10} \times \dfrac{1}{10}\right) = \square \qquad$ associative property (grouping factors for multiplication)

$8,041 \times \dfrac{1}{100} = \dfrac{8,041}{100}$

$8,041 \times .01 = 80.41 \quad$ renaming

From the observation of the results of many computational examples, ranging from very simple to more complex, the generalization about placement of the decimal point in the product is to be formulated.

Division.   As with multiplication, the computation for division with decimals is similar to division with whole numbers, with the difficulty of correctly locating the decimal point in the quotient. Except for introductory illustrations, pupils' understandings of placement of the decimal point in the quotient are developed through application of their previously acquired arithmetical abilities. A relatively high level of mastery with division with whole numbers should be a prerequisite for division with decimals.

Most elementary mathematics programs introduce division with decimals with partitioning situations in which the number represented by a decimal is partitioned into a given number of equal-sized parts. Locating the decimal point in the quotient of a decimal divided by a whole number will not be difficult for children because it can be concretely illustrated that the quotient will have the same number of decimal places as the dividend. The relationship of division to multiplication should be stressed, and positional-value diagrams for the computation can be used.

Consider introductory examples such as

$$\text{a.} \quad .46 \div 2 = \square \qquad \text{and} \qquad \text{b.} \quad 8.7 \div 3 = \square$$

a.   .46 is to be partitioned into two equal parts:
$$2 \times \square = .46 \qquad 2\,\overline{)\,.46}$$

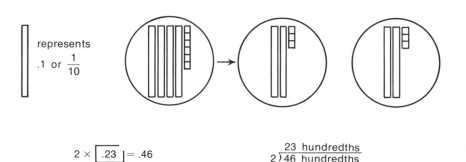

represents
.1 or $\frac{1}{10}$

$$2 \times \boxed{.23} = .46$$

$$\begin{array}{r} 23 \text{ hundredths} \\ 2\,\overline{)\,46} \text{ hundredths} \end{array}$$

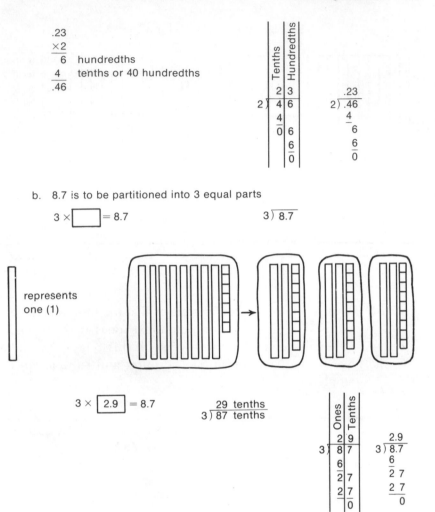

.23
×2
———
6   hundredths
4   tenths or 40 hundredths
———
.46

b.   8.7 is to be partitioned into 3 equal parts

$3 \times \boxed{} = 8.7$ 3⟌8.7

represents
one (1)

$3 \times \boxed{2.9} = 8.7$ 29 tenths
3⟌87 tenths

There may be some learning advantages in illustrating measurement-type division situations in which the computation involves division of a whole number by a decimal fraction. Consider a problem in which the question is "How many groups of .6 (six tenths) each are contained in a group of 3 (three)?"

Illustration and counting using square regions and the number line can demonstrate the correct result. The result can also be obtained by subtraction, which can be performed by first renaming the 3 as 30 tenths or which can be performed by using ideas of subtracting decimals. The division operation can then be related to repeated subtraction or to the operation of multiplication.

$$3 \div .6 = \square \qquad \text{or} \qquad \square \times .6 = 3$$

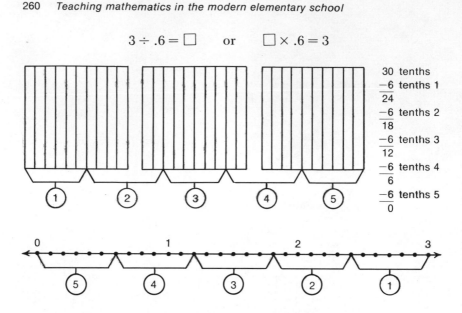

```
30 tenths
-6 tenths 1
——
24
-6 tenths 2
——
18
-6 tenths 3
——
12
-6 tenths 4
——
6
-6 tenths 5
——
0
```

Note: This is one of the few instances that the number line can be used to develop computational ideas with decimals. Other instances are the reverse of this type of problem, $5 \times .6 = \square$, and in simple addition and subtraction examples.

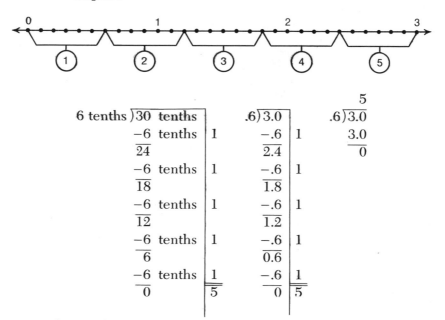

```
                                                    5
6 tenths )30  tenths         .6)3.0            .6)3.0
         -6  tenths | 1      -.6  | 1            3.0
         ——                  ——                  ——
         24                  2.4                  0
         -6  tenths | 1      -.6  | 1
         ——                  ——
         18                  1.8
         -6  tenths | 1      -.6  | 1
         ——                  ——
         12                  1.2
         -6  tenths | 1      -.6  | 1
         ——                  ——
         6                   0.6
         -6  tenths | 1      -.6  | 1
         ——                  ——
         0          | 5       0   | 5
```

Such introductory problems and illustrations may give pupils some intuitive understanding of how the decimal point must be placed in the quotient. However, the complexity of illustrations and the computations for problems involving uneven division requires the development of a procedure that is universally applicable.

Placement of the decimal point in the two other possible types of division examples—(1) division of a whole number by a decimal and (2) division of a decimal by a decimal—is established by arithmetically converting each to an example of dividing a decimal by a whole number. Children's proficiencies with dividing a decimal by a whole number should be firmly established before other types of examples are introduced.

All division expressions either in the form of number sentences or in computational form may be said to name numbers. They name the same number that the sought quotient will name. Whether the division is concerned with whole numbers or with decimals, there are an infinite number of division expressions that name the same number. The procedure that is to be developed for both dividing a whole number by a decimal and dividing a decimal by a decimal is one of substituting an equivalent name or expression of division for the original one.

The substituted equivalent name is not arbitrarily selected. It is established by multiplying the original number name by one. The name for one used in the multiplication is from the set $\left\{ \dfrac{10}{10}, \dfrac{100}{100}, \dfrac{1000}{1000}, \ldots \right\}$. Consider the ideas: $n \times 1 = n$ and $\dfrac{a}{b} \times \dfrac{c}{c} = \dfrac{ac}{bc}$. $\dfrac{c}{c}$ is a name for 1, and $\dfrac{ac}{bc}$ is an equivalent name for $\dfrac{a}{b}$. Note how these ideas are used in establishing equivalent division expressions. The name for one, $\left\{ \dfrac{10}{10}, \dfrac{100}{100}, \dfrac{1000}{1000}, \ldots \right\}$, is chosen such that the multiplication will result in a whole number divisor.

$$2.3\overline{)4.25} = \frac{4.25}{2.3} = \frac{4.25}{2.3} \times \frac{10}{10} = \frac{42.5}{23} = 23\overline{)42.5}$$

$$.47\overline{)5.381} = \frac{5.381}{.47} = \frac{5.381}{.47} \times \frac{100}{100} = \frac{538.1}{47} = 47\overline{)538.1}$$

After children understand the procedure for establishing an equivalent division expression by multiplying the dividend and the divisor by the same power of 10, the procedure can be shortened by performing the multiplication in the computational example. The *caret* has traditionally been used to indicate the position of the decimal point in the equivalent decimal expression.

$$4.28 \overline{)5.276} \quad \rightarrow \quad 4.28_\wedge \overline{)5.27_\wedge 6} \quad \rightarrow \quad 428 \overline{)527.6}$$

The multiplication of dividend and divisor by the same power of ten is indicated by the caret, the decimal point is located in the quotient, and the division is performed as with whole numbers.

$$23.5_\wedge \overline{)6.1_\wedge 38} \qquad .235_\wedge \overline{)6.138_\wedge}$$

As described in a previous chapter, division with whole numbers does not always obtain an exact whole number quotient. When this occurs, the undivided part is stated as a remainder or the part is divided and an exact quotient is stated in terms of a whole number plus a fraction. When division with decimals does not obtain an exact quotient, we usually do not state remainders or use common fractions in the quotient. An *approximate* quotient is determined by *rounding off* the quotient to the decimal position used in the dividend. The quotient can be no more precise than the dividend. The procedure is to annex a zero to the dividend, to continue the division one place beyond the original dividend, and to use the value of the final quotient digit to *round off* the quotient.

a. $3.62 \div 2.7 = \square$ b. $5.97 \div 3.2 = \square$

$$
\begin{array}{r}
1.34 \\
2.7_\wedge \overline{)3.6_\wedge 20} \\
2\,7 \\
\hline
92 \\
81 \\
\hline
110 \\
108 \\
\hline
2
\end{array}
\quad \rightarrow \quad 1.3
\qquad
\begin{array}{r}
1.86 \\
3.2_\wedge \overline{)5.9_\wedge 70} \\
3\,2 \\
\hline
2\,77 \\
2\,56 \\
\hline
210 \\
192 \\
\hline
18
\end{array}
\quad \rightarrow \quad 1.9
$$

In example a, 1.34 is closer to 1.3 than it is to 1.4; in example b, 1.86 is closer to 1.9 than it is to 1.8.

Terminating and nonterminating decimals

By applying their knowledge and skills of dividing with decimals, children can convert all rational numbers stated as fractions to equivalent decimals. The fraction can be interpreted as an unperformed division in which the numerator is the dividend and the denominator is the divisor. The observed quotient will be the decimal equivalent of the fraction. Since we are converting to a decimal (base ten) equivalent, only those fractions (when named in lowest terms) whose denominators have prime factors of only 2 and 5 will result in an exact or *terminating* decimal.

$$
\frac{3}{4} = 4\overline{)3.00} \qquad \frac{5}{8} = 8\overline{)5.000} \qquad \frac{13}{40} = 40\overline{)13.000}
$$

$$
\begin{array}{c}
.75 \\
4\overline{)3.00} \\
\underline{2\,8} \\
20 \\
\underline{20} \\
0
\end{array}
\qquad
\begin{array}{c}
.625 \\
8\overline{)5.000} \\
\underline{4\,8} \\
20 \\
\underline{16} \\
40 \\
\underline{40} \\
0
\end{array}
\qquad
\begin{array}{c}
.325 \\
40\overline{)13.000} \\
\underline{12\,0} \\
1\,00 \\
\underline{80} \\
200 \\
\underline{200} \\
0
\end{array}
$$

If the denominator of the fraction (named in lowest terms) has one or more prime factors that are not 2 or 5, the decimal equivalent will not terminate. However, performance of many divisions and observation of the quotients should lead to the generalization that the decimals are *nonterminating*, but are *repeating* decimals. A repeating pattern of digits will occur in the quotient if the division is carried far enough.

$$
\frac{1}{6} = 6\overline{)1.00000} \qquad \frac{2}{15} = 15\overline{)2.00000} \qquad \frac{2}{13} = 13\overline{)2.00000000000000}
$$

$$
\begin{array}{c}
.16666 \\
6\overline{)1.00000} \\
\underline{6} \\
40 \\
\underline{36} \\
40 \\
\underline{36} \\
40 \\
\underline{36} \\
4 \\
\cdot \\
\cdot \\
\cdot
\end{array}
\qquad
\begin{array}{c}
.13333 \\
15\overline{)2.00000} \\
\underline{1\,5} \\
50 \\
\underline{45} \\
50 \\
\underline{45} \\
50 \\
\underline{45} \\
5 \\
\cdot \\
\cdot \\
\cdot
\end{array}
\qquad
\begin{array}{c}
.1538453845384 \\
13\overline{)2.00000000000000} \\
\underline{1\,3} \\
70 \\
\underline{65} \\
50 \\
\underline{39} \\
110 \\
\underline{104} \\
60 \\
\underline{52} \\
80 \\
\underline{65} \\
50 \\
\underline{39} \\
110 \\
\underline{104} \\
60 \\
\cdot \\
\cdot \\
\cdot
\end{array}
$$

One way of indicating the repetition in the decimal is to draw a bar over the repeated patterns: $\frac{1}{6} = .1\overline{6}$; $\frac{2}{15} = .1\overline{3}$; $\frac{2}{13} = .1\overline{53846}$.

Can all rational numbers be expressed either as a terminating or as a repeating decimal? The division may have to be carried to a great many places before the repetition is observed, but all decimal equivalents of rational numbers either terminate or have a repeating pattern of digits.

Can a decimal occur that is not terminating and not repeating? Consider merely writing such decimals as .123456789101112 . . . and .2468101214161820 . . . so that a repeating pattern of digits does not occur. Also consider computing the relationship of the circumference of a circle to its diameter (*pi*), or computing $\sqrt{1}$, $\sqrt{2}$. Decimals that do not terminate or repeat are representations of *irrational* numbers. Children are not likely to encounter any ideas of irrational numbers until they reach the upper levels of the elementary program. When they are introduced to problems involving pi, $\sqrt{1}$, or other irrational numbers, the decimal representations of these numbers are rounded off and treated as rational numbers. Children should learn that decimals need not always be terminating or repeating and that there is a class of numbers called irrational numbers. A natural inquiry from pupils as to the possibility of decimals that are nonterminating and nonrepeating may be the teachable moment for the introduction of this idea.

Locating the decimal point in multiplication and division

At least two other generalizations should result from children's experiences with multiplying and dividing decimals. One deals with the location of the decimal point in the result of multiplying or dividing a decimal by a power of ten. The other deals with the use of estimation as a *rough* verification of the location of the decimal point in the product or quotient.

As children develop ideas of multiplication and division with decimals and practice computation with those ideas, their knowledge of multiplication and division with whole numbers should be used to estimate results and to verify the location of the decimal point in the result.

42.68 $6 \times 40 = 240$; therefore the integral part of the decimal
×6.5   product should be in terms of hundreds and the deci-
             mal point so located.

$6.5 \overline{)42.68}$ $42 \div 6 = 7$; therefore the integral part of the decimal quotient should be in terms of ones and the decimal point so located.

Children should have sufficient experiences with multiplying decimals by 10, 100, and 1000 to develop the generalization that the product contains the same sequence of digits as the decimal and the decimal point in the product is located one place to the right for *each* factor of ten in the multiplier. A short procedure for multiplying by powers of ten is simply to move the decimal a correct number of places to the right.

$$10 \times 5.3786 = 53.786$$
$$10^1 \times 5.3786 = 53.786$$
$$\rightarrow 5.3\,7\,8\,6$$

$$100 \times 5.3786 = 537.86$$
$$10^2 \times 5.3786 = 537.86$$
$$\rightarrow 5.3\,7\,8\,6$$

$$1000 \times 5.3786 = 5378.6$$
$$10^3 \times 5.3786 = 5378.6$$
$$\rightarrow 5.3\,7\,8\,6$$

Similarly, a short procedure for dividing a decimal by a power of ten is to locate the decimal point a correct number of places to the left.

$$624.7 \div 10 = 62.47$$
$$624.7 \div 10^1 = 62.47$$
$$\rightarrow 6\,2\,4.7$$

$$624.7 \div 100 = 6.247$$
$$624.7 \div 10^2 = 6.247$$
$$\rightarrow 6\,2\,4.7$$

$$624.7 \div 1000 = .6247$$
$$624.7 \div 10^3 = .6247$$
$$\rightarrow 6\,2\,4.7$$

Negative decimal numerals

In the early elementary grades children may be introduced to numbers less than zero by locating points on a number line. Introduction to the *negative integers* may stem from experiences of moving markers on a number line of whole numbers.

Consider a learning activity in which pupils are asked to move the marker on a number line according to directions given by other pupils. The marker is at "2" and a child directs that the marker is to be moved five spaces backward or to the left. What happens to the marker? Can it be moved? Does it fall off the line or disappear? Or can we extend the line, locate and name points, and continue the activity? Children should agree that the line can be extended and that points can be located. Discussion can be directed toward naming the points in such a way so that confusion will not exist between the names for the points to the right of zero and points to the left.

The term *negative* and a symbol to indicate negative are introduced. The symbol for "negative three" should be written "$^-3$" instead of "-3" to avoid confusion with the operational symbol for subtraction. The negative symbol is to be interpreted as part of the numeral and the numeral $^-2$ is to be read as "negative two." It will not be necessary to prefix a symbol for positive to the positive integers at this level. As children name the points (representing units of one) to the left of zero, they will be developing the set of negative integers: $\{. . ., \, ^-4, \, ^-3, \, ^-2, \, ^-1\}$. As they develop the set, they should be guided to observe that each member of the set of new number names can be thought of as the opposite of one of the numbers they have been using.

Learning activities structured on the movement of markers on a number line can now include the use of both positive and negative integers. Concepts of negative integers can be applied in reading the thermometer and recording or graphing the temperature or in any other instances where a scale below zero is required. "Countdowns" to a predetermined time can also be used to illustrate negative numbers.

When children who have had such experiences are naming points on the number line with fractions, it will not be unusual for them to want to name and locate points representing the negative fractions. The same children will probably want to locate the negative decimals when the number line is being used to develop ideas of order, comparison, and equivalence with decimals. Such activities are to be encouraged and are intended only to introduce children to very elementary but fundamental ideas of negative numbers. Concepts can be developed that pertain to names and symbols, order and sequence, comparisons, and the symmetry of negative and positive numbers.

$$\begin{array}{cccccccccccccc}
\frac{^-6}{10} & \frac{^-5}{10} & \frac{^-4}{10} & \frac{^-3}{10} & \frac{^-2}{10} & \frac{^-1}{10} & \frac{0}{10} & \frac{1}{10} & \frac{2}{10} & \frac{3}{10} & \frac{4}{10} & \frac{5}{10} & \frac{6}{10}
\end{array}$$

$$^-0.6 \quad ^-0.5 \quad ^-0.4 \quad ^-0.3 \quad ^-0.2 \quad ^-0.1 \quad 0.0 \quad 0.1 \quad 0.2 \quad 0.3 \quad 0.4 \quad 0.5 \quad 0.6$$

It seems logical to develop these concepts with negative rational numbers (integers, fractions, decimals) before the operational algorithms with signed numbers (negative and positive) are introduced. No new facts and few new operational procedures are introduced in the algorithms for signed numbers. The major difficulty will be in determining the negative or positive value of the result. If children have mastered the algorithms with whole numbers, and if they have acquired the cited foundational understandings of negative rational numbers, they should be able to apply any new learnings about algorithms with signed numbers to integers, fractions, and decimals. Because operations with negative numbers are generally not topics of study in contemporary elementary mathematics programs, and because the authors of this text are not highly favorable toward including that topic in the elementary program, procedures for teaching those operations will not be included in this volume.

Suggested activities

1. Construct a collection of instructional aids that will help children understand decimal fractions and decimals.

3. Collect newspaper and magazine articles that use decimals to describe number.

3. List the prerequisite learnings children should have before division with decimals is introduced and developed.

4. Develop a set of exercises in which *only* the placement of the decimal point in a product is practiced.

5. Prepare a lesson plan that will introduce the existence of irrational numbers.

Selected references

Bouwsma, W. D., C. G. Corle, and D. F. Clemson, Jr., *Basic Mathematics for Elementary Teachers*. New York: The Ronald Press Company, 1967, Chapter 15, "Decimal Representation and Real Numbers," pp. 280–314.

Crouch, R., G. Baldwin, and R. J. Wisner, *Preparatory Mathematics for Elementary Teachers*. New York: John Wiley & Sons, Inc., 1965, Chapter IX, "Decimal Representation and the Real Number System," pp. 371–413.

Mueller, F. J., *Arithmetic — Its Structure and Concepts*. Englewood Cliffs, N.J.: Prentice-Hall, Inc., 1964, Unit 21, "Decimals: Sums and Differences," and Unit 22, "Decimals: Products and Quotients," pp. 259–287.

Ohmer, M. M., C. V. Aucoin, and M. J. Cortez, *Elementary Contemporary Mathematics*. Waltham, Mass.: Blaisdell Publishing Company, 1964, Chapter 8, "Decimals and the Real Number System," pp. 268–313.

Youse, B. K., *Arithmetic — A Modern Approach*. Englewood Cliffs, N.J.: Prentice-Hall, Inc., 1963, Chapter 7, "Decimals," and Chapter 8, "Infinite Decimals," pp. 80–107.

Teaching 11
ratio, proportion,
and percent

In preceding chapters our major use of number has been to refer to specific quantities or measures. In this chapter we undertake the development of another use of number — to describe a relationship or correspondence between specific quantities or measures. There are many applications in quantitative situations for number to be used in this manner to provide information and to solve problems.

When we make such statements as "It is *three* times as far from John's home to school as it is from Terry's home to school" or "Joe has *one half* as many pencils as Mary," we are describing the relationship or correspondence between the number properties of two sets without mention of those number properties. In the first example, the actual measure of one of the two distances could be any number, but the relationship must always be such that the longer is *three* times the length of the shorter. Similarly, Joe might have any number of pencils, but Mary must have *two* times as many. The correspondence between the two unmentioned numbers in both statements remains constant, and each statement merely provides information about that correspondence.

Contemporary elementary mathematics programs introduce and develop the use of number to describe or express correspondences earlier than programs of the past. Developing the concept of *ratio* is of major importance in helping children to use number in this way. Their understandings that ratios can be compared and that equal ratios or *proportions* can be determined will help them to solve problems involving paired correspondences including problems concerning *percent*.

Ratio

An expression used to state the constant or consistent correspondence that exists between two numbers is called a *ratio*. A
ratio describes the relationship between the number properties
of two sets and requires the use of referent terms for each set.
Several equivalent expressions or ratios may be used to describe
the numerical correspondence between two sets. However, the
relationship is best communicated when the referent terms are the
smallest whole numbers possible. The relationship is generally
stated in some form similar to "the ratio of the number of set A
to the number of set B is $\square$ to $\bigcirc$."

In each of the following illustrations two sets are numerically
compared and a ratio is stated.

1. Set A

   Set B

The ratio of $n(A)$ to $n(B)$ is 1 to 1.

2. Set C

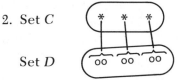

   Set D

The ratio of $n(C)$ to $n(D)$ is 1 to 2.

3. Set E

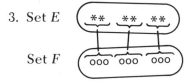

   Set F

The ratio of $n(E)$ to $n(F)$ is 2 to 3.

4. Set G

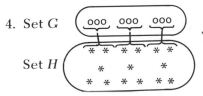

   Set H

The ratio of $n(G)$ to $n(H)$ is 3 to 5.

The stated ratios imply that one of the sets in each pair operates as a base for comparison and the other is the set being compared to the base. In the statement of a ratio the second set referred to is the base set, so *order* is an important aspect when expressing ratios. It is important that the base set is clearly identified when the ratio is stated. In each of the preceding illustrations and ratios, the base set could be changed and the ratios could be stated as

1. The ratio of $n(B)$ to $n(A)$ is 1 to 1.
2. The ratio of $n(D)$ to $n(C)$ is 2 to 1.
3. The ratio of $n(F)$ to $n(E)$ is 3 to 2.
4. The ratio of $n(H)$ to $n(G)$ is 5 to 3.

However, it should be clear that the ratio of 2 to 3 is not the same ratio as 3 to 2.

In the early primary grades children have many experiences in comparing the number properties of sets of objects. Most of these activities deal with determining whether or not a one-to-one correspondence exists between the elements of two sets. Such activities should be extended in the upper primary and lower intermediate levels to include comparisons of two sets where the correspondence is 1 to 2, 1 to 3, 2 to 3, and so forth. Early introduction of the term ratio and discussion of the correspondence of the elements in such set situations will allow children to use number in this manner to describe correspondence situations in other learning activities.

Because we are concerned only with the number properties of the sets, it is not necessary for the elements of the two sets to be similar objects to discuss the correspondence or ratio between those number properties. Some textbook programs make a distinction between problems that involve comparing the number properties of sets composed of similar objects (*comparison*) and those that involve comparing the number properties of two sets that have dissimilar objects (*rate*). This distinction is necessary only if the teacher feels it will help pupils understand the problem situations. The computational procedures used in solving problems in either situation are identical.

Initially, the ratios are to be observed from physical representations with objects and orally stated. The first written descriptions should probably be in word form similar to those in the preceding illustrations. Introduction of a unique symbolism for expressing ratios should utilize the colon, and pupils should be taught to read the notations as

Written	Read
1 : 1	"one to one"
1 : 2	"one to two"
2 : 3	"two to three"
3 : 5	"three to five"

Expressing ratios as fractions (1/1, 1/2, 2/3, 3/5) should be delayed until problems involving the comparison of ratios or establishing an equivalent ratio are introduced. When fractional numbers are introduced as a means of expressing ratios, it should be made clear to children that the fraction is being used to indicate a comparison and is not being used to describe equal parts of an object or a group and does not indicate an unperformed division. When a fraction is used to express a ratio, a comparison of the numerator to the denominator is implied. At approximately the same level, when equivalent ratios are being introduced, tables of numerals and ordered pairs may be introduced to tabulate or record equivalent ratios.

Stars	* * * *	* * * *	* * * *	* * * *
Circles	o o o	o o o	o o o	o o o

Stars	4	8	12	16
Circles	3	6	9	12

(4, 3), (8, 6), (12, 9), (16, 12), . . .

Proportion

After children have demonstrated that they can use ratios to express the correspondence between the number properties of two sets, preferably using the smallest possible whole numbers, and can describe those ratios in fraction form, emphasis should be given to establishing equivalent ratios. In the earlier activities children may have observed that the same ratio was derived from different set situations. When specific attention is to be given to determining equivalent ratios, they may be established by combining sets of the same correspondence, as in illustration A below, or by separating in similar correspondence, as in illustration B,

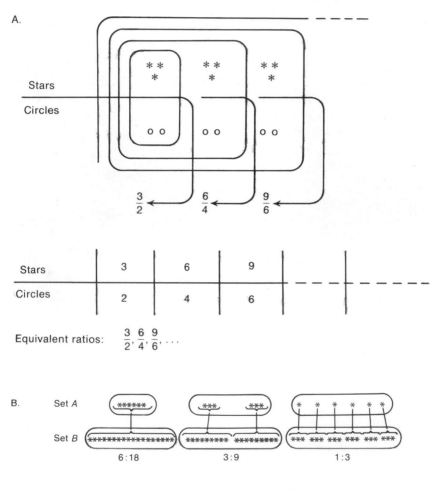

A.

Stars	3	6	9		
Circles	2	4	6		

Equivalent ratios: $\dfrac{3}{2}, \dfrac{6}{4}, \dfrac{9}{6}, \dots$

B.

Set A

Set B

6:18   3:9   1:3

Set A	6	3	1
Set B	18	9	3

Equivalent ratios: $\dots, \dfrac{6}{18}, \dfrac{3}{9}, \dfrac{1}{3}$

When the equivalence of two ratios written as fractions is expressed as an equation $\left(\dfrac{3}{2}=\dfrac{6}{4},\dfrac{1}{3}=\dfrac{3}{9},\text{ and so forth}\right)$, the expression is called a *proportion*. Attention should be called to the fact that although these expressions have the same appearance as equations involving fractions that name the same number, a proportion is an equation expressing equivalent ratios. It is important that children are clearly aware of the distinction between common fractions that name numbers and ratios or correspondences between numbers that are expressed in fraction form. Most of the problems involving ratios that children will encounter can be solved by utilizing the arithmetic of fractions. However, one notable exception is that the ratio of one correspondence cannot be added to the ratio of another correspondence as fractions are added to obtain a new ratio that describes the correspondence of the numbers of the combined sets.

					not
Circles	o o	o o		o o o o o	$\dfrac{2}{3}=\dfrac{10}{15}$
Stars	* * *	* * * * *	$\longrightarrow$	* * * * * * * *	$+\dfrac{3}{5}=\dfrac{9}{15}$ $\dfrac{19}{15}$
$\dfrac{\text{Circles}}{\text{Stars}}$	$\dfrac{2}{3}$	$\dfrac{3}{5}$		$\dfrac{5}{8}$	

After tabulating equivalent ratios and writing proportions, pupils should be guided to discover that both terms of a ratio can be multiplied or divided by the same number to obtain an equivalent ratio.

$$\frac{3}{2}=\frac{3\times 2}{2\times 2}=\frac{6}{4};\ \frac{3}{2}=\frac{3\times 3}{2\times 3}=\frac{9}{6};\ \frac{3}{2}=\frac{3\times 4}{2\times 4}=\frac{12}{8};\cdots$$

or

$$\frac{3}{2}=\frac{3\times 2}{2\times 2}=\frac{3\times 3}{2\times 3}=\frac{3\times 4}{2\times 4}=\frac{3\times 5}{2\times 5}\cdots\frac{3\times n}{2\times n}$$

$$\frac{6}{18}=\frac{6\div 2}{18\div 2}=\frac{3}{9};\ \frac{6}{18}=\frac{6\div 3}{18\div 3}=\frac{2}{6};\ \frac{6}{18}=\frac{6\div 6}{18\div 6}=\frac{1}{3}$$

The development of this generalization will allow children to understand the procedure in which they will use proportions to solve problems. These problems will involve knowing that two ratios are equivalent and that a proportion can be stated, but a term in one of the ratios is missing.

1. If 4 pencils cost 18 cents, what will 12 pencils cost?

$$\frac{4}{18} = \frac{12}{N}$$

2. If 4 pencils cost 18 cents, how many pencils can I buy for 9 cents?

$$\frac{4}{18} = \frac{N}{9}$$

Children should be able to find the missing number by manipulating objects to make sets that have the same correspondence as the known ratio. Simple problems should be used to allow children to apply their knowledge that multiplying or dividing the numerator and denominator of one ratio by the same number will result in an equivalent ratio.

$$\frac{4}{18} = \frac{4 \times \bigcirc}{18 \times \bigcirc} = \frac{12}{N} \qquad 4 \times \circled{3} = 12, \text{ so } N = 18 \times 3; \; N = 54$$

$$\frac{4}{18} = \frac{4 \div \square}{18 \div \square} = \frac{N}{9} \qquad 18 \div \boxed{2} = 9, \text{ so } N = 4 \div 2; \; N = 2$$

Two approaches might be suggested for helping children to develop the formal or adult procedure for finding the missing term of a proportion. The formal procedure is based on the idea that two ratios, $\frac{a}{b}$ and $\frac{c}{d}$ ($b \neq 0$, $d \neq 0$), are equivalent if and only if $a \times d = b \times c$. Thus, to find the missing term in the proportion $\frac{7}{9} = \frac{35}{N}$, we can write the equation $7 \times N = 9 \times 35$ and solve the equation for N.

$$7 \times N = 9 \times 35$$
$$7 \times N = 315$$
$$N = \frac{315}{7}$$
$$N = 45$$

Many of us learned this procedure by stating the proportion as $7:9 = 35:N$ and applying the rule "The product of the means is equal to the product of the extremes." The *extremes* are those terms farthest from the equal sign and the *means* are those terms nearest the equal sign: $7 \times N = 9 \times 35$.

By using the formal procedure, children will be able to solve problems involving any type of numbers and difficult computation. One approach to developing this procedure is to record many of the proportions children have observed through simple techniques in problem situations and to help them make a generalization about all the proportions. That observation is that the product of the first term of the first ratio and the second term of the second ratio is equal to the product of the second term of the first ratio and the first term of the second ratio. A common term used to describe this procedure is *cross multiplication*.

$$\frac{2}{3} = \frac{6}{9} \qquad\qquad \frac{7}{8} = \frac{49}{56}$$

$$2 \times 9 = 3 \times 6 \qquad 7 \times 56 = 8 \times 49$$
$$18 = 18 \qquad\qquad 392 = 392$$

$$\frac{3}{4} = \frac{N}{16} \qquad\qquad \frac{4}{13} = \frac{20}{N}$$

$$3 \times 16 = 4 \times N \qquad 4 \times N = 13 \times 20$$
$$48 = 4 \times N \qquad 4 \times N = 260$$

$$\frac{48}{4} = N \qquad\qquad N = \frac{260}{4}$$

$$12 = N \qquad\qquad N = 65$$

In this approach proof is not required and children accept this procedure for verifying or establishing proportions because they have seen that it was true for all their easily checked examples.

A second approach involves greater understanding of solving equations and more arithmetic computation. This approach is based on the idea that both the equivalent parts of an equation may be multiplied by the same number and the result will be a new equation—a statement of equality.

$$\frac{3}{7} = \frac{N}{56}$$

$$7 \times \frac{3}{7} = \frac{N}{56} \times 7 \text{ - - - - - - - - -} \quad \text{Multiplying both parts of the equation}$$
by 7 so that the

$$3 = \frac{N}{56} \times 7 \text{ - - - - - - - - -} \quad \text{first expression } \left(7 \times \frac{3}{7}\right) \text{ is renamed as}$$
3.

$$56 \times 3 = 56 \times \frac{N}{56} \times 7 \text{ - - - - - -} \quad \text{Multiplying both parts of the equa-}$$
tion by 56 so that the

$$56 \times 3 = N \times 7 \text{ - - - - - - - - -} \quad \text{second expression } \left(56 \times \frac{N}{56} \times 7\right) \text{ is}$$
$$168 = 7 \times N \qquad\qquad\qquad \text{renamed as } N \times 7$$

$$\frac{168}{7} = N$$

$$24 = N \qquad\qquad \text{When this equation is established, the}$$
method of solution is the same as that
used in the first approach.

This approach leads to the same generalization ($56 \times 3 = 7 \times N$) and is based on a mathematical concept, but it is probably less appropriate for children in the intermediate or upper grades. However, it might be used to expand the understandings of better pupils.

Practice exercises dealing with proportions need not always take the form of "solving for N." Pupils can be asked to determine whether the product of the means is equal to the product of the extremes or whether a statement about ratios is a proportion in exercises such as the following:

Place one of the symbols $=$ or $\neq$ in each of the circles to make each of the following a true statement about ratios.

a. $\frac{3}{4} \bigcirc \frac{6}{9}$ b. $\frac{2}{3} \bigcirc \frac{8}{12}$ c. $\frac{10}{12} \bigcirc \frac{5}{6}$

d. $\frac{15}{12} \bigcirc \frac{5}{3}$ e. $\frac{24}{72} \bigcirc \frac{72}{216}$ f. $\frac{38}{24} \bigcirc \frac{152}{120}$

Which of the above expressions are proportions? _____

_____

Children should also have opportunities to make decisions as to whether one ratio is greater than or less than another ratio. Practical problem situations can be utilized that require children to ascertain which ratio is more favorable (greater than) or less favorable (less than) when two ratios concerning similar situations are known.

"Mary bought a box of 8 crayons for 20 cents. John bought a box of 16 similar crayons for 39 cents. Who made the better buy?"

The two ratios are $\frac{8}{20}$ and $\frac{16}{39}$ and the method of finding the products of the means and of the extremes could be used first to determine that the ratios are not equivalent. There is also a technique for using cross multiplication to determine which ratio is greater than the other, but this method of comparison is complex in decision making and not the most appropriate for children. The technique involves the following procedure:

$$\frac{8}{20} \bigcirc \frac{16}{39} \qquad 8 \times 39 = 312 \qquad \text{and} \qquad 20 \times 16 = 320$$

$$312 < 320, \quad \text{so} \quad \frac{8}{20} < \frac{16}{39}$$

More appropriate procedures for helping children compare and order ratios include

A. Renaming one or both of the original ratios as equivalent ratios so that
   1. The numerators of the new ratios are equated. The denominators can then be compared and a decision made.

$$\frac{8}{20} \bigcirc \frac{16}{39} \qquad \frac{16}{40} < \frac{16}{39}, \text{ so } \frac{8}{20} < \frac{16}{39}$$

   2. The denominators of the new ratios are equated, the numerators are compared, and a decision is made.

$$\frac{8}{20} = \frac{8 \times 39}{20 \times 39} = \frac{312}{780} \qquad \text{and} \qquad \frac{16}{39} = \frac{16 \times 20}{39 \times 20} = \frac{320}{780}$$

$$\frac{312}{780} < \frac{320}{780}, \quad \text{so} \quad \frac{8}{20} < \frac{16}{39}$$

B. Each of the ratios (fractions) can be converted to decimals, the decimals can be compared, and a decision about the original ratios can be made.

$$\frac{8}{20} = 20\overline{)8.000} = .400 \qquad \text{and} \qquad \frac{16}{39} = 39\overline{)16.000} = .410$$

$$.400 < .410, \quad \text{so} \quad \frac{8}{20} < \frac{16}{39}$$

Changing the ratios to decimals can be interpreted as equating the denominators and comparing the numerators because the decimals could have been restated as fractions with the same denominators.

Percent

Perhaps the most common applications of ratio are those situations in which the base number is 100. Historically, such ratios were so commonly used for purposes of taxation and commercial transactions that a unique term and a unique symbol evolved. The term *percent* is derived from the Latin *per* meaning by or for each and *centum* meaning hundred. The symbol % (read percent) is the last or latest of a variety of related symbols that have been used to describe "for every hundred" during the past centuries. Thus the numeral 8% is composed of two symbols, represents a ratio of 8 compared to 100, and is read "eight percent."

Helping children learn to apply concepts of percent to the solution of quantitative problem situations has traditionally been given a considerable amount of attention at the intermediate and upper elementary school levels. Statements of percent continue to be widely used in reporting comparisons, and concepts of percent are still needed to solve or to make decisions about everyday problems. Because of children's contemporary and future needs, developing their abilities to understand and use concepts of percent in communication and problem solving should continue to be a major area of concern in elementary mathematics programs. However, we would hope that the confusion and difficulties children encountered with percent in programs of the past would not continue in modern programs. Children's difficulties with the topic of percent might be traced to two major sources: (1) confusion in interpretation and (2) lack of the mathematical skills to perform the necessary computations.

In a well-planned and sequential elementary mathematics program, children should have few difficulties with the mathematical skills required to solve problems involving percent. Previously acquired abilities with whole numbers, fractions, decimals, and proportions will be applied to percent problems. No new mathematical skills will be needed.

Difficulties in interpretation may stem from efforts to approach percent as a singularly different topic, unrelated to other concepts that children have previously acquired. The concept of ratio may not have been well developed or the relationship between or similarity of ratio and percent may not have been emphasized. Every statement of percent or problem concerned with percent involves the ratio comparison of the number properties of two sets. The number property of one set is compared to the number property of a base set and that ratio is stated by a percent numeral.

In the past, difficulties of interpretation were further intensified by categorizing problems involving percent into three cases. Approaches and procedures for solving problems of the following three types were fragmented and differentiated and identification of type was a major issue.

1. The ratio in percent and the number property of the base set is known. The number property of the set that is compared to the base is to be determined. 30% of $810 = N$
2. The number properties of the base set and the set that is compared to the base are known. The ratio in percent is to be determined. $N\%$ of $68 = 17$
3. The ratio in percent and the number property of the set compared to the base are known. The number property of the base set is to be determined. 20% of $N = 25$

As implied in the following discussion, identification of a problem by case and application of one of three distinct procedures or formulas is not the most appropriate approach for teaching children how to apply concepts of percent.

Assuming that children have acquired the prerequisite mathematical skills, two approaches are suggested for developing pupils' abilities to solve problems with percent. One of these is based upon children's abilities to express problems in number sentences or equations and to solve those equations. The other pertains to using equations in the form of proportions to describe the problem and finding the missing term of the equation or proportion. The authors suggest that neither of these approaches be used to the exclusion of the other. Our recommendation is that a dual approach is to be employed—both techniques are to be used in a near simultaneous manner, and the procedures should be related to each other.

Converting percents to equivalent numerals.   Children's introductory experiences with percent should deal with describing the comparison of two number properties with a percent numeral. Concrete illustrative aids used to develop these skills of interpretation and communication meaningfully are similar to the rectangular regions previously used to develop concepts of ratio. Collections of objects and other types of regions may also be used. The illustrations used should be relatively easy for children to interpret with the base number of 100 visible.

After children are proficient in describing such comparisons as percents, the same materials can be used to help children rename the percent, expressing the comparison with decimal or fractional numerals that describe the same ratio. The ability to convert percents to decimal numerals is a prerequisite to solving problems involving percent. Computations are not performed with the percent symbolism. Children will need to be able to convert state-

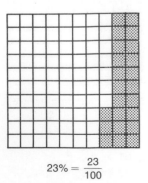

$$23\% = \frac{23}{100}$$

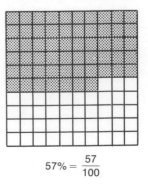

$$57\% = \frac{57}{100}$$

ments of percent into numerals (fractions and decimals) that can be used in computational procedures.

Initially, some conversions can be made by observations of shaded parts of a region that has been partitioned into 100 equal parts. Because the expression 23% is a ratio in which the base number is 100, it can be interpreted as 23 parts per 100 parts. A fraction can be written that expresses the same idea.

Children should be helped to develop the following generalization: To convert a percent to a fraction, replace the % symbol with a denominator of 100. In algorithmic form the conversion from a percent to a fraction can be developed as

$$23\% = 23 \text{ parts per hundred} = \frac{23}{100}$$

$$60\% = 60 \text{ parts per hundred} = \frac{60}{100} \quad \text{and} \quad \frac{60}{100} = \frac{6}{10} = \frac{3}{5}$$

$$12\tfrac{1}{2}\% = 12\tfrac{1}{2} \text{ parts per hundred} = \frac{12\tfrac{1}{2}}{100}$$

$$\frac{12\tfrac{1}{2}}{100} = 12\tfrac{1}{2} \times \frac{1}{100} = \frac{25}{2} \times \frac{1}{100} = \frac{25}{200} \quad \text{and} \quad \frac{25}{200} = \frac{1}{8}$$

$$125\% = 125 \text{ parts per hundred} = \frac{125}{100} \quad \text{and} \quad \frac{125}{100} = 1\frac{25}{100} = 1\frac{1}{4}$$

Percents can be converted to decimals if the interpretation of the % symbol is modified from *parts per hundred* to *hundredths*.

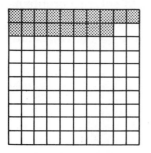

18% = 18 hundredths = .18

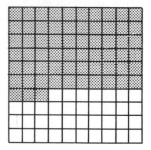

63% = 63 hundredths = .63

or

$$18\% = 18 \text{ hundredths} = 18 \times .01 = .18$$
$$63\% = 63 \text{ hundredths} = 63 \times .01 = .63$$

$$8\tfrac{1}{2}\% \text{ or } 8.5\% = 8.5 \text{ hundredths} = 8.5 \times .01 = .085$$
$$116\% = 116 \text{ hundredths} = 116 \times .01 = 1.16$$

Children are to be helped to develop the following generalization: To convert a percent to a decimal, remove the % symbol and move the decimal point two places to the left.

As described in the following section, conversion of percents to fractions or decimals is necessary for computation of solutions for problems in which the ratio in percent is known and the number property of one of the compared sets is to be determined. Computation for problems that seek the ratio in percent (the number properties of the compared sets are known) results in a fraction or decimal numeral that expresses the ratio. The fraction or decimal must then be converted to a percent.

Converting a decimal to a percent is not difficult and involves the reverse procedure of converting a percent to a decimal. The decimal is first interpreted in terms of hundredths. Then the hundredths is replaced by the equivalent symbol %.

$$.95 = 95 \text{ hundredths} = 95\%$$
$$.43 = 43 \text{ hundredths} = 43\%$$
$$.7 = 70 \text{ hundredths} = 70\%$$
$$.065 = 6.5 \text{ hundredths} = 6.5\% \text{ or } 6\tfrac{1}{2}\%$$
$$3.24 = 324 \text{ hundredths} = 324\%$$

Before children are asked to convert other decimals to percents, a sufficient number of decimals with only two places (hundredths) should be converted to percents to help them develop the following generalization: To convert a decimal to a percent, move the decimal point two places to the right and annex the % symbol.

Converting any fraction to a percent will not be too difficult for children if they have had enough experiences with converting a fraction to a decimal. In many instances the procedure requires changing the fraction to a decimal and then converting the decimal to a percent.

$$\frac{5}{8} = 8\overline{)5.000}^{\,.625} = 62.5 \text{ hundredths} = 62.5\% \text{ or } 62\tfrac{1}{2}\%$$

$$\frac{3}{16} = 16\overline{)3.0000}^{\,.1875} = 18.75 \text{ hundredths} = 18.75\% \text{ or } 18\tfrac{3}{4}\%$$

$$\frac{5}{6} = 6\overline{)5.000}^{.83\overline{3}} = 83.\overline{3} \text{ hundredths} = 83.\overline{3}\% = 83\tfrac{1}{3}\%$$

$$\frac{5}{4} = 4\overline{)5.00}^{1.25} = 125 \text{ hundredths} = 125\%$$

Some fractions are easier to convert to percents. If all the prime factors of the denominator are from the set {2, 5}, the fraction expressing the ratio can be renamed to a fraction having a denominator of 100. The fraction with a denominator of 100 can then be easily converted to a percent.

$$\frac{1}{2} = \frac{1}{2} \times \frac{50}{50} = \frac{50}{100} = 50 \text{ parts per hundred} = 50\%$$

$$\frac{3}{4} = \frac{3}{4} \times \frac{25}{25} = \frac{75}{100} = 75 \text{ parts per hundred} = 75\%$$

$$\frac{4}{5} = \frac{4}{5} \times \frac{20}{20} = \frac{80}{100} = 80 \text{ parts per hundred} = 80\%$$

$$\frac{3}{10} = \frac{3}{10} \times \frac{10}{10} = \frac{30}{100} = 30 \text{ parts per hundred} = 30\%$$

$$\frac{14}{25} = \frac{14}{25} \times \frac{4}{4} = \frac{56}{100} = 56 \text{ parts per hundred} = 56\%$$

Children should not be required to memorize fraction-decimal-percent equivalent names until they have recognized the equivalence of the ratio or have converted from one name for the ratio to the others. For purposes of practice and for later use as a reference, teachers might ask pupils to complete a table such as the following:

Equivalent ratios

Fraction	$\tfrac{1}{4}$		$\tfrac{2}{5}$	$\tfrac{1}{2}$			
Decimal	.25	.33$\overline{3}$				.375	
Percent	25%		40%	80%			

Solving problems with percent. All problems concerning percent have three component parts: a ratio between two number properties stated as a percent, the number property of the base set, and the number property of the set that is compared to the base. When the ratio stated as a percent is converted to a ratio stated as a fraction, it has two parts: a base number of 100 and a number compared to that base. In any one problem situation, any one of the three component parts may be incomplete or missing, and the solution requires finding the missing number property. The base number of 100 in the percent ratio is never missing.

In traditional arithmetic programs, these three problem situations were treated as separate cases. In some of these programs, problems and computational procedures dealing with the first case were supposedly well developed before problems of the second case were introduced. Similarly, problems and techniques with the second case were to be well mastered before problems of the third case were introduced. Then problems of all three cases were practiced, and the pupils were expected to (1) identify the "case" of the problem, (2) select the distinct computational technique for that case, and (3) compute the correct solution.

In other programs of the past pupils were expected to memorize the conditions and computational techniques of all three cases early in their work with percent and to apply the memorized rules in practice problems of all types. In many instances the practice problems were not closely related to the needs or interests of pupils.

Efforts to improve instructional techniques with the topic of percent include the use of problems closely related to the everyday experiences of children and techniques for solution that are similar for all types of problems. The current trend in techniques of solution is toward using equations to state the problem and the solution of those equations. The use of equations with problems dealing with percent is consistent with the earlier introduction and greater use of number sentences in modern mathematics programs. Prior to using equations to help solve problems with percent, children will have had many experiences in using equations or number sentences with whole numbers, fractions, and decimals; and they will have applied their computational abilities and their understandings of the inverse relationships of operations to finding solutions for "unknowns" in equations. If the proper foundations for working with percent have been developed, they will also be familiar with finding the missing number property in a proportion.

Equations for problems concerning percent can be expressed in two forms: as a number sentence and/or as a proportion. As stated previously, the authors suggest that both types of equations should be used in helping children understand and solve problems involving percent. In the introductory and developmental activities, two equations should be expressed for each problem. Later, preference may be given to one technique.

> "On a spelling test of 40 words, Paul spelled 34 correctly. What percent of the spelling words did Paul spell correctly?"

a. $N\%$ of $40 = 34$ b. $\dfrac{N}{100} = \dfrac{34}{40}$

$N\% \times 40 = 34$

In the following discussion, examples of types of percent problems are stated, two equations are written for each problem, and a suggested algorithm for solution is illustrated. The reader should note the similarity of the equations and methods of solution for all problems.

If similar procedures are to be used to solve all types of problems with percent, the decision as to which type of problem to introduce first will depend upon which situation is easiest for pupils to interpret. Realistically, this decision should be made by each teacher in consideration of his own class. However, teachers may find that when pupils' interpretations and necessary computations are considered, the order of the following illustrations is most appropriate.

Problems in which the percent is to be found may be the easiest for children to understand. The number properties of two sets that are to be compared are given and the ratio is to be stated in the form of percent. The greatest difficulty in this type of problem is in determining which set is the base set. When the base set has been ascertained, the two equations for the problem can be written. In the proportion the comparison of the number properties of the two sets is expressed as the fraction form of the ratio. The same fraction is evident in the solution of the other equation, and in each instance that ratio is to be converted to an equivalent percent.

> "When shooting baskets with a basketball, Mike made 9 out of 25 attempts. What percent of his shots did he make?"

a. $N\%$ of $25 = 9$ b. $\dfrac{N}{100} = \dfrac{9}{25}$

$^{1}N\% \times 25 = 9$ $N \times 25 = 9 \times 100$

$N\% = \dfrac{9}{25}$ $N \times 25 = 900$

$N\% = 25\overline{)9.00}^{\,.36}$ $N = \dfrac{900}{25}$

$36\% = .36$ $N = 36$

$\dfrac{36}{100} = 36\%$

Traditionally, teachers have introduced percent problems that sought the number compared to the base as the "first case." The advantage of introducing percent problems with this type was solely in the ease of computing from the memorized formula: *base × rate = percentage*. All the pupil needed to do was to change the rate or percent to a decimal fraction and multiply. Meaningful interpretation or understanding was not required, and other formulas were needed for the two other types of problems. Note that the terms rate and percentage are not used in our discussion of percent problems. Use of the terms with children may be more confusing than it is helpful. The advantage of ease in computation in problems seeking the number of the set compared to the base is lost when an equation approach to percent is utilized because the same computational pattern is used in all percent problems.

Finding the missing number property of the set compared to the base involves converting the ratio given as a percent to a fraction or decimal stating the equation, and solving for the unknown. The missing number is represented by N or any other symbol that has been used by children to represent "unknowns." In the ratio comparing the number properties of the two sets, that symbol (N) becomes the numerator.

"The sales tax in the city where Jane lives is 5%. If Jane makes a purchase of $4.60, how much sales tax will she have to pay?"

[1] Although $N\%$ is not a numeral that can be used in computation, children know that percent can be changed to computational numerals.

a. 5% of $\$4.60 = N$ b. $\dfrac{5}{100} = \dfrac{N}{4.60}$

$.05 \times \$4.60 = N$ $5 \times 4.60 = 100 \times N$

$\$.23 = N$ $23.00 = 100 \times N$

$\dfrac{23}{100} = N$

$\$.23 = N$

Percent problems in which the number property of the base set is missing and sought should be no more difficult for pupils than the preceding types. After children have interpreted the situation, the same equation approaches are used. The ratio between the two numbers expressed in percent is converted to a decimal and/or fraction, and the number sentence is written using a familiar symbol to represent the missing number. The proportion is expressed between the percent ratio that has been converted to a fraction and the ratio of the number properties of the two sets that are being compared. In these problem situations the number property of the set being compared to the base is known, and the base is unknown. The symbol representing the missing number property of the base is used as the denominator of the ratio of the two number properties.

"Marie bought a dress on sale for 75% of its original price. She paid $\$9.75$ for the dress. What was its original price?"

a. 75% of $N = \$9.75$ b. $\dfrac{75}{100} = \dfrac{9.75}{N}$

$.75 \times N = 9.75$ $75 \times N = 100 \times 9.75$

$N = \dfrac{9.75}{.75}$ $75 \times N = 975$

$N = 13$ $N = \dfrac{975}{75}$

$N = 13$

The preceding examples illustrate the advantages of using an equation approach—number sentences and proportions—to solve problems with percent. After children are able to interpret and understand the component parts of problems and to use those parts in structuring equations, a similar approach is used for all situations. Distinction between "cases" and the memorization of unique procedures for each case are unnecessary. A further advantage of developing ideas of percent on the concept of ratio is that those instances in which the percent is greater than 100% should cause no major difficulties. As illustrated in the following examples, procedures for solution will be similar to those used with percents less than 100%.

a. 130% of 80 $= N$

$$\frac{130}{100} = \frac{N}{80}$$

$1.30 \times 80 = N$

$130 \times 80 = 100 \times N$

$104.00 = N$

$10,400 = 100 \times N$

$$\frac{10,400}{100} = N$$

$104 = N$

b. 210% of $N = 105$

$$\frac{210}{100} = \frac{105}{N}$$

$2.10 \times N = 105$

$210 \times N = 100 \times 105$

$$N = \frac{105}{2.10}$$

$210 \times N = 10,500$

$N = 50$

$$N = \frac{10,500}{210}$$

$N = 50$

c. $N\%$ of $60 = 93$

$$\frac{N}{100} = \frac{93}{60}$$

$N\% \times 60 = 93$

$N \times 60 = 100 \times 93$

$$N = \frac{93}{60}$$

$N \times 60 = 9,300$

$N = 1.55$

$$N = \frac{9,300}{60}$$

$155\% = 1.55$

$N = 155$

$$\frac{155}{100} = 155\%$$

Verifying solutions to problems involving percent

When children are solving problems with percent or computing results for practice exercises, they should be encouraged to verify their solutions. To verify the solution of the number sentence type of equation, the observed result is substituted for the unknown in the equation and the indicated operation is performed. If an accurate computational operation indicates that the number sentence is a true statement, the observed result is correct.

$$85\% \text{ of } N = 29.75 \qquad 85\% \text{ of } \boxed{35} = 29.75$$
$$.85 \times N = 29.75 \qquad .85 \times 35 = 29.75$$
$$N = \frac{29.75}{.85}$$
$$\begin{array}{r} 35 \\ \times .85 \\ \hline 175 \\ 280 \\ \hline 29.75 = 29.75 \end{array}$$
$$N = 35$$

A similar procedure is followed in verifying the result of the computational procedures used to find the missing number in the proportion. The observed result is substituted for the unknown in the original proportion and computational techniques are used to compare the ratios in the proportion to determine whether they are equal.

$$\frac{85}{100} = \frac{29.75}{N} \qquad \frac{85}{100} = \frac{29.75}{\boxed{35}}$$
$$85 \times N = 100 \times 29.75 \qquad 85 \times 35 = 100 \times 29.75$$
$$85 \times N = 2{,}975 \qquad 2{,}975 = 2975$$
$$N = \frac{2{,}975}{85}$$
$$N = 35$$

Children's verification of solutions for problems with percent involve utilization of previously learned concepts of ratio and proportion. The more meaningfully these concepts are taught to children, the more effective and efficient children will be in their application of these concepts in describing quantitative situations and in solving problems. The same general principles that pertain to good instructional techniques and procedures in other areas of the elementary mathematics program also pertain to the introduction and development of concepts of ratio, proportion, and percent.

Suggested activities

1. Develop a list of examples from classroom situations from which the ratios of correspondences between the number properties of two sets can be illustrated as 1:2, 1:3, 2:3, and so forth.

2. Collect from magazines and newspapers examples of ratios being used in life situations to describe comparisons.

3. Prepare a set of transparencies and overlays for use with the overhead projector that will illustrate equivalent ratios or proportions.

4. Collect from magazines and newspapers comparisons expressed as percents. Include in the collection illustrations and circle graphs.

5. Refer to pupils' textbooks for problems involving percent. Select several of those problems and solve them using both types of equations.

6. Select several modern textbook series and compare approaches in teaching pupils to solve problems with percent.

Selected references

Fehr, H. F., and T. J. Hill, *Contemporary Mathematics for Elementary Teachers*. Boston: D. C. Heath and Company, 1966, Chapter 16, "Applications of Mathematics," pp. 319–337.

Mueller, F. J., *Arithmetic — Its Structure and Concepts*. Englewood Cliffs, N. J.: Prentice-Hall, Inc., 1964, Unit 23, "Ratio, Proportion, and Probability," and Unit 24, "Per Cent," pp. 289–313.

Schaaf, W. L., *Basic Concepts of Elementary Mathematics*. New York: John Wiley & Sons, Inc., 1965, Chapter 11, "Mensuration," pp. 313–358.

Webber, G. C., and J. A. Brown, *Basic Concepts of Mathematics*. Reading, Mass.: Addison-Wesley Publishing Company, Inc., 1963, Chapter 9, "Applications," pp. 174–188.

Teaching 12
geometry and measurement

The early introduction of geometric concepts into the elementary mathematics program is one of the major content modifications in recent curriculum development. Traditionally, some aspects of geometry have been taught as a part of the study of measurement and from an arithmetic viewpoint at the upper elementary level. The geometric concepts currently being introduced as early as kindergarten and spirally developed at following levels are not based upon ideas of measurement and thus are not arithmetically oriented. The geometry in contemporary elementary programs is directed toward the intuitive development of ideas of geometry and is concerned with the properties and spatial relationships of such geometric entities as points, lines, angles, figures, and solids. The intuitive development of ideas differs from a formal approach in that it does not rely upon definitions, axioms, theorems, or proofs. It allows the child to use his intuition, general knowledge, and recognition to see and develop ideas in an informal manner.

Several reasons can be given for the early inclusion of geometry in the elementary program. Every child entering school possesses some knowledge of comparing magnitudes and of spacial relationships and will continue to expand this knowledge in his out-of-school experiences. Young children are using some of the vocabulary. Many are applying simple geometric concepts to their physical world and will make further applications as they grow. A well-planned and well-conducted classroom program that develops geometric ideas sequentially will be much more instructionally efficient than the pupils' self-directed learning. In addition, teachers who have introduced concepts of geometry with procedures in which children explore and develop ideas intuitively have found that not only do the children learn but that they also enjoy the activities. Their enjoyment tends to serve as a motivational factor and may help to develop more favorable attitudes toward the study of mathematics. Recently reported studies indicate that pupils need not be above-average achievers to understand geometric ideas and to perform simple constructions with a straightedge and compass.

The early introduction of geometric concepts is also advantageous in terms of pupils' later learning experiences. Those pupils who have intuitively developed geometric facts or ideas will be able to comprehend the content better and to establish the proofs required in the formal study of geometry at the secondary level. The inquiry approach used in the early intuitive development of geometric ideas and generalizations is quite likely to transfer to the development of other mathematical knowledge and perhaps to other areas of study. Early applications of geometric concepts to physical models will be useful in the later study of art, science, social studies, and industrial arts and even in many vocational endeavors.

The development and application of measurement techniques have also received renewed interest as an important part of a complete program in elementary mathematics. Although some published programs and some experimental and curriculum development projects are virtually void of any application of mathematical concepts outside the field itself, other programs and projects emphasize measurement as an application of geometry and arithmetic. The current trend appears to be toward greater emphasis on applications of mathematics and the integration of those applications in modern elementary science and social studies programs with the mathematics program.

Our reason for combining the discussion of teaching geometry and measurement in one chapter is that a truly modern elementary mathematics program attempts to develop and integrate concepts of geometry, arithmetic, and elementary algebra from kindergarten on. At the elementary level, measurement is the vehicle of integration for these concepts. Although the ideas of geometry are to be introduced and developed intuitively, concepts and physical representations or models of those concepts will be applied to measurement activities. Geometry is to be taught in the elementary school because of its merit and not strictly because it can be considered a prerequisite for measurement, but it is not completely correct to state that the geometry of the elementary school program does not concern measurement or that it is *nonmetric*. Measurement deals with the comparison of magnitudes. Initially, geometric ideas are introduced without such a reference, but those ideas are soon used to develop models that will be used in comparison situations. Measurement is one of the most important applications of geometry and arithmetic.

Singular chapters or volumes could be written to describe the content and teaching of geometry and measurement in the elementary school. Our endeavor in this chapter will not be to describe the scope and sequence of content in these major areas nor to describe and illustrate distinct appropriate techniques for teaching specific concepts. Instead, we shall be concerned with general principles and classroom practices related to helping children understand and apply major ideas in these areas.

Introducing geometric concepts

Mathematics educators agree that some of the main ideas of geometry can and should be taught in the elementary grades. There is general consensus that each child in the early grades should become familiar with the basic ideas of geometry and that these ideas should be nonmetric. There is also agreement that the introduction and development of geometric ideas at this level should be intuitive, in which children see, handle, discuss, and develop generalizations from all sorts of geometric models.

The same extent of agreement does not exist in regard to the specifics of geometry in the elementary school program. Several questions of curriculum development that have not yet been definitively answered are

1. What are the basic ideas of geometry that should be developed in the elementary grades?
2. When or in what sequence should these ideas be taught?
3. What instructional procedures should be used in teaching specific geometric ideas to young children?

4. From an evaluative or objective viewpoint, what shall children know or demonstrate before we consider them "familiar" with a basic idea?
5. What special efforts should be made to relate or teach and apply geometric concepts to areas such as science, social studies, and art?

An analysis of the reports of special committees, curriculum development projects, and commercially published materials will indicate some small differences in what are to be considered the basic ideas of nonmetric geometry that are to be taught at the elementary level. Greater differences will appear in the suggested order or sequence in which these ideas are to be taught. Differences in the sequence in which the ideas are to be taught imply that there are also differences in the instructional procedures to be used because techniques will take advantage of children's previous knowledge.

The following diagram is an attempt to illustrate schematically most of the basic geometric ideas that are to be included in the elementary program. Children are to be introduced to the entities and ideas of geometry, which they will learn to recognize and to name. They will observe properties, characteristics, or facts about geometric entities. To help children organize their geometric ideas, entities should be classified according to their possession of common characteristics, generalizations about comparisons of the size and shape of entities should be developed, and the relationships of ideas or concepts should be considered.

The entities or "things" of geometry with which elementary school children will be concerned are subsets of points in space and that space is considered to be the set of all points around us. The term *point* is undefined, but we can discuss it with children as having no dimensions of length, width, or thickness; thus no size and no shape. All a specific point has is a place or position. A point, then, is an abstract idea, and, because geometric entities are composed of sets of points, they, too, are abstract ideas. Points cannot be seen and neither can the geometric entities that are subsets of points.

In the elementary program, geometric entities should be discussed as sets of points. Lines and curves are sets of points; angles are sets of points; triangles, quadrilaterals, circles, and other figures

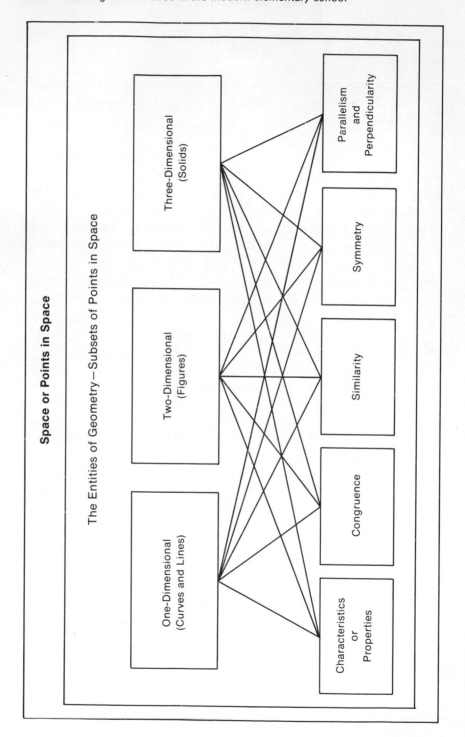

Space or Points in Space

The Entities of Geometry—Subsets of Points in Space

Three-Dimensional (Solids)

Two-Dimensional (Figures)

One-Dimensional (Curves and Lines)

Parallelism and Perpendicularity

Symmetry

Similarity

Congruence

Characteristics or Properties

are sets of points; planes are sets of points; and solid regions are sets of points. The use of "set language" will allow children to be precise in their discussion of geometric ideas.

Because the entities of geometry cannot be seen, representations or models of those things are used as a means of study. To help children to name geometric entities, classify geometric entities, establish properties of geometric entities, and to make generalizations about geometric entities, physical models and line drawings are used as representations of those geometric entities. Using physical models to represent geometric entities is analogous to using counters or objects to represent numbers. Using line drawings to represent geometric entities is analogous to using numerals to represent numbers.

Children's familiarity with the basic ideas of geometry are developed at the elementary level through observation, through seeing and feeling, and by construction of both physical models and line drawings. Their familiarity with basic ideas of geometry is not effectively developed through vocabulary exercises in which names, definitions, descriptions, and rules are presented abstractly.

Means of developing basic ideas of geometry

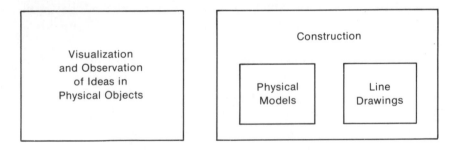

Use of physical models. When physical objects are used to introduce geometric ideas, children should be allowed to handle the objects, to make observations, and to express ideas in their own words. Children should be encouraged to recognize familiar shapes in the physical models and to associate descriptive terms or names with those shapes. Careful teacher questioning can guide pupils to discover the geometric properties or characteristics of the physical objects and generalizations can be developed that include descriptions and definitions. Misuse of specific terms, misconceptions, and incorrect ideas are to be corrected. As special vocabulary is needed, it is introduced and used, but no effort should be made to force or to limit children to the use of precise terms and definitions in their discussions. As children participate in these activities and discussions, they will expand their vocabulary and make their statements about geometric ideas more precise.

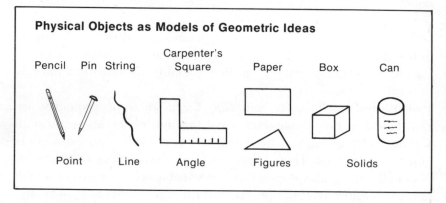

Physical Objects as Models of Geometric Ideas

			Carpenter's			
Pencil	Pin	String	Square	Paper	Box	Can
Point		Line	Angle	Figures		Solids

At this level the development of geometric ideas is concrete in that the abstractions are represented by physical things that can be seen or felt. However, it should be clear to teachers that the purpose of these activities is not merely to identify characteristics of the objects, but to emphasize the geometric ideas that are illustrated or present in those objects.

Constructions. Some geometry programs do not use physical objects in introductory experiences, but introduce geometric ideas with constructions of either physical models or line drawings. Because children should be able to see, handle, and feel the representations of ideas, it would seem appropriate to utilize constructed physical models before children are asked to make line drawings.

Physical representations of geometric entities with one or two dimensions can be constructed with string, rubber bands, and pegs and pegboard. By constructing geometric entities on a pegboard and discussing them, children can generalize about the characteristics or properties of those things and develop basic ideas about congruence, similarity, symmetry, parallelism, and perpendicularity. One of the few geometric entities with fewer than three dimensions that cannot be constructed on a pegboard is a circle. However, children are interested in trying to do so and from their trials can generalize about the characteristics or properties of a circle.

Teachers should remember that in a spiral plan of curriculum all the basic ideas about geometric entities will not be introduced and developed from one sequence of experiences. The same topic or idea will be reintroduced at later stages in the program, and the concepts related to those entities will be expanded and extended. Just as with developing ideas from physical objects, specific and precise use of vocabulary is not a requirement in early experiences. Children should use their own words to describe ideas. Understanding of the idea is to be considered more important than knowing the name for that idea. For example, the idea of congruence can be discussed as "entities having the same size and the same shape"; similarity can be referred to as "entities with the same shape but not the same size"; and perpendicularity can be described as "lines making a square corner."

In pegboard constructions, pegs represent points with specific positions and the strings or rubber bands represent sets of points. For the best development of geometric ideas from pegboard constructions, each child should have his own small pegboard and rubber bands and a large pegboard should be available for teacher and pupil illustrations and demonstrations that a group of pupils can observe and discuss. To facilitate constructions, the pupils' pegboards can have the points (pegs) permanently fixed, perhaps as driven nails. For the large pegboard, pegs used as points should be movable.

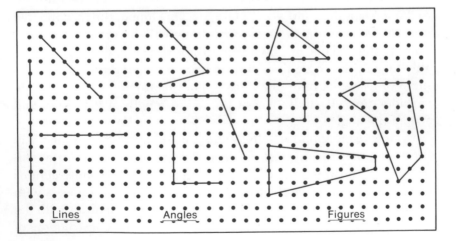

As children are constructing models and developing geometric ideas, they should be identifying many geometric shapes. Some of these geometric shapes will have common properties, and children should be encouraged to classify geometric entities into subsets that have common properties. With some guidance they can establish the idea that geometric figures can be classified according to the number and relative size of the angles and/or the number and relationships between the sides of the figures. As with the development of other mathematical skills, pupils' attempts at classification should proceed from those that are relatively simple to those that are more complex. For example,

1. Figures may be classified according to the number of angles or sides.
2. Angles may be classified as right angles (square corners), less than right angles, or greater than right angles.
3. Triangles may be classified by establishing whether the three sides are unequal in length, two sides are equal in length, or all three sides are equal in length.
4. Triangles may be classified as to the size of the angles: one right angle and two acute angles; three acute angles; one obtuse angle and two acute angles.
5. Quadrilaterals may be classified according to the relationship of the sides.

Classification activities should help children establish and associate names, illustrations, and definitions of geometric entities. As understandings and vocabulary are developed, the terminology used by children in their classifications will be refined. In addition, as their skills of classification are developed, they will be able to consider more than one characteristic referent in categorizing. For example, their classification of quadrilaterals will include consideration of parallelism of the sides, length of the sides, and size of the angles.

A few contemporary elementary mathematics programs pay little attention to physical models and introduce geometric concepts with constructions of line drawings. Pegboard constructions can be more appropriately used to develop geometric concepts with younger children because they will have fewer difficulties with the constructions. Learning activities related to the construction of

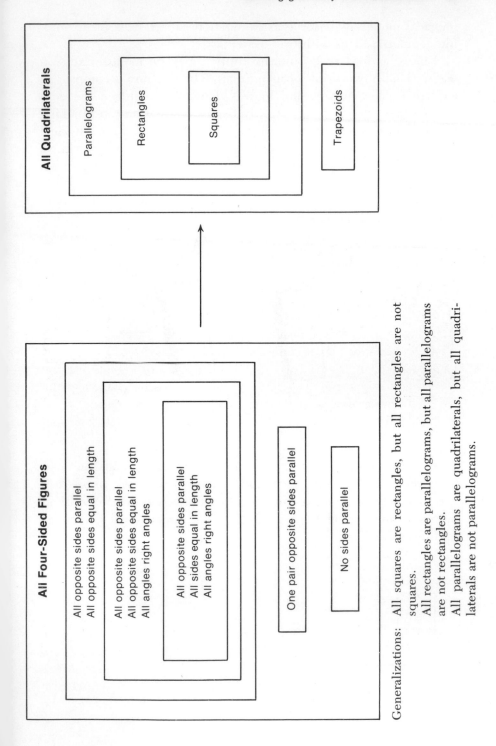

All Quadrilaterals

Parallelograms

Rectangles

Squares

Trapezoids

All Four-Sided Figures

All opposite sides parallel
All opposite sides equal in length

All opposite sides parallel
All opposite sides equal in length
All angles right angles

All opposite sides parallel
All sides equal in length
All angles right angles

One pair opposite sides parallel

No sides parallel

Generalizations: All squares are rectangles, but all rectangles are not squares.
All rectangles are parallelograms, but all parallelograms are not rectangles.
All parallelograms are quadrilaterals, but all quadrilaterals are not parallelograms.

physical models will serve as foundation experiences for extending geometric ideas with line drawings.

Line drawings of geometric entities may be made in several ways. Usually we think of using a straightedge and a compass to construct lines, angles, and figures. However, children can construct some line drawings simply by using a pattern and making a pencil mark along or around it. The patterns used are physical objects. For example, a straightedge is a pattern for drawing a straight line, the bottom of a can is a pattern for drawing a circle, and so forth.

Children may find it interesting to construct some of their own patterns by folding paper:

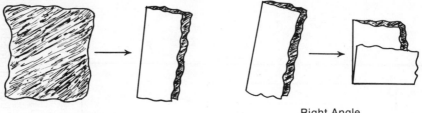

Straightedge

Right Angle
(Square Corner)

By making other appropriate folds, children can construct patterns for triangles, rectangles, and squares. If desired, pupils can use such patterns to make drawings that can be cut out, folded, and pasted to make models of solids or three-dimensional geometric entities.

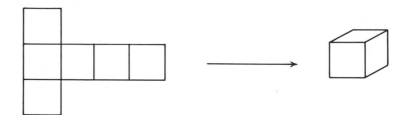

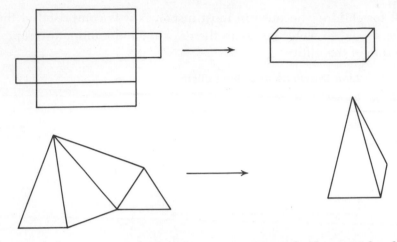

Line drawings made from patterns, primarily the straightedge, can be used to extend previous learnings and to introduce new ideas. In these activities, geometric entities continue to be discussed as sets of points, and children should be made aware of the distinction between geometric concepts and the models or drawings used to represent those ideas. The distinction can be made by discussing with children the idea that we can make drawings or models of geometric ideas such as points, lines, angles, and figures. The geometric ideas are abstractions and cannot be seen, but we can use models or drawings to study about them.

In line drawings, dots are used to represent specific points that can be named with capital letters, and the elongated pencil mark represents a line or set of points. Note that a geometric line is a *straight* line. Concepts that can be developed with simple line drawings include

1. The infinite length of a line
2. A ray as a line with one end point
3. A line segment as a line with measurable length or two end points
4. The properties and characteristics of angles
5. The properties and characteristics of figures

The symbolism used to describe geometric entities represented by line drawings is often introduced to children when they are learning to make those constructions. The symbolism is not difficult for children because in most instances it is comprised of the letters used to name points in the drawing and a miniature reproduction of the entity.

Line Drawings and Symbolism

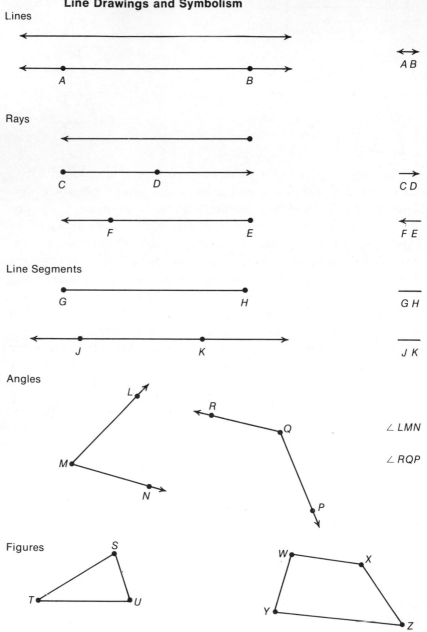

Lines

AB

Rays

CD

FE

Line Segments

GH

JK

Angles

∠ LMN

∠ RQP

Figures

Before children are expected to make geometric constructions with a compass, they should be allowed sufficient time to explore with the device and to discover what can be done with it. The compass has two "legs" joined at one end with a pencil "point" at the end of one leg and a metal "point" at the end of the other. It is the variable distance between these two "points" that is of major importance in using the compass.

Children's first directed experiences with a compass should involve using the instrument to compare the measurement of distance between several points. Are points B and C the same distance from point A?

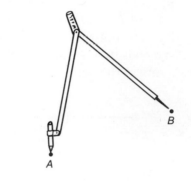

The procedure is to adjust the compass so that the end points of the instrument are "on" two of the points, A and B in the illustration, and to compare that distance with the distance between A and C.

Following many similar experiences, children can be asked to construct line segments that are congruent (the same length) to given line segments and to compare angles to determine whether they are congruent. To construct a line segment that is of the same length as a given line segment, the pupil must first use a straightedge to draw a line that is longer than the given segment. Then using the compass, he transfers the length of the given line segment to a segment on the line he has drawn. The construction is completed when he names the end points of the segment on the line he constructed.

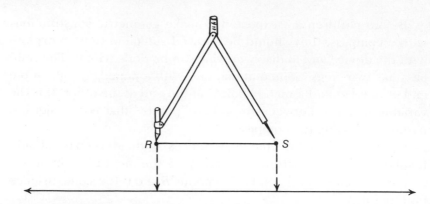

To compare angles to determine whether they are congruent, the illustrated procedure is to (1) use the compass to establish points on the sides of the two angles that are equidistant from the vertices, $\overline{AB} = \overline{AC} = \overline{DE} = \overline{DF}$. The compass is then used to (2) establish the distance between those two points in one of the angles. That distance is then compared (3) to the distance between the identified points in the other angle.

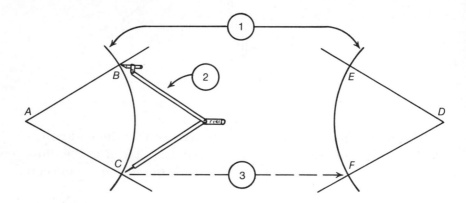

Succeeding constructions will include drawing circles, constructing angles congruent to given angles, constructing a line perpendicular to a given line at a given point, bisecting angles, constructing a line parallel to a given line, and constructing a figure congruent to a given figure. All these constructions will involve using the compass as an instrument to transfer measurements (distance between points). To help children develop geometric ideas from line constructions, teachers must themselves be proficient in the use of the straightedge and compass.

Through learning activities that emphasize the use of physical objects, constructions of physical models, and constructions of line drawings to represent geometric entities, children in modern elementary mathematics programs should become familiar with the basic ideas of geometry. The basic ideas have been briefly described as the identification of geometric entities and their properties or characteristics, the classificaticn of geometric entities, and the consideration of possible relationships between geometric entities. Well-planned elementary mathematics programs should use a unit teaching approach to develop geometric ideas with children rather than isolated one-day lessons and will spirally develop, expand, and extend concepts of geometry at all levels in the program.

The geometry currently considered appropriate for the elementary program is concerned with sets of points in space. To many teachers it appears to be the same geometry that they were taught in the secondary school, but the discussion in this chapter should have made clear that in the elementary program we are not concerned with theorems and formal proofs. It is the same *Euclidean geometry*, but in contemporary elementary programs the objectives are to develop major ideas intuitively from concrete representations.

In addition to utilizing the suggestions in this chapter dealing with objects, models, and constructions, teachers should investigate the possibilities of conducting simple experiments in topology, using projective devices, making scale drawings, and plotting points on coordinates as means of expanding children's understanding and use of geometric ideas.

Developing concepts of measurement

In the broadest sense, *measurement* is concerned with finding the quantity, size, or amount of either physical objects or geometric entities. This definition implies that there are two types of measurement. One type deals with counting or naming a number of *discrete* objects and the measurement results in an exact number described by an integer. If related to a number line, this type of measurement employs only the positive integers.

The term measurement is generally used in reference to a second type of activity that involves associating a number with variables that have a *continuous* quality such as amounts of length, surface, volume, time, and temperature. When related to a number line or scale, the possible values of continuous variables are uninterrupted and consist not only of integers, but of all real numbers. Measurements are determined by using some appropriate unit as a basis for comparison and stating the measurement as a ratio between the measured quantity and the unit. In this chapter, emphasis is placed upon the measurement of continuous variables.

The measurement of continuous variables can be further categorized into two types of procedures. When some unit is used as a basis for comparison by applying it directly to the thing or quantity being measured, the procedure is called *direct measurement*. Examples of direct measurement are using a ruler to measure length, using a model of a square inch to measure surface, and using a cup to measure capacity. Sometimes the measurement is arrived at by indirect means. Examples of *indirect measurement* are measuring temperature by the expansion of liquid in a tube or metal in a coil, measuring time by the hands on a clock, or any other instance when a physical model of the unit is not directly used.

Before measurement as a topic is introduced in the elementary program, children will have had many experiences with both direct and indirect measurement. In some of their activities they will have physically compared magnitudes in a direct manner and will probably have made some observation or generalization from the comparisons. Most of these early environmental experiences will have dealt with measures of capacity. For example, children may have observed that it is possible to get two cups of milk from one small bottle of milk called a pint. In other direct measurement activities, they will have compared the length, height, width, and size of several objects and made decisions concerning those comparisons.

Young children's observations from indirect measurements will not be as clearly developed and may simply be related to the instrument used to make the measurement. From their experiences, children may conclude that (1) to "tell" the time, we look at or "read" a clock; (2) to "tell" the temperature or how cold it is, we "read" the thermometer; and (3) to "tell" how much we weigh, we look at or "read" the numerals on the scale. In many instances, such observations from children are completely unrelated to the major idea that measurement deals with the comparison of magnitudes.

In the first year of school experiences, children are ready to be introduced to some of the basic ideas of measurement. The systematic or formal development of measurement concepts with children should stress activities of direct measurement in which they are actively engaged in making comparisons. It is only after children understand the use of measurement units in comparison situations that indirect measurements become meaningful. Initial experiences need not involve number names, but might deal only with the comparison of two "things" and the use of comparative terms such as longer or shorter and more or less. As children learn to use number names and units for comparison, concepts are to be broadened and extended through a spiral organization of the content of measurement in the elementary mathematics program.

Some instructional programs introduce children to the topic of measurement by acquainting them with some of the most commonly used measuring devices. The procedure is to introduce a particular device and to discuss the uses of the instrument. Teacher demonstrations of the purposes of the instrument are often followed by pupil attempts to use the instruments. Pupil proficiency with the devices is extended by structuring situations that require greater precision. Such programs are to be commended for their efforts to help children learn about measurement by actually measuring, but in many instances these experiences deal only superficially with the basic ideas underlying measurement and a small amount of pupil success in using a device is often misinterpreted as understanding and mastery of a measurement process.

In primary programs it is not unusual to find as much emphasis being placed upon instruments of indirect measurement such as the clock and the thermometer as there is upon instruments used in direct measurement. However, most of the activities related to the clock and the thermometer are not really measurement activities that involve a comparison of the use of measurement units. Instead, such experiences are more directed toward interpreting or reading data that is presented by these instruments and should probably be approached as developing techniques of "reading" the information from the device.

Measurement activities in the elementary mathematics program are concerned with measurements of linear distance, surface or area, weight, volume, and capacity and in some instances measurement of angles. Instructional procedures should be designed to help children understand the nature of measurement and to introduce and develop major ideas of measurement such as those cited by Scott.[1]

1. The comparative nature of all measurement
2. The likeness between the measurement referent and the measured characteristic
3. The arbitrariness of the measurement referent
4. The desirability of standard reference units
5. The inexact characteristic of measurement
6. The aspect of precision
7. The treatment of error
8. The use of indirect measurement

Common procedures.   Concept and skill development activities that are concerned with measurement should always be initiated with some type of comparison in a direct measurement approach, preferably with a problem situation that requires description of some geometric characteristic. However, children's measurement experiences should not begin with the use of common measuring devices. Early experiences and activities should allow children to explore with units of measure and to make generalizations about the measurement. Learnings gained from such activities will lead to pupils' use of common measurement devices.

After the need for a measurement description of a geometric characteristic or quantity has been established, a way of describing the characteristic by reference to some unit is introduced. The first units used in the comparison of the quantity to be measured can be units proposed by children in the form of models. Attention should be called to the need for the proposed units to possess the same characteristic as that which is to be measured. If length is to be measured, the proposed unit must have the characteristic of length; if amount of surface is to be measured, the proposed unit must have the characteristic of surface; and so forth. The proposed units need not be of a definite size or be named. For the sake of classroom discussion, they could simply be called "Jimmy's unit" or "Mary's unit."

---

[1] Scott, Lloyd, *Trends in Elementary School Mathematics.* Skokie, Ill.: Rand McNally & Company, 1966, p. 84.

To determine the length of a rod, Jimmy suggested this unit of length⊏▭⊐ and Mary suggested this unit⊏▭▭⊐. Both Mary and Jimmy used pieces of drinking straw for their models of units of measurement.

Children are to be given the opportunity to measure the object with the model units they propose and with the units that were suggested by other pupils. The measurements are made by actual comparison of the quantity of the object to be measured to the quantity of the suggested model units.

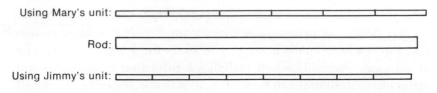

This activity naturally leads to a discussion of (1) the inexact characteristic of measurement and (2) the need for a common or standard unit.

When Mary's unit is used for measurement of the rod, the decision would be that the rod is *about* six of those units long. When Jimmy's unit is used, the decision would be that the rod is *about* or *approximately* eight of those units long. Even if some pupil felt that the model unit he suggested resulted in an exact comparison number, the same model used by another pupil might not result in the same decision. Through these kinds of experiences, children will learn that we measure as accurately as we can with the instruments we have and that measurements can never be absolutely exact.

When children are asked for suggestions concerning a common or standard unit, the commonly used units and measuring devices will probably be suggested. If the suggestion is not forthcoming from the pupils, the device or unit must be introduced by the teacher. At this point, some historical information pertaining to the origin of the standard unit commonly used today will be of interest to many pupils.

Children's use of standard units will reinforce the idea of the inexactness of measurements and will lead them toward being as precise in their measurements as the instruments they use and the number concepts they possess will allow. Children's abilities to be precise in their measurement activities are closely related to their understandings, knowledge, and skills with number. As children develop concepts involving fractions and become familiar with their use, they should describe and record measurements in terms of fractions or rational numbers. Measurement activities in problem-solving situations should be an integral part of the development of number concepts.

Teachers should introduce children to instruments of measurement that will allow them to be more precise as their skills develop and should encourage them to work toward a greater degree of preciseness in their measurements. One of the generalizations that they should be helped to develop is that they can measure with a greater degree of preciseness when a small unit is used than they can when a larger unit is used. For example, length can be measured more precisely when utilizing a ruler that is scaled to one-sixteenth inch than it can be with a ruler that is scaled to one-fourth inch.

As children work with the idea of preciseness, they should be helped to understand that the measurements they record are not *true* measurements but approximations. They should generalize that a better approximation of the measurement could always be recorded if the unit of measurement used were smaller, and a smaller unit of measurement can always be thought of. In all their measurements, children should be concerned with making a measurement with a degree of precision that is appropriate to their purpose.

Children should also be led to discover that when a smaller unit of measurement is used, the size of the possible error of measurement is reduced. The greatest possible error of measurement is equal to one half of the unit being used. Consider measuring the length of a line segment with rulers that are scaled in (1) inches, (2) one-half inches, (3) one-fourth inches, and so forth.

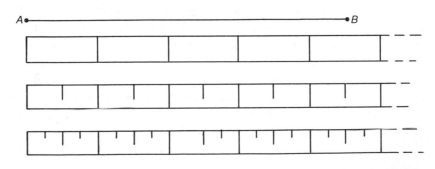

The recorded measure and the greatest possible error when using each ruler is

Ruler scaled to	Recorded measure	Greatest possible error
One inch	5 inches	$\frac{1}{2}$ inch
One-half inch	$4\frac{1}{2}$ inches	$\frac{1}{4}$ inch
One-fourth inch	$4\frac{3}{4}$ inches	$\frac{1}{8}$ inch

The greatest possible error is also often called *tolerance*. The term tolerance can also be used to refer to a "goodness of fit" in which the measured object is to have a minimum and a maximum measure. For example, if a rod is to be cut that is not longer than $4\frac{1}{2}$ inches and not shorter than $4\frac{3}{8}$ inches, the tolerance is the difference between the two requirements or $\frac{1}{8}$ inch.

As children progress in a spiral development of measurement concepts, they will be introduced to many measuring devices. Several of these devices will be designed to measure the same characteristic, and pupils should have opportunities to select the most appropriate instruments for the purposes of problem situations.

As they work with various measurement units, pupils should become familiar with the relative size of those units. Familiarity with the size of units will make reasonable estimations of measurements possible. Activities that require children to estimate measurements in relation to the measurement units that are being studied are an important part of the learning experiences dealing with measurement, and efforts should be made to help children improve their skills in estimation.

It may be very difficult to introduce the measurements of time and temperature with activities that deal with direct measurement —the actual comparison of a unit to the quantity that is to be measured. Some ingenuity can be used to establish units of time with sun dials, egg timers, water clocks, and so forth, to make the measurement of time more meaningful, but it may be more appropriate for young children to deal with these topics as indirect measurements. Standard units on the measuring devices, clocks and thermometers, can be emphasized and children can be taught to make measurements by accurate reading of the device.

As children develop concepts of area and volume, they will establish short procedures using linear measurements and computation to arrive at measurements of surface and capacity. These short procedures or indirect measurements will be much more meaningful to pupils if they have had previous experiences with directly measuring those geometric characteristics.

Specific suggestions

As previously stated, children's development of understandings and abilities to use the various units of measurement should generally involve direct measurement. Activities and experiences should be structured and directed by teachers so that basic or foundational ideas of measurement are emphasized in each topic or area of measurement that is undertaken. In summary, those basic ideas are concerned with measurement as comparison, the need for standard units, and the desirability of precision in measurement. In addition to consideration of the previously described common elements in instructional procedures, the following specific suggestions are made for particular topics of measurement study in the elementary program.

Linear measure. The development of concepts pertaining to linear measure or distance is directly related to the development of the geometric concepts of points and line segments. Children should have a good intuitive understanding of lines and line segments before the systematic study of linear measurement is begun. Because the ruler or instruments for linear measurement are primarily number lines, children should have constructed number lines using units of varying length before they are asked to apply a number line to measuring situations. They should, in fact, construct some rulers for their own use. As their knowledge of fractions or rational numbers is expanded, the constructed number lines or rulers will include rational numbers and their measurements should become more precise.

The measurement of perimeters of geometric figures should be approached as a measurement of distance that determines the total length of the line or line segments comprising the figures or polygons. To avoid confusion with the measurement of surface, activities in which the perimeter of polygons are to be determined should not be simultaneous with activities concerning the measurement of area or surface. Pegboard constructions, line drawings, string, and rulers should be used to help children determine perimeters, and formulas are to be developed by children from many actual measurement activities. Measurements of the linear characteristics of circles should be developed as measures of distance and relationships between those measures should be meaningfully established through measurements and comparisons. For example, the linear characteristics of many physical models of circles can be measured, recorded, and compared to establish ideas of the relationship of the diameter to the radius and the circumference to the diameter.

Area.   Children's understanding of the concept of area is dependent upon the recognition of a plane region as a surface comprised of points—the union of the closed curve and its interior. This idea may be developed by having children cover geometric regions with pencil marks or color representing points and illustrating surface.

Most elementary programs introduce the concept of area by presenting a problem situation in which the amount of surface of a rectangular region is to be determined. Children are encouraged to find the amount of surface in the region using their own units of measurement to "cover" the surface. In this early activity, children need to recognize that to measure a region, a unit that is itself a region is required. Different pupils may use unit regions that are unequal in size. One might use the side of a book and another might use a sheet of paper, but each must make sure that the entire region is measured.

After children agree on the need for a common or standard unit, they should be helped to select as the standard units to be used the square regions that are commonly used to measure area. Following direct measurement activities in which these standard units are placed or drawn on rectangular regions and counted to determine the area, children should be asked to develop a formula that would allow them to measure indirectly or to compute the area. They might proceed to develop the formula for the area of a rectangular region as

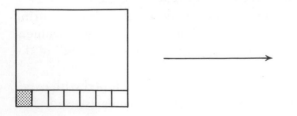

(the number of rows) × (the number of units in each row)
    = the total number of units in the region

Or, if the standard unit were a square inch,

6 rows with 7 square inches in each row = 42 square inches

With the teacher's guidance, the abstract formula for the area of a rectangular region should evolve: Area = length × width or $A = lw$.

When pupils recognize that the measure of a region can be determined by finding the number of square units that are needed to cover the region, they will be able to find the areas of other polygons (geometric regions). The measurement of the area of other geometric regions will be related to and developed from the measurement of the area of rectangles. Direct measurement of triangular regions and regions with the shape of parallelograms will lead to the establishment of appropriate formulas for computing those areas.

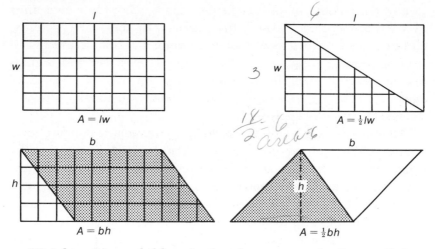

Weight.   Many children in the elementary school can tell their weight in terms of some number name but have little understanding of the direct measurement of weight or what that number means. In too many instances, pupils' experiences with measuring weight are of an indirect nature in which the measuring instrument indicates a numeral that is to be regarded as the "weight" of the object being measured.

Concepts of measuring weight should be developed with experiences of direct measurement in which a balance is used. The weight of objects can be determined in units of marbles, dominoes, or some other unit. Standard units can be introduced to show that measurements made with such units are more precise. From such experiences, children are much more likely to understand units of weight and to be able to use those units in problem-solving situations.

Capacity. The measurement of capacity or liquid measure can be developed from activities built around containers used to package products used in the home. When children are asked to bring bottles, jars, or cartons from home, a variety of shapes and sizes will be collected. Filling and pouring the containers with sand or water can lead to interesting activities of comparison. One of the children's first conclusions will be that some of the containers have the same capacity (hold the same amount) but do not have the same shape.

Reference to standard units will allow children to determine which containers have the capacity of one pint, which have the capacity of one quart, and so forth. By comparison of the capacities of standard units, pupils will be able to develop their own reference table of liquid measures.

Volume. The development of concepts pertaining to volume requires pupils' understanding of a space region—the union of a closed surface (which appears to be a solid) and its interior. It is very difficult to use an approach to volume in which children suggest varying units of measure to be used. In the earliest activities with volume, children should be helped to understand that to measure volume, they must use a unit that has the characteristic of volume. The idea of a cubic unit is quickly introduced and children might be asked to make models of cubic units.

The concept of volume is generally introduced with a problem situation that requires finding the amount of volume or cubic units that are needed to fill a box. One-inch cubes and boxes that can be filled with these cubes are appropriate instructional aids for developing concepts of volume. However, when such boxes are used, it is necessary to emphasize that it is the inside volume of the box that is being determined.

As children fill the box with cubes, they will find that the base or bottom of the box is covered with a number of cubes that is equal to the measure of the length multiplied by the measure of the width or the measure of the area of the base of the box.

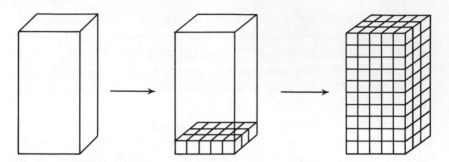

Continuing to fill the box, they will find that a certain number of these "layers" will fill the box and be able to determine the volume as the number of cubic units in one layer multiplied by the number of layers. With several such problems and proper guiding questions from the teacher, children should be able to establish a formula that will allow them to compute the volume in cubic units of any rectangular solid.

The measure of the base layer = length × width of the base

$$(A = lw)$$

The measure of the volume = the measure of the base

× height of the prism

Volume = (length × width) × height

$$V = lwh$$

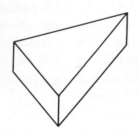

Area of the base $= \frac{1}{2} bh$

Volume of prism = area of base × height

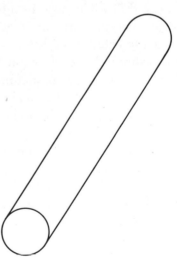

Area of base $= r^2\pi$

Volume of cylindrical region $= r^2\pi h$

Emphasis upon determining the number of cubes in the base "layer" by determining the area of the base is important because this concept can be extended to determining the volume of other solids.

Angles. To associate a measurement or comparison idea with angles, some angle must be chosen as a referent unit. Perhaps the first referent angle that children will use is the right angle (square corner), which they can construct by paper folding. This model can then be used for comparison purposes to determine whether other angles are greater than, equal to, or less than a right angle.

When children learn to bisect angles, they can bisect a right angle and establish another unit angle that could be used for comparison purposes. This procedure of bisecting the new unit angle could be repeated to arrive at new unit measures. Because the units of comparison are becoming smaller, the angles to be measured will be measured with a greater degree of preciseness. The constructed unit angles could even be used to construct an instrument for measuring angles.

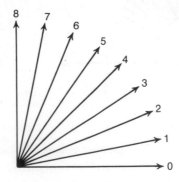

At a later level, the *degree* as a standard unit for measuring angles will be introduced. The introduction may be a statement concerning the number of degrees around a common vertex (360), or the idea may be introduced with a statement about the number of degrees in a right angle (90) and a question concerning the number of degrees possible around a common vertex.

When pupils are ready to use an instrument to measure the size of angles, teachers should introduce the *protractor*. To indicate an-

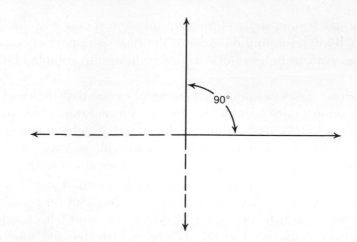

other use of degrees, reference might also be made to the compass that is used to indicate direction.

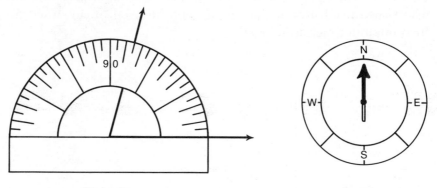

Protractor   Compass

The metric system.   No specific reference has been made to the metric system of measurement in the preceding discussion because instructional techniques and procedures for developing concepts of measurement with metric units do not differ from those for developing abilities with the English system. Readers should not interpret previous omission as a suggestion that the metric system of measurement is not to be studied in the elementary school. The metric system is widely used around the world for all measurement situations and in the United States in scientific endeavors. Because of its wide use, measurement activities involving the metric system should be a part of both the elementary mathematics and science programs.

The metric system of measurement is a decimal system in that larger units are repeatedly comprised of 10 small units. Thus the metric system can and should be developed in its relationship to our base ten system of numeration. Measurements in the metric system are recorded in decimal notation and the study of the system provides excellent opportunity to reinforce children's understandings and skills with decimals and computations with decimals. Activities and experiences with metric measurement should be directed toward developing basic ideas of measurement with metric units. Little is to be gained from practice exercises that are directed toward converting English measures to metric measures and *vice versa*.

Suggested activities

1. Make a collection of physical objects that can be used to illustrate geometric concepts.

2. Use a straightedge and a compass to practice line drawing constructions that include
   a. Constructing line segments congruent to given line segments
   b. Constructing the perpendicular bisectors of given line segments
   c. Constructing lines parallel to a given line
   d. Constructing bisectors of given angles
   e. Constructing figures (triangles and quadrilaterals) that are congruent to given figures

3. Develop a sequence of learning experiences concerning pegboard constructions that are designed to develop
   a. Basic ideas of geometry
   b. Basic ideas of linear measurement

4. Use paper folding to construct models of a straightedge, a right angle, and a rectangle.

5. Make a set of three-dimensional models that can be used to help illustrate problems concerning the surface of solids and volume.

6. Design a bulletin board to develop interest and motivation for a unit of study dealing with measurement at a particular grade level.

7. Compare several elementary textbook series in regard to the approaches used to develop basic ideas of geometry and understandings and abilities of measurement.

8. Collect sets of work problems that are concerned with linear measurement, area, weight, volume, and capacity.

Selected references

The Arithmetic Teacher. 14:82–140, Feb. 1967. (This issue deals with geometry in the elementary school.)

Bourne, H. N., "The Concept of Area," *The Arithmetic Teacher*, 15:233–243, March 1968.

Crouch, R., G. Baldwin, and R. J. Wisner, *Preparatory Mathematics for Elementary Teachers.* New York: John Wiley & Sons, Inc., 1965, Chapter X, "Geometry and Measurement of Geometric Sets," pp. 414–487.

Helgren, F. J., "The Metric System in the Elementary Grades," *The Arithmetic Teacher*, 14:349–353, May 1967.

Keedy, M. L., and C. W. Nelson, *Geometry—A Modern Introduction.* Reading, Mass.: Addison-Wesley Publishing Company, Inc., 1965.

Ringenberg, L. A., *Informal Geometry.* New York: John Wiley & Sons, Inc., 1967.

Robinson, G. E., "The Role of Geometry in Elementary School Mathematics," *The Arithmetic Teacher*, 13:3–10, Jan. 1966.

Schaaf, W. L., *Basic Concepts of Elementary Mathematics.* New York: John Wiley & Sons, Inc., 1965, Chapter 10, "Measurement," and Chapter 11, "Mensuration," pp. 288–358.

Smart, J. R., and J. L. Marks, "Mathematics of Measurement," *The Arithmetic Teacher*, 13:283–287, April 1966.

Swart, W. L., "A Laboratory Plan for Teaching Measurement in Grades 1–8," *The Arithmetic Teacher*, 14:652–653, Dec. 1967.

Webber, G. C., and J. A. Brown, *Basic Concepts of Mathematics.* Reading, Mass.: Addison-Wesley Publishing Company, Inc., 1963, Chapter 12, "Measurement: A Mathematical Approach," and Chapter 13, "Measurement in Practice," pp. 236–271.

Teaching 13

problem solving

The primary purpose of teaching mathematics in the elementary school is to assist the child in developing understandings and skills related to concepts, principles, and operations and the ability to apply these to problem-solving situations involving mathematics.

What is a problem? In the context in which problem solving is discussed in this chapter, a *problem* is a mathematical situation for which the child does not have an immediate answer or an obvious mathematical operation or method for determining the answer. A problem is not defined this broadly in most books. In fact, a distinct differentiation is made in some books between a problem and a computational example. The authors believe, however, that the more inclusive definition, as used in this book, is warranted.

Problem solving has many aspects, any or all of which may constitute a problem for the child as he attempts to find solutions to mathematical situations that confront him. A situation does not have to be in "story" form to present a problem. Many writers would classify $42 \div 7 = \square$ as a computation example rather than a problem, but if a pupil does not know what $42 \div 7$ is, he faces the problem of determining a way of finding the answer. A mathematical situation, then, whether described in words or with mathematical symbols, may be a problem to one child and no problem at all to another child of approximately the same age or in the same grade. For instance, a child may know that $12 \times 67 = ?$ requires the multiplication operation. However, if the child does not know how to perform the computation using the multiplication operation, he is faced with a problem to be solved before he can find an answer to the mathematical question. Verbal problems, word problems, or story problems are an important aspect of a mathematics instructional program in problem solving, but they should not constitute the total program.

The importance of using mathematical problems in the instructional program

Each person faces many mathematical questions, both within and outside of school for which he needs to find answers. The attitudes, understanding, abilities, skills, and techniques needed to solve mathematical problems can best be developed through a carefully planned program of problem-solving experiences appropriate to the maturity of the learner.

Problems can be used to facilitate the attainment of a variety of goals. Sometimes "real-life"-type problems are more appropriate for the objective; sometimes "fantastic" problems may be more appropriate. At various times during the year, a teacher may wish to use problems to

1. Demonstrate to pupils the need for learning mathematics
2. Introduce a new concept or idea
3. Illustrate a mathematical principle
4. Help youngsters more easily recognize the importance of number operations and the relationships between operations
5. Provide interesting and meaningful practice
6. Assist children in seeing uses and applications of mathematics in the real world
7. Provide experiences leading to better reading ability
8. Motivate interest and promote a more positive attitude toward mathematics
9. Illustrate that a variety of methods can be used to find the answer to a mathematical question
10. Provide experiences with many problem situations that can lead to a more experimental attitude and ultimately to new mathematical ideas

Because one of the aims of all instruction is to assist the individual to analyze situations and bring to bear significant data in arriving at decisions, problem solving in mathematics should be related to all areas of the curriculum.

If children are to become effective and efficient in finding solutions to problems, teachers need to plan so that problem solving is an integral part of all phases of mathematics instruction, rather than a few lessons in a book or a now-and-then experience during the year.

Begin problem solving early

A program of experiences to help the child build competence and confidence in solving problems involving mathematics should begin the first year the child is in school. If the young child is encouraged and guided to find solutions to problems within his limited world, he may increase his problem-solving interest instead of developing fear as he moves through the school years.

Problem solving involves more than a command of number combinations and skill in computation. Early experiences with problems should be within the interest and experience of the child. Although, when first entering school, the child usually can neither read nor write, the teacher needs to recognize that solutions to most problems appropriate to this age youngster do not require paper-and-pencil arithmetic.

Logical reasoning is generally recognized as an essential element in problem solving. Some children can reason better than others. For most people, however, the ability to reason well has been developed over a relatively long period of time and from experiences that require logical thinking. Pupils in the early grades, therefore, should be *encouraged and given time to think —* to think about problem situations within their experiences, to recognize and understand the problem, and to work out, on their own, methods of attack.

Activities involving concrete materials that the pupil can manipulate and arrange in various ways are especially valuable in the primary grades as a means of providing first-hand experience with mathematical concepts and their uses. By manipulating objects, a child can solve problems that are orally described. "Here are two bags of marbles. Can you find out if one bag contains more marbles than the other?" Without recognizing or writing numerals, a child can solve this problem by simply removing at the same time a marble with his left hand from one bag and a marble with his right hand from the other bag until both bags are empty at the same time or only one bag is empty.

If children can count and recognize the number symbols to 30, many realistic problem situations can be built around the calendar. "This is Monday, March 13. Tom's birthday is Friday, March 24. How many more days before we can celebrate Tom's birthday?" This problem may be solved in several ways in the primary grades depending on the maturity of the children.

S	M	T	W	T	F	S	
			1	2	3	4	
5	6	7	8	9	10	11	
12	13	14	15	16	17	18	TOM
19	20	21	22	23	(24)	25	
26	27	28	29	30	31		

A child may look at the calendar and count the days to get the answer 11. Another child may know that there are 7 days after this Friday, so he counts 4 more days to get 11. Still another child with more mathematical understanding may think $7 + 4 = 11$ or $24 - 13 = 11$. When faced with a mathematical situation, children should be encouraged to think through the problem and use what they know to solve the problem in the easiest way they can. In the early grades, particularly, there should be *much discussion* about problem situations drawn from the daily activities of youngsters and the way the problems can be solved.

The enterprising early elementary teacher can capitalize on opportunities that arise in the activities of the school to improve continually the child's mathematical understanding and problem solving ability. Some of these activities are

1. Grouping of toys or objects
2. Checking daily attendance
3. Buying savings stamps
4. Ordering milk for pupils
5. Playing store
6. Putting away the toys
7. Weighing, and measuring time
8. Dramatizing stories
9. Making a map of the immediate area

10. Making change in the lunchroom
11. Planning refreshments for a party

Reading and problem solving

Reading ability is clearly related to success in solving word problems presented in written form. Some pupils who are recognized good readers experience difficulty with mathematical story problems. Reading story problems involving mathematics requires different skills and techniques than reading material in other curricular areas such as the reading book, the literature book, or the social studies book. A child cannot be expected to solve story problems presented in written form unless he possesses the skills necessary to read and comprehend the problem.

Problem solving requires careful, detailed, analytical reading. Mathematical material is generally characterized by its conciseness. The teacher needs to help pupils recognize the nature of the material and the purpose for which it is being read. Most people find it profitable to read a story problem rapidly to get the over-all picture of what it is about. Then they reread the material more slowly and carefully, as many times as necessary, to fill in the details of the over-all picture. A good problem-solver must also recognize the mathematical relationships existent in what he reads. A good check on the child's understanding of a story problem is to have him restate it in his own words, perhaps without using number names.

Language factors in story problems have long been associated with difficulty in problem solving. If a child does not understand terms used in a problem, he certainly is in no position to solve the problem. In a recent study on problem solving, Lyda and Duncan found that ". . . direct study of quantitative vocabulary contributes significantly to growth in problem solving."[1] In teaching pupils to read and interpret problem situations, teachers need to help them develop meaning both for words that relate to the social setting and those that relate to the technical vocabulary of mathematics.

When a written verbal problem is encountered, good problem-solvers invariably read the problem carefully and thoughtfully be-

---

[1] Lyda, W. J., and F. M. Duncan, "Quantitative Vocabulary and Problem Solving," *The Arithmetic Teacher*, 14:291, April 1967.

fore attempting a solution. Most children need teacher guidance in learning to read a mathematical story problem meaningfully. This can be provided without establishing a pattern of steps that every child must always follow. If children apparently do not understand certain terms, provide help in understanding these terms before asking pupils to read the problems.

After pupils have had time to read the problem situation and think about it, but before they compute the answer, teachers have found it good practice to ask such questions as

1. Does the problem involve combining groups? Separating a group? Comparing groups?
2. What were you asked to find?
3. What data were given that you can use?
4. Will you need any data not given?
5. Are there data in the problem that you don't need?
6. What will you do to find the answer?
7. What do you already know that will help you?
8. Can you draw a diagram or write a mathematical sentence to show the relationship between what is given and what you are to find?
9. About what do you think the answer will be?

After discussing the questions and responses, have children read another problem with the idea they will be asked similar questions about it. Now ask pupils to compute answers to the problems and to compare the answers with their earlier estimates.

Improving ability to solve verbal problems

Problem solving has been an important objective of mathematics instruction for many years, yet many people in general are not very good problem-solvers. What can teachers do to improve the effectiveness of the problem-solving program in the elementary school? The following approaches offer no panacea, but have proved to be effective techniques for motivating and assisting pupils to improve their reasoning and problem-solving power. Where and how each approach can best be used will depend upon the purpose in mind and the needs and interests of a particular group of children.

Use interesting problems. Teachers can do much to make problem solving an interesting and enjoyable as well as a profitable experience by carefully planning problem-solving activities. These activities, generally, should deal with things and conditions within the children's experiences. In this way the problems will be real to the children and will be easier to visualize and solve. This is especially true in the early years of school and when using problems to introduce new concepts. If the problem situation is interesting and has meaning for the pupil, he is more likely to *want to solve* the problem.

Numerous opportunities exist both inside and outside the school to construct problem situations that are within the child's experience and that are of interest to him. For example,

1. Count the number of pupils present today.
2. Tomorrow is Janet's birthday. Three people have agreed to bring cookies. How many cookies will each have to bring if every member of the class has two cookies?
3. It is spring and many people are planting gardens. How many seeds would be needed for a 20-foot row, if the seeds are planted 6 inches apart?
4. Bill had 45 cents. He earned 10 cents for taking out the trash and 35 cents for raking leaves. How much money does Bill have?
5. Laying out a plan for a mural may be an interesting problem for the girls.
6. Laying out a softball diamond on the playground may be a good problem for the boys.

Concrete objects, drawings, diagrams. People of all ages and ability levels find it easier to solve many problems if objects, drawings, or diagrams are used. These can be used effectively to clarify the problem, to find a solution, or to verify the answer. Children should be encouraged to use these aids to solve problems in the early grades and to continue their use throughout the elementary school. For instance, in the lower grades, objects or drawings may be used to illustrate problems such as

I had three marbles and someone gave me two more. How many do I now have?

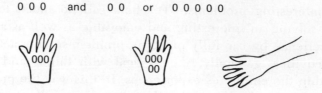

My brother had five puppies and three of them ran away. How many are left?

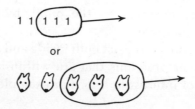

Drawings and diagrams may be used in the middle grades to solve problems such as the following:

David walks 2/3 of a mile to school and Jimmy walks 4/6 of a mile to school. Who walks the longer distance?

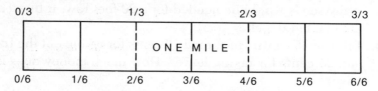

The drawing shows that each boy walked the same distance. It also illustrates that 2/3 and 4/6 are different names for the same number.

In the upper grades drawings and diagrams may be used with problems such as

a. Four girls wish to share equally three donuts. What part of a donut will each girl get?

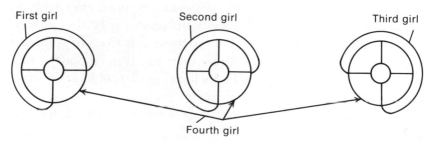

b. The Scouts are having a cookie or candy sale as a money-raising project. Make a chart or graph showing the number of boxes each Scout in the room sold on each of the first four days of the sale.

Dramatizations.   Dramatizing or acting out story problems not only stimulates and motivates children, but also makes problems more realistic. Conditions, concepts, and relationships presented in the problem situation can be clarified through dramatization. Through dramatizations, children can readily learn how mathematics is related to out-of-school situations such as making purchases in a store and making and checking change.

A child goes to the store with a $5.00 bill and buys an article for a certain amount, a second article for a certain amount, and a third article for a certain amount. How much money did he get back?

This problem can be meaningfully dramatized by two children, a buyer and a seller, in a make-believe store with play money and articles for sale at various prices. Play-store activities provide a good means of helping children in the early grades see the relationship between mathematics and economics.

Other excellent classroom opportunities for dramatizations involving mathematics are:

A group of pupils joining another group of children to illustrate the relationship of addition to union of two disjoint sets.

Making a deposit or writing a check at a make-believe bank.

Planning for a school camping trip or serving as a clerk in the "camp store."

Multilevel problems.   Regardless of grouping procedures used within the school or within the room, children in a classroom differ in terms of interest, motivation, and mathematical maturity. Problems assigned to a pupil to solve should be difficult enough to challenge him, but not so difficult as to continually frustrate him.

The teacher has a most important guidance function in trying to match the difficulty level of the story problem with a child in terms of his experience background, his reading level, and his mathematical understanding. If a child is to continue trying to improve his problem-solving ability, he needs to experience frequent success as he attempts to solve problems of increasing difficulty. The concerned teacher provides this opportunity through appropriate differentiated assignments.

Recognizing relationships.   There are several relationships that are important factors in finding solutions to problems. Successful problem-solvers recognize the number system interrelationships and the relationships between number operations. Emphasizing the *process* in problem solving as well as deriving answers helps youngsters concentrate attention on understanding the nature of the problem and the relationships inherent in it.

Recognizing and understanding relationships requires specific mathematical insights that, for the most part, have to be developed either prior to or concurrent with problems that call for application of these insights.

A child may wish to find how much he would save if he could buy an article in a store for $1.73 and the same article in another store for $1.81. When considering two numbers, a pupil needs to recognize which number represents the smaller quantity and which represents the larger quantity.

Many problem situations involve data relative to certain measurement relationships that need to be recognized to solve successfully the problem. Some of these relationships that need to be developed are

1. Penny—nickel—dime—quarter—half dollar—dollar
2. Year—month—week—day—hour—minute—second
3. Inch—foot—yard—mile
4. Cup—pint—quart—half-gallon—gallon
5. Length—width—perimeter—area
6. Distance—speed—time
7. Price—number of items—cost

When the relationships between data in a problem are recognized, the problem solver still needs to recognize the relationships among number operations to apply the best one in finding the answer. A pupil who understands the following relationships is a better problem-solver than one who does not see the relationships:

1. Addition is the operation that will name the total number when two or more disjoint, equivalent or nonequivalent, sets are combined.
2. The multiplication operation is a faster means of finding the total number when two or more equivalent sets are combined.
3. Division is the operation that can be used when separating a given set into equivalent subsets or finding how many equivalent subsets are in a given set.
4. The subtraction operation is used either to find how many more or less is in one set than another or to find the missing subset when the other subset and the original set are known.

Mathematical sentences.   Most current programs make much use of mathematical sentences as a means of focusing attention on problem solving. A mathematical sentence is a statement of the story of the problem expressed in the symbols of mathematics. The most common type of mathematical sentences used in the elementary school are of the equation form, for example, $3 + 2 = 5$, a true sentence; $3 + 2 = 8$, an inequality or untrue sentence; $3 + 2 = \square$, an open sentence. The $\square$, called a variable or placeholder, stands for the number that must be found to make the sentence a true statement. Some programs use letters of the alphabet, some use ?, and some use geometric shapes to represent the variable.

Mathematical sentences are also used to express the relationship between numbers, for example, $6 > 4$, six is "greater than" four; $3 < 7$, three is "less than" seven; $2 + n < 8$, what number(s) plus 2 is less than eight?

Formulas may be developed with children and expressed as mathematical sentences that can be used as models for solving problems describing a situation of similar type. For example, $a \times b = b \times a$ describes the commutative property for multiplication; $L \times W = A$ may be used to find the area of rectangular regions.

The ability to write a mathematical sentence that can be used in solving the problem indicates the child's ability to listen carefully or to read and interpret the verbally stated problem situation.

Sometimes it is good practice to ask the child to state the problem in a word sentence before writing the mathematical sentence. Another profitable experience for some pupils is to write mathematical sentences *for the solution* of several problems without actually finding the replacement for the variables. These kinds of experiences encourage the pupil to *think* about and *analyze* the problem situation before attempting to compute the answer.

A child should begin to write mathematical sentences soon after he understands number as expressed by our basic numerals and has had experience in combining and separating sets of objects. A set of blocks is placed on the table. Another set of blocks is placed on the table. How many blocks do we have on the table?

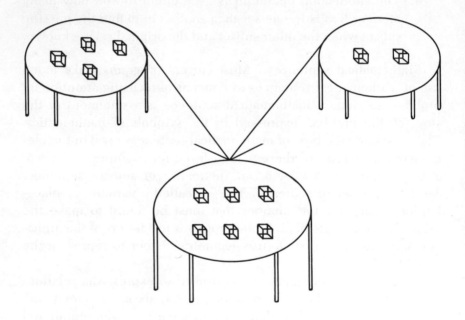

Further questions and discussion may ensue such as

1. How many blocks in first group?
2. How many blocks in second group?
3. What did we want to find?
4. How did various youngsters go about finding the answer?

The teacher may approach the writing of mathematical solutions by saying, "The problem we have just talked about can be written in a short, simple form using mathematical symbols instead of words. Can anyone help me write a mathematical sentence for the problem?" With help of pupils, the teacher writes $4 + 2 = N$. What does the 4 and 2 stand for? The number of blocks in each group. What does the N stand for? All the blocks, or another name for $4 + 2$. How can we find a replacement for $4 + 2$? By counting or by adding the two numbers. Write the true mathematical sentence that answers the problem. $4 + 2 = 6$. What does the 6 mean? In this problem it means the number of blocks on the table.

If an approach similar to that described is followed in the early elementary years, perhaps fewer problems than formerly will be dealt with. The emphasis, however, in these years is *thinking* about problems and *learning how* to solve problems so that the pupil can solve problems with increasing independence. Students need to have many experiences in interpreting a problem and writing a mathematical sentence *for its solution.*

Solve problems in many ways.   An individual should strive to develop a plan for attacking and solving problems. If this plan is to be an effective, workable one for the pupil, he must be free to suggest, explore, and try out many approaches to solving problems. The teacher must resist having pupils solve problems "my way" or the "textbook" way. Solving problems many ways will increase motivation and interest and provide variety to the learning experiences, but more importantly it provides a pupil, when faced with a problem, a *basis for choosing the method* that is easiest and most appropriate for him.

Evidence is growing that pupils gain more insight into a problem situation, better understand the interrelationships in our number system, and do more quantitative thinking when they solve one problem many ways than when they solve several like or similar problems one way. The teacher should occasionally discuss with the total group several ways in which a problem has been solved because what is interesting and is understandable to one pupil may not be interesting or understandable to another pupil. Also, in this way a child can have the benefit of other children's thinking.

Depending on the maturity level of the child, he may use any one or several of the following procedures to solve the problem, "I want some pieces of string $\frac{3}{4}$ foot long; how many pieces of this length can I get from a 6-foot-long string?" Start at one end, measure 9 inches, cut. Continue this as long as you can get a 9-inch-long piece. You will get eight pieces. Use a number line to represent a string 6 feet long.

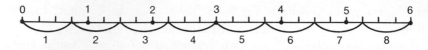

Divide the number line into six equal parts. Divide each of the whole number segments into fourths. Count the number of $\frac{3}{4}$'s.

Another child who sees there are four $\frac{3}{4}$'s in 3, may think there would be twice that many in 6, and arrive at an answer of 8.

The problem may be solved by adding $\frac{3}{4}$ eight times. There are eight $\frac{3}{4}$'s in 6.

$$\frac{3}{4}+\frac{3}{4}+\frac{3}{4}+\frac{3}{4}+\frac{3}{4}+\frac{3}{4}+\frac{3}{4}+\frac{3}{4}=6$$

Start with 6 and subtract $\frac{3}{4}$ until the remainder is zero. Count the number of times $\frac{3}{4}$ was subtracted.

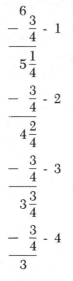

Consider the partial solution at the left of the page. Some children would not need to do any more subtracting. They would know there would be as many more $\frac{3}{4}$ in 6 as they have already subtracted; therefore the answer would be 8.

The "invert and multiply" method of division could be used.

$$6 \div \frac{3}{4} =$$

$$6 \times \frac{4}{3} = \frac{24}{3}$$

$$\frac{24}{3} = 8$$

Another child may find the "common denominator" method more appropriate for him.

$$6 \div \frac{3}{4} =$$

$$\frac{24}{4} \div \frac{3}{4} = 8$$

Six feet could be changed into 72 inches. Three-fourths foot could be changed into 9 inches: $72 \div 9 = 8$.

If we wish to think of $\frac{3}{4}$ as .75, we could divide 6 by $\frac{3}{4}$ and get 8 as an answer.

$$\begin{array}{r} 8 \\ .75\overline{)6.00} \\ \underline{6\,00} \end{array}$$

Estimation. The child could be encouraged and given guidance to estimating answers. This experience should begin in the early grades and continue until it becomes a natural thing to do before attempting to solve a mathematical problem. Most of the problems faced in daily living (some claim as high as 85%) require an approximate answer, not an exact answer. Even when problems do ultimately require an exact answer, the habit of first estimating the answer focuses attention on details of the data in the problem and provides a basis for judging the reasonableness of answers.

Facility in estimating answers can be developed through experiences such as

1. Is 7 more than 5? Is 7 less than 10? Is seven more than 6 and less than 8? A number line may be used in this situation advantageously.
2. Is 42 nearer 40 or 50?
3. Is 28 nearer 20 or 30?
4. Sometimes when estimating the sum of several numbers, it is helpful to round the number to the nearest 10. $42 + 28$ may be thought of as $40 + 30$. Suzie bought 3 books for 39 cents each. About how much did she spend for books?
5. 5×21 is about 90, 100, 110?
6. When dividing $5.1\overline{)15.3}$, it is helpful to think I am dividing a little more than 15 by a little more than 5. The answer should be about 3.
7. You made purchases of $2.98, $1.49, and 29 cents. You have $5.00, do you have enough money to pay for what you bought? About how much change should you receive?
8. Round each factor to the nearest 100, then estimate the product. $389 \times 423 = \square$.

Problems without numbers. Presenting problems without numbers and asking pupils what they would do to solve the problem is a valuable means of developing problem-solving ability. Because there are no numbers or an answer with which to be concerned, the pupil can concentrate his attention on analyzing the situation and determining what method(s) would be applicable in arriving at a solution if the numbers were given.

1. Jeff knows how much he earned each day on his paper route. How can he find how much he earned last month from delivering papers?
2. You went to a movie, bought a bag of popcorn and a coke. How can you find how much you have left from your week's allowance?
3. How would you find the average weight of a football team?

Inadequate or irrelevant data. Solving problems with inadequate or extraneous data tends to force pupils to examine the data critically before trying to solve the problem. Paying attention to detail should be emphasized because solving everyday problems necessitates selecting and organizing data essential to the solution.

Sometimes a problem situation does not provide enough information to solve the problem and at other times more information is given than is needed. In the solution of problems it is important to know what additional information must be collected as well as to know how to use the information that is given. An occasional good practice is to have pupils, after reading a problem, to tell or write the information given but not needed to solve the problem or the information needed for the solution but not given.

Problem situations similar to the following ones may be constructed to provide pupils with needed practice in selecting between needed and unneeded data.

1. In driving from Lansing to Chicago we used 19 gallons of gasoline. How many miles per gallon of gasoline did we get?
2. Jim and his father fished for 4 hours. Jim caught nine fish and his father caught seven fish. How many fish did they catch altogether?
3. An airplane flies 640 miles per hour. How much fuel will it consume in a 3-hour flight?
4. The school gym is 110 feet long and 60 feet wide. How far will Timmy run if he runs the length of the gym 5 times?

Making up problems.   Pupils at all levels of the elementary school can improve their problem-solving ability by making up problems for solution in class. Teachers who have tried this approach find that children tend to make the problems as difficult as possible, thinking that if no one can find a solution, it is a good problem. To offset this tendency, some teachers require that a pupil must either be able to solve the problem he constructs or else be able to tell why it cannot be solved.

The teacher, particularly in the lower grades, will usually supply data and ideas children may use in constructing problems. If children are reticent to try formulating problems, the teacher may start the activity with some problems she has made up.

Problems may be developed out of classroom activities in the various subject areas, school parties, and so forth, or out of school experiences such as a field trip, a vacation, purchases at the store, or ads and charts and graphs from newspapers and journals. Sometimes the directions may be to formulate a problem that requires discussion, that requires both addition and subtraction, that illustrates the relationship between time, rate, and distance, or some other specific concept.

Problem solving should be an integral part of mathematics instruction throughout the elementary school program. Problem-solving situations offer an effective means of introducing new concepts, developing understanding and skills, and evaluating learnings. Activities developing inquiry and problem-solving ability through dealing with mathematical situations should be correlated with activities in other areas of the curriculum such as science and social studies.

Suggested activities

1. Construct several mathematical problem situations that would be appropriate for children in the early grades to solve orally.

2. Develop a plan for assisting pupils to read a "story problem" meaningfully.

3. What can you do to develop a positive attitude in youngsters toward problem solving?

4. Choose a grade level (3–6) and write several problem situations that would be both interesting and profitable for the pupils to solve.

5. Teachers should make a serious attempt to match the difficulty level of story problems to the variabilities of youngsters in the class. What implications does this have for lesson planning?

6. Select several problems from a textbook at the grade level you are most interested in teaching and try to solve each problem in as many ways as you can.

Selected references

Cohen, L. S., "Open Sentences—The Most Useful Tool in Problem Solving," *The Arithmetic Teacher*, 14:263–267, April 1967.

Cohen, L. S., and D. C. Johnson, "Some Thoughts about Problem Solving," *The Arithmetic Teacher*, 14:261–262, April 1967.

Dorrie, H., *100 Great Problems of Elementary Mathematics*. New York: Dover Publications, Inc., 1965.

Earp, N. W., "Problem Solving: Arithmetic's Persistent Dilemma," *School Science and Mathematics*, 67:182–188, Feb. 1967.

Johnson, D. C., "Unusual Problem Solving," *The Arithmetic Teacher*, 14:268–271, April 1967.

Lerch, H. H., and H. Hamilton, "A Comparison of a Structured-Equation Approach to Problem Solving with a Traditional Approach," *School Science and Mathematics*, 66:241–246, March 1966.

Lyda, W. J., and F. M. Duncan, "Quantitative Vocabulary and Problem Solving," *The Arithmetic Teacher*, 14:289–291, April 1967.

Neureiter, P. R., "Problem Solving without Tears," *Instructor*, 75:36, June 1966.

Swenson, E. J., "How Much Real Problem Solving?" *The Arithmetic Teacher*, 12:426–430, Oct. 1965.

Trimble, H. C., "Problems as Means," *The Mathematics Teacher*, 59:6–8, Jan. 1966.

Wilson, J. W., "What Skills Build Problem Solving Power?", *Instructor*, 76:79–80, Feb. 1967.

Evaluation 14

For many years the emphasis in elementary school mathematics was on the development of computational ability. Efficiency in computation is, and will undoubtedly continue to be, an important aspect of mathematical instruction at the elementary school level along with the development of meaningful concepts, functional understanding, and reasoning ability. As the objectives and methods of instruction changed and broadened, so has the need for appropriate and effective evaluation increased.

What is evaluation?

Evaluation as used in this book refers to all the techniques and instruments used in appraising the outcomes of instruction. When one considers (evaluates) what he set out to do and how well it has been done, he is making both quantitative and qualitative value judgments based upon some criteria of excellence. Evaluating how well an objective has been accomplished calls for a carefully planned program for gathering pertinent data, recording the data in usable form, and interpreting or analyzing the data. Evidence collected through both formal and informal techniques not only provides a basis for evaluating previously set objectives, but it also provides guidance in making judgments relative to future goals and the means of achieving them.

Evaluation is a crucial aspect of the educative process and should be considered an integral part of the day-to-day instructional program in mathematics. Evaluative judgments are more valid if based on data collected over a relatively long period of time using many techniques and instruments in a variety of situations involving mathematics and its usage.

What do we evaluate?

When we evaluate the learning of mathematics with respect to established goals, we are making value judgments about the appropriateness and effectiveness of the program of experiences, the materials of instruction, and the methodology of teaching as well as appraising pupil progress.

Program of experiences. Many changes have been made in elementary school mathematics programs within recent years. The intent of these curricular changes has been to improve the learning of children. Evaluation is basic to the development and maintenance of an appropriate and effective program of experiences. A teacher should frequently seek answers to such questions as

1. Are these the mathematical concepts, understanding, and skills this age or grade level youngster should learn?
2. Are they appropriate for these pupils and this community?
3. Is the scope of curriculum too broad or too narrow?
4. Might the curricular experiences be organized differently?

Materials of instruction. For years teachers have been urged to use a variety of materials to assist pupils in learning mathematics. In recent years many new and interesting materials have been produced commercially for classroom use. Since a number of choices is possible, teachers need to evaluate carefully the relative merits of materials available to use with a specific topic or with a particular group of children. In evaluating materials, a teacher may consider such criteria as the following:

1. Is the main purpose of using the material to arouse interest, develop a concept, build vocabulary, provide practice, supplement or replace the textbook?
2. Will the material(s) be primarily used by the teacher or by the pupils? Would the purpose be accomplished best by using reading materials, audiovisual aids, manipulative devices, concrete objects, or games?

3. Was the time required to use the selected material most wisely spent?
4. Do certain kinds of materials bring a better response than others?
5. Is there a place for programmed learning materials in the instructional program? If so, for what specific purpose(s)?

Methodology of teaching.   In an attempt to make learning of mathematics a challenging, enjoyable, and successful experience, teachers are experimenting with significant changes in the methodological approach to instruction. A methodological approach that works well for one teacher may not be an effective teaching technique for another. Also, a method that is effective in teaching a topic may not be successful with another due to differences in the concepts or to the human variabilities within groups of children.

A "good" teacher evaluates his effectiveness in teaching-learning situations and makes whatever adjustments are warranted. Whether using old, altered, or new methods, instructional effectiveness in teaching mathematics is likely to be increased if the teacher evaluates his methodological approach on such criteria as the following:

1. Is the learning of mathematics geared to an automatic response or to an adventure in discovery?
2. Does instruction emphasize the *why* as well as the *what* and *how* of mathematics?
3. Are learners helped to recognize recurring fundamental concepts?
4. How well does the program of learning experiences correlate with the sequential interrelated nature of mathematics?
5. Are there more questions asked than answers given?
6. Is the methodological approach structure orientated rather than rule orientated?
7. Does the learning environment encourage children to explore and try out their "hunches"?
8. Are pupils encouraged to solve problems in many different ways?
9. Is there a variety of practice experiences that accompany understandings?

Pupil progress.   Teachers have a responsibility for evaluating the several aspects of pupil growth toward those objectives that are held to be important in a modern mathematics program. All objectives currently emphasized in mathematics instruction should be kept in mind in evaluating pupil achievement. Teachers have shown a tendency to evaluate only in terms of objectives that are easy to test or measure. Improvement in evaluation techniques and instruments has not kept pace with improvement in the instructional program. As a result, many important outcomes are being slighted or neglected in the evaluative program.

Before any evaluation program is attempted, the teacher should carefully determine the objectives of the mathematics program deemed appropriate for the children in his class. When goals are clearly stated in behavioral terms—what the pupil should be able to do as a result of the experience—the extent to which the learner has progressed toward the desired objective can be easily determined.

Pupil progress toward objectives could be more realistically appraised if teachers in a school building would cooperatively develop the objectives for various aspects of mathematics K–6. The objectives should then be stated in terms that describe expected behavior at various levels of maturity. For example, the concept of measurement is studied from kindergarten through grade 6. Examples of expected behavioral goals at various levels might be stated as follows:

1. First year in school—can determine whether one object is longer or shorter than another.
2. Second and third year—using a "common ruler" can measure the length of an object to the nearest inch and half inch.
3. Fourth and fifth year—can illustrate and explain why we need standard units of linear measure.
4. Sixth and seventh year—selects appropriate standard measuring unit and determines perimeters of various geometric regions.

The writings in recent years have stressed the importance of making instruction meaningful and functional. A modern mathematics program is concerned with attitudes, understandings, meanings, concepts, generalizations, communication, skills, and reasoning ability as well as the development of computational proficiency. The remainder of this chapter will be devoted to techniques and instruments a teacher can use in evaluating pupil progress in terms of current instructional objectives.

Formal evaluative procedures

Most educators would agree that paper-and-pencil tests are only one part of a well-rounded program of evaluation in mathematics. Such tests, however, have always been and probably will continue to be one of the most valuable means of obtaining evidence of pupil achievement. Although testing instruments may provide only one type of evidence, they nevertheless contribute much useful data to the total program of evaluating mathematical learnings. Test results are valuable to the extent that the teacher knows what he is testing for and selects or develops an instrument that is likely to yield the most valid and reliable results in terms of the purpose.

Tests commonly used in the elementary school can be classified into three general types: (1) standardized tests, (2) textbook tests, and (3) teacher-constructed tests.

Standardized tests.   Many standardized achievement and diagnostic tests are available on the commercial market. These tests are carefully prepared by well-qualified people. The standardized test score permits the teacher to compare a student's performance in mathematics with that of other students of the same grade or age. Sometimes this may be desirable in adjusting the curriculum to the needs and abilities of students.

By the very nature of the test, a teacher should not expect a commercially produced standardized achievement test to cover all the concepts currently taught or all the objectives held for a given group of children. Generally, standardized tests are most useful in providing a measure of a child's general computational efficiency, mathematical vocabulary, competence in solving verbal problems, and graph-reading skills. In selecting a standardized test, particular attention should be given to its validity, reliability, usability, and objectivity. Remember that a test may have high validity for one purpose but have little or no validity if used for a purpose other than for which it was designed. Comprehensive bibliographies and critical reviews of recently published tests can be found in Buros (ed.), *The Sixth Mental Measurements Yearbook* (Highland Park, N. J.: The Cryphon Press), 1965.

Textbook tests.   Most of the recently published elementary school mathematics textbook series have tests that parallel each book. These tests are generally well constructed and offer the teacher a rather easily available means of measuring a pupil's progress and diagnosing his needs in terms of what he has recently been studying in the textbook program. In addition to end-of-chapter tests, some of the textbook companies have available mid-year and year-end comprehensive tests. Most textbook tests contain only a limited number of items to sample the work covered. Even though the tests are designed to accompany a designated textbook, some of them cover a rather broad range of current mathematical content and would therefore be appropriate to use with other textbooks.

Teacher-constructed tests.   Teacher-constructed paper-and-pencil tests have been the most commonly used classroom test to measure pupil progress. In recent years a greater effort has been exerted by test publishers to develop tests that measure aspects of mathematical growth other than computational skill and verbal problem-solving ability. Yet, most published tests do not measure pupil progress in more than a limited number of the many aspects of today's mathematics instruction.

The changing nature of both mathematical content and methodological approach make it nearly impossible for publishers of standardized tests to keep current with what happens in the classroom. A continuing need exists for well-conceived teacher-constructed tests to make sure that many important outcomes of contemporary mathematics instruction are not neglected in the testing program.

One of the most common shortcomings found in both textbook and standardized tests, as pointed out by writers in the field, is that comparatively little attention is devoted to the understandings and reasoning ability of the person being tested. A single test cannot measure all the objectives of a well-rounded program of mathematics instruction. Preliminary to actual test construction, the test-maker must decide upon the purpose or objective of the test. Let us assume that the primary purpose of the test is to appraise more objectively, than is now being done, objectives of mathematical instruction other than computational proficiency, namely, understandings and reasoning ability. The authors are convinced that such an evaluation instrument needs to be and can be developed either by an individual teacher or by a group of teachers in a building or school system working together.

After the objective(s) or purpose(s) of the test has been established, attention is focused on determining the content to be covered by the test. If the test is to aid the teacher in evaluating and diagnosing individual pupil progress, it needs to be closely related to the pupil's program of experiences. Depending upon the usage, a test may be developed to cover one topic, several topics, or all the main topics taught during the year.

After the preceding decisions have been made, the test-maker must decide on the kind of test item that is likely to yield the data being sought. Many forms of test items are in general use, such as essay, true-false, short answer, matching, completion, and multiple choice. A study of the strengths and weaknesses of the various item forms, as expressed in the literature, seems to indicate that the multiple-choice-type item with four response choices, when carefully constructed, offers the most promise for providing a measure both of the pupil's understanding and reasoning ability.

The appropriateness and adequacy of items used in a teacher-constructed test for the described purpose can be improved if gauged against a set of criteria such as the following:

1. Items should be valid in terms of instructional objectives and curriculum content.
2. Items should simulate real-life situations as closely as possible.
3. Item content should be stated in simple terms so that vocabulary and language structure does not block the reasoning process.
4. An effort should be made to avoid stereotyped textbook phraseology both in the stem and in the responses.
5. All responses should be plausible answers.
6. None of the items should require the pupil to actually "work out" the problem.

Space does not permit the inclusion of test items appropriate for all objectives and content of a modern mathematics program. A few sample noncomputational items are given that might be used to get an indication of a pupil's understanding and reasoning ability in each of 12 selected mathematical concepts commonly taught today in grades 5 and 6.

APPROXIMATION

Sunday afternoon you went with your family for a drive in the country. Your father stopped at a service station and bought 10 gallons of gas at 34 cents a gallon. About how much did the gas cost him?

_____ a little less than $4.00

_____ a little more than $4.00

_____ exactly $4.00

_____ almost $5.00

When rounded to the nearest thousand, which of these numbers would be 12,000?

_____ 12,245

_____ 12,510

_____ 12,720

_____ 12,990

AVERAGES

If you know how far you traveled in a day and how long it took, you can find the average speed per hour by

_____ subtracting the time from the distance

_____ adding the distance to the time

_____ dividing the distance by the time

_____ multiplying the distance by the time

Robin is a good basketball player. In the first six games this season he has scored 24, 32, 29, 21, 37, and 32 points. You would find his average score per game by

_____ adding the points Robin scored in each game and dividing the total by six

_____ dividing the number of points Robin scored by the number of points scored by the rest of the team

_____ dividing the total number of points scored in each game by the number of points Robin scored in each game

_____ adding Robin's highest and lowest score and dividing the sum by two

COMMON FRACTIONS

You can serve more friends from a can of orange juice if you give each person

_____ $\frac{1}{4}$ cup   _____ $\frac{2}{3}$ cup

_____ $\frac{1}{2}$ cup   _____ $\frac{3}{4}$ cup

Multiplying both terms of a common fraction by the same
number

_____ increases the value of the fraction

_____ does not change the value of the fraction

_____ decreases the value of the fraction

_____ changes the fraction to a whole number

DECIMALS AND PERCENT

The children in a school want to raise $25 for the Junior Red
Cross. They now have $20. How would you find what percent
of their goal has been reached?

_____ Subtract $20 from $25 and change the answer to percent.

_____ Divide $25 by $20 and change the answer you get
to percent.

_____ Multiply $20 times 100%.

_____ Divide $20 by $25 and change the answer you get
to percent.

Which of these decimals is the same as 42%?

_____ .042

_____ .42

_____ 4.2

_____ 42.00

FUNDAMENTAL OPERATIONS

Joe had $12. He gave one third of it to his sister. She spent
$3 for a sweater. How can we find out how much she had left?

_____ find one third of $12; add $3.

_____ find one third of $12; subtract $3.

_____ Subtract $3 from $12; find one third of the money left.

_____ Add $3 and $12; find one third of the sum.

The teacher bought four circus books, two animal books, and
three airplane books. What would you do to find out how many
books the teacher bought?

_____ Add the number of animal books and the number of
circus books.

_____ Add the number of airplane books and the number
of animal books.

_____ Multiply the number of animal books by the number
of airplane books.

_____ Add the number of circus books, the number of animal
books, and the number of airplane books.

Tommy's mother went shopping. She bought him a ball glove for $4.50 and a pair of tennis shoes for $2.00. Which is the best way to find how much change she got from a $10.00 bill?

_____ Subtract $4.50 from $10.00. Add what is left to $2.00.

_____ Add $4.50 and $2.00. Subtract this total from $10.00.

_____ Subtract $2.00 from $4.50. Add what is left to $10.00.

_____ Add $4.50 and $2.00. Add this total to $10.00.

GRAPHIC REPRESENTATION

Which of these figures has about 75% of its area shaded?

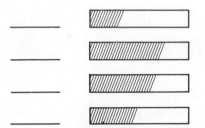

Dates in history are often shown by a line like the example below. This line begins with the year 1600 A.D. and ends with 2000 A.D. Four years during this period are shown by the letters A, B, C, and D. Which one shows the year 1918?

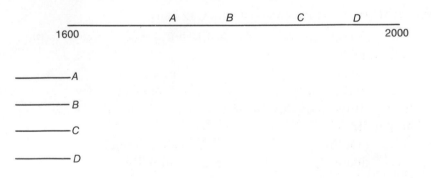

INSUFFICIENT DATA

Dick's father took an automobile trip of 180 miles. He gets 18 miles to a gallon of gasoline. What else do you need to know to find out how much he spent for gasoline?

_____ how many times he stopped for gasoline

_____ how many miles a day he drove

_____ how fast he drove

_____ how much 1 gallon of gas costs

Tim is working after school to earn money for a baseball and bat. The baseball cost $1.00 and the bat cost $1.50. What else must you know to find out how long Tim will have to work to get enough money to pay for the baseball and bat?

_____ how much the baseball and bat cost
_____ how much he gets paid per hour or per day
_____ what kind of work he does
_____ when he plans to buy the baseball and bat

IRRELEVANT-RELEVANT DATA

Which of the facts below do you *not* need to find how much longer it took John than Jim to swim the pool?

_____ The pool is 6 feet deep.
_____ They swam a 60-foot pool.
_____ John swam the pool in 30 seconds.
_____ Jim swam the pool in 20 seconds.

Which of the facts below do you *not* need to find how many eggs the grocer has left?

_____ My grocer buys eggs from the farm.
_____ He bought 60 eggs.
_____ He put the eggs in boxes that hold a dozen eggs each.
_____ He sold only 36 of the eggs.

MATHEMATICAL TERMS AND GENERALIZATIONS

The gas tank on Fred's car holds 20 gallons. The 20 gallons is the tank's

_____ capacity   _____ area
_____ perimeter   _____ dimension

Jack's father pays his insurance every 3 months. How does he pay it?

_____ monthly   _____ semiannually
_____ quarterly   _____ annually

MEASUREMENT AND GEOMETRY

The Monday morning news report said the temperature at the airport was 35. This means the temperature was

_____ very high
_____ a little above freezing
_____ a little below freezing
_____ very low

If you know the measurement of a living room in feet, how can you find the number of square feet of floor space?

_____ Add the lengths of the sides.

_____ Multiply the height by the length by the width.

_____ Divide the length by the width.

_____ Multiply the length by the width.

PLACE VALUE

In which of these numbers does the 6 stand for six thousand?

_____ 82.916   _____ 36,040

_____ 4,562   _____ 67,281

In which of the numbers below is the figure for one's place 3, for thousand's place 2, for ten's place 7, and for hundred's place 0.

_____ 2,073   _____ 3,072

_____ 2,703   _____ 3,702

QUANTITATIVE RELATIONSHIPS

What is the number *next* larger than 7,399?

_____ 7,390   _____ 7,490

_____ 7,400   _____ 73,991

Three girls left for summer vacations at the same time. Helen's vacation lasted 6 weeks. Pat's vacation was 24 days. Judy had a vacation of 1 month. This shows that

_____ Pat's vacation was longer than Judy's.

_____ Helen's vacation was the longest.

_____ Judy's and Pat's vacations were the same length.

_____ Judy's vacation was longer than Helen's.

Without measuring, which line below is $\frac{3}{7}$ as long as this sample line *but otherwise like it*?

Sample line: ___ ___   ___   ___   ___   ___   ___

_____   — — — — — — — —

_____   ___ ___   ___   ___

_____   ___   ___   ___   ___

_____   ___ ___   ___   ___

Informal techniques and procedures

Tests are important elements of a program of evaluation, but a variety of informal methods should also be used to secure adequate data upon which to make valid judgments about pupils' progress in mathematics. Just as no one test measures all areas of growth, no one informal method of evaluation can be used to collect evidence in all aspects of pupil development. In practice, teachers find it an impossible task to collect evidence on every aspect of pupil experiences every day. A more practical as well as a more effective approach is to concentrate on evaluating one aspect some days and another aspect on other days. We realize that some of the evidence gained through day-to-day informal procedures is subjective in nature; such evidence is nevertheless considered vital to an adequate program of evaluation.

Directed observation.   To diagnose pupil needs and to plan the most appropriate set of mathematical experiences, a teacher needs to know as much as possible about each pupil. Much important information can be gained by observing pupils both while they are studying mathematics and outside the regular mathematics time.

Observing the pupil as he works reveals much about his interest and attitude as well as his understanding and achievement. Does the pupil appear to be interested and excited or does it seem that he would rather be doing almost anything else? Does the child nearly always need help or can he usually attack the problem at hand and carry through on his own? If he makes errors, are they mostly in thought process or in computation? Can the pupil make drawings or diagrams to illustrate a problem situation and its solution? Does he explore several ways of solving a problem and checking the computation? Is there evidence that the pupil makes good use of mathematics when studying other school subjects, for instance, social studies, science, and art? Do you see evidence that he applies mathematics, for instance, measurement concepts, during the gym period, on the playground, or at the lunch counter? Answers to questions such as these may be found through directed observations.

Teachers need to develop plans for recording observations in usable form if they are to be of help in adapting instruction to the needs, interests, and abilities of youngsters. A recorded series of observations sometimes referred to as anecdotal records should prove helpful in judging whether behavior is consistent or the nature and extent of behavioral changes.

Individual pupil interviews.   Interviews permit the teacher to go into more depth than do observations in diagnosing a child's understandings and abilities or the lack of them. Elementary teachers have a full day and interviews take time, but with careful planning, a teacher can hold two or three interviews with each child during the school year. When this is done, both the teacher and pupil generally feel the time was profitably spent. The interview technique may be the most revealing of any evaluation procedure on an individual pupil's strongest areas, weakest areas, particular difficulties he is encountering, attitudes, and the effectiveness of the instructional program.

The interview should be as personal and nonthreatening as possible. If held during the regular school day, the room should be arranged so the teacher and pupil have privacy in a quiet corner. The interview session can be a good teaching situation in that it may offer the teacher on-the-spot opportunities to clarify misconceptions and misunderstandings expressed by the child.

If both people are willing, it may be a good idea to tape the interview. This permits either or both parties to replay the tape at perhaps a more convenient time or as many times as desired. In this way overlooked aspects that should be discussed or added insights may be discovered.

Check lists and rating scales.   Some teachers find it convenient to develop a check list or rating scale to collect special information believed necessary on a particular type of pupil behavior, program objective, or instructional procedure. A check list and a rating scale are similar in that both usually consist of a set of statements, although some consist of a set of questions relative to the topic about which information is sought. The two instruments differ in the way a person's reaction is indicated. On a check list you simply check the items that seem most appropriate. On a rating scale you use a symbol indicating your reaction to the item in terms of some kind of judgmental scale. Frequently a three-point scale is used such as one of the following:

A — Agree	U — Undecided	D — Disagree
A — Always	S — Sometimes	N — Never
F — Frequently	L — Little	N — Never

In the lower grades teachers may find either of the described instruments helpful in keeping a record of behaviors observed or children's oral reactions. In the middle and upper grades, teachers may wish to give a copy of the instrument to each pupil and ask them to indicate their reactions. For instance, a teacher may use a check list similar to the following example to determine her pupil's feeling about problem solving.

Directions: Place a ✔ mark in front of each statement that expresses your feelings about problem solving.

_____ I enjoy doing arithmetic problems.

_____ I wish we could do more problems than we do.

_____ Problem solving is easy for me.

_____ I need a lot of help with problem solving.

_____ I only try to work problems when I have to.

_____ I hate arithmetic when we have to solve problems.

_____ Reading is my favorite subject.

_____ I enjoy arithmetic as much as I do reading.

_____ I try to solve problems in many ways.

The check list could be converted to a rating scale by changing the directions: Indicate your reaction to each item by placing the appropriate capital letter in front of the statement. A—Agree, U—Undecided, D—Disagree.

Evaluation as an integral part of instruction and learning in mathematics has been stressed. Teaching requires value judgments relative to the mathematics curriculum, materials of instruction, methods of teaching, and pupil progress. This demands collecting, recording, and analyzing a wealth of data. Particular emphasis was devoted to diagnosing and evaluating pupil growth toward objectives currently held to be important. A variety of formal and informal procedures were discussed for helping a teacher plan a comprehensive program of evaluation.

Suggested activities

1. Select a topic of study for a grade or age level and write the hoped-for outcomes or objectives in behavioral terms.

2. Write a brief description of what "evaluating mathematical learnings" means to you.

3. List the techniques or procedures you would use in evaluating pupil progress in grades K–2. For what purpose would you use each?

4. Choose a topic studied at a grade level (3–6). Construct three multiple-choice test items designed to measure the pupil's understanding.

5. What kinds of evidence might best be obtained through informal evaluation techniques?

6. A child is experiencing much difficulty with multiplication. What approach would you use in attempting to diagnose the cause of the difficulty?

7. List the advantages and disadvantages of standardized, textbook, and teacher-constructed tests.

8. Develop an outline plan for evaluating pupil progress in your classroom over a 3-month period.

Selected references

Abrego, M. B., "Children's Attitudes toward Mathematics," *The Arithmetic Teacher*, 13:206–208, March 1966.

Ashlock, R. B., "What Is His Trouble in Mathematics?", *Instructor*, 77: 80–81, Oct. 1967.

Dutton, W. H., *Evaluating Pupils Understandings of Arithmetic*. Englewood Cliffs, N.J.: Prentice-Hall, Inc., 1964.

Epstein, Marion, "Testing in Mathematics: Why? What? How?", *The Arithmetic Teacher*, 15:311–319, April 1968.

Flournoy, F., "Study of Pupils' Understanding of Arithmetic in the Intermediate Grades," *School Science and Mathematics*, 67:325–333, April 1967.

Gray, R. F., "Approach to Evaluating Arithmetic Understandings," *The Arithmetic Teacher*, 13:187–191, March 1966.

Hammitt, H., "Evaluating and Reteaching Slow Learners," *The Arithmetic Teacher*, 14:40–41, Jan. 1967.

National Council of Teachers of Mathematics, *Evaluation in Mathematics*, Twenty-sixth Yearbook. Washington, D.C.: The National Council of Teachers of Mathematics, Inc., 1961.

Pace, A., "Understanding of Basic Concepts of Arithmetic: A Comparative Study," *Journal of Educational Research*, 60:107–120, Nov. 1966.

Toward Better Evaluation of Learning. Washington, D.C.: NEA Council on Instruction, 1962.

Index

Abacus, as an aid to teaching, 59–60, 86, 247
  when not to use, 104–105
Absence of value, zero as an indicator of 48, 58
Addends
  addition operation and, 75, 88–89
  regrouping of, in addition operation, 88–91, 98, 99, 101
    as a means of verification, 108
  relationship to minuend and subtrahend, 115
  renaming of, 89, 90, 99, 100
  sum and, 75, 88–89
Addition, as a binary operation, 74
Addition facts; *See* Addition operation
  addends; *See* Addends
  establishing and mastering, 81–106
  nature of, 81–84
  recommendations for teaching, 84–100
    additive inverse, 92–93
    allowing child to form his own generalizations, 86–87
    associative idea, 90–91, 92, 98, 99, 101, 108
    commutative idea, 92, 98, 99
    drill, 93–94
    identity element, 92
    introduce orally, with problem situations from classroom environment, 84
    manipulative materials, use of, 85–86, 89–91
    number houses and squares, 95–96
    number lines, 94–95
    number sentences, 95
    regrouping procedure, 88–91, 98, 99, 108
    summary schema for sequence of concepts, 98–100
  taught with subtraction facts, by use of "families" involving three numbers, 119–120, 123
Addition operation
  addends and sum, 75, 88–89; *See also* Addends
  addition facts; *See* Addition facts
  algorithm of, 100–104, 114, 120
  associative property of, 78–79
    use of, 90–91, 98, 99, 101, 108
  closure property of, 79
  commutative property of, 78
    use of, 89, 98, 99
  on decimals; *See* Decimals: addition of developing understanding and mastery of, 100–106
    renaming numbers with expanded notation, 101–104
    using addition facts, 101
    using manipulative objects, 104–105
  on fractions; *See* Fractions: addition of identity element of, 78
    use of, 92, 98
  inverse of, 79–80, 92–93

272
definition of, 270
expressed as a fraction, 205, 211–213,
    272, 273, 274
illustrations of, 270, 272
symbolism for, 272
Rational numbers; *See* Fractions
decimal fractions and, 241
Ratios, equivalent; *See* Equivalent ratios
Rays, 304
Regrouping procedure
in addition operation, 88–91, 98, 99,
    101
    as means of verifying sums, 108
in addition and subtraction of deci-
    mals, 252
in multiplication operation, 151, 158,
    161
in subtraction operation, 123, 127, 130,
    131, 132, 133, 134
Remainder, 173, 177, 185–187
Renaming addends, 89, 90, 99, 100
Renaming factors, 151, 161, 162, 257
Renaming numbers, in expanded nota-
    tion, 61, 65, 101–102
Repeated addition, and the multiplica-
    tion operation, 138–139
Repeated subtraction, and the division
    operation, 180–181, 259–260
Repeating decimals, 263–264
sign to indicate, 264
Repetitive principle used in
Egyptian numeration system, 37
Roman numeration system, 42
Roman numeration system, 41–44
additive and repetitive principles, 42
modern usage of, 41
multiplicative principle, 43
subtractive principle, 42–43
symbols used in, 42
Rule of Likeness, 129, 221, 224

School Mathematics Study Group, 3, 11
Sequential schema for developing pu-
    pils' understanding and skills in
addition, 98–100
division by one-digit divisors, 195
division by two-digit divisors, 196–197
subtraction, 133–135
Set, the
description of

using symbols, 17
using words, 18
identifying property of, 16
meaning of the term, 15–16
members or elements of, 16 *ff.*
separation of, into two distinct subsets,
    111–112, 114, 115, 116
tabulations of, 17
Set concepts
equivalence, 30
    methods of teaching, 50–52
one-to-one correspondence, 20, 30, 35,
    50
    counting and, 50–51
procedures for introducing and utiliz-
    ing, 31
symbols used in, 17, 18–19, 20, 21, 22,
    23, 24, 27–29
use of, 14–31
Venn diagrams and, 26–30
Sets
associative operation on, 26
common property of, 50–51
commutative operation on, 25
disjoint, 24, 27, 28, 29, 98
    comparison of, 111–112, 114, 115
    comparison of the numbers of, 175–
    176
empty, 18, 21, 48, 52
equal, 19–20, 28
equivalent, 19–20, 30
    cardinality of number and, 20, 50
    method of illustrating, 50–51
finite, 18
infinite, 18–19
intersecting, 23, 28
intersection of, 22–24
matching, 30; *See also* Equivalent sets
missing number properties of
    subtraction and, 111–114, 133
nonequivalent, determination of, 50
null; *See* Empty set
number and, 34–35
number properties of, correspondence
    between the, 270–271, 272
number property of
    addition operation and, 73–75
    multiplication operation and, 138–
    139
operation on, 22–26
subsets and, 20–22, 26, 27